INLAND PASSAGE

INLAND PASSAGE

Knox Randall was down to three dollars and forty cents when he read the ad in the Miami paper: Wanted: Experienced man to take 74 ft. cruiser to N. Y. via inland waterway. Start Sunday. Phone——"

It looked good until he realized that all of his seven passengers seemed either to have something to hide or to be running away. And when the Miami police stopped them two days out at Eau Gallie to tell them that the owner of the Julia *had been murdered, events had gone too far for any turning back.*

Not all of those who started that trip arrived in New York, and the real answers came to Randall only after the trip was over. What he did then furnishes the climax to a colorful, swift-moving story that measures well up to the standard Mr. Coxe's other books have set.

GEORGE HARMON COXE

Inland Passage

ALFRED · A · KNOPF   NEW YORK

1

THERE WAS nothing ominous in the two-line classified advertisement that Knox Randall discovered in the
morning paper. There was no hint of death in its message, no overtones of danger in its phrasing. There was
a possible suggestion of mild adventure involved, but it
was not for that reason that Randall was interested. To
him it offered a solution to a pressing economic problem that he had not fully realized until twenty minutes
earlier when he jumped out of bed and counted the
money he had emptied from his pockets the night before.

After nearly three months of Miami, the three thousand dollars he had started with had dwindled to a neat
three dollars and forty cents on this early April morning,
and, estimating conservatively, he figured he could get
to Palm Beach in reasonable comfort. It was the distance
between that point and New York which had sent him
turning to the classified ads before breakfast.

What he was looking for was one of those notices
which offered free transportation to a careful, experienced man in exchange for driving an empty car—a
Cadillac convertible preferred—to New York. Instead

he found himself reading an intriguing and somewhat
cryptic announcement which said:

> WANTED: EXPERIENCED MAN TO TAKE 74 FT.
> CRUISER TO N. Y. VIA INLAND WATERWAY. START
> SUNDAY. PHONE ————

Later when he told Lenore Calvert about it, and she
found out who owned the boat, she expressed certain
doubts and misgivings, all of which went unheeded;
still later, when he began to realize how right her pre-
monitions had been, he was hopelessly involved and
unable to extricate himself. Now, however, his mind
occupied with more pleasant possibilities, he hastened
to the nearest telephone booth, and twenty minutes
later he was knocking on the door of Lenore's apartment, prepared to make his preliminary report.

An amply curved, auburn-haired girl clad in a trailing housecoat and little else, Lenore Calvert allowed
herself to be hugged. The soundness of the kiss surprised her a little. It was not a lover's kiss nor born of
passion; rather it was inspired by friendliness and exuberance, and though she recognized it as such her green
eyes were watchful as she drew back.

"Why all the early morning ardor?"

"It isn't ardor," Randall said. "I just feel good. I think
the catharsis is complete."

"Is that good?"

Randall explained. He said he was cleansed, purged
of the past, his sickness forgotten.

Lenore was a realist and not given to flights of fancy.
"Some sickness," she said. "You mean you've finally forgotten that little number in New York?"

"If you're referring to Louise, she's but a hazy memory."

Lenore shook her hair out and tightened the belt of her robe. "It took you long enough," she said dryly. "Because she broke your engagement so she could marry a guy with more money you quit your job—"

"I got a leave of absence."

"—and started making passes at every girl in sight," said Lenore, not to be denied, "and drinking all the Bourbon in reach, and feeling oh, so sorry for yourself. So now you're cured?"

Randall put his folded newspaper aside, a strongly built man, neither tall nor short, with dark eyes and hair that had a tendency to curl when damp. At twenty-nine, he was good-looking in a rugged, square-faced sort of way, and the Florida sun had tanned him deeply so that when he smiled his teeth seemed unusually white.

"I'm like a guy who has been convalescing without knowing it," he said. "Getting better day by day until finally one morning he gets out of bed and discovers he's well again."

Lenore folded her arms, hugging her breasts. "I can see why you're a writer."

"A copywriter."

"Well?"

"It's different."

"You put words on paper. You think thoughts like that." She watched him, her smile hidden. "You want one egg or two?"

Randall said one and Lenore took him by the arm. In the kitchenette she handed him two oranges and motioned towards the squeezer while she put heat under the coffee.

At the table he showed her the advertisement while he ate, and she nodded, her glance thoughtful. "So you're going back."

"I have to," Randall said. "I'm down to my last three bucks. I don't want to wire the office and this way I can make it for free."

Lenore put down her cigarette and examined the nails of one hand while Randall sipped coffee and studied her. She was a big girl, generously fashioned but not horsy, with a well-proportioned body and, he remembered, nice legs. She had a wide, mobile mouth and white soft skin, tending to slackness in the face, with a hint of a second chin which made him wonder if she were not a little older than her announced twenty-six, though this, he realized, might be caused by her lack of enthusiasm for exercise in any form, dancing excepted.

"I'd sort of like to go back, too," she said, not looking up.

"Well, why don't you?"

She made no reply to this, but picked up her cigarette and tapped off the ash. Presently she said: "There'll probably be ten guys after that job."

"But I've got the inside track." Randall winked at her and took out a piece of paper on which he had scribbled an address. "I talked to this lawyer fellow who represents the owner. His name is Gifford; the lawyer, I mean. I gave him the vital statistics he wanted and I've got a date with him at ten thirty. He's got an office just off Flagler."

She arched her brows at him. Underneath them a smile grew slowly. Making a fist of her right hand she reached across the table, put it against the side of his jaw and pushed, pantomiming a right cross.

"Okay, Bruiser," she said, and stood up.

He carried things into the kitchenette and when he

came back Lenore was putting her handbag down. Beside it were two twenty-dollar bills. He looked at her, his glance suspicious.

"What's that for?"

"You have to live this week, even if you get the job."

"Un-unh." He grinned at her. "I've got my rent paid for a week. I've got a fifty-dollar deposit on that Drive-Yourself car I've been using. I ought to get twenty bucks back on that."

"Look." She regarded him severely, arms akimbo. "For a month now I've been helping you spend your money. You're entitled to a refund so leave us not get stuffy."

He started to argue, thought better of it. He picked up one of the twenties, dark eyes amused. "I'll take one of them," he said, "because I want to buy you dinner tonight and tell you all about it." He put his arm about her shoulder and gave it a friendly squeeze. "Okay?"

"Okay," she said. "And good luck, honey."

Eaton Gifford was a tall, well set-up man of thirty-five or so with wavy, medium-blond hair and light brown eyes. He had a toothy smile that flashed briefly as he shook hands with Knox Randall and waved him to a chair; then he settled himself behind the heavy flat-topped desk which had been placed across one corner of the extravagantly furnished office.

"Now let's see, Mr. Randall," he said, examining some notes he had made from the earlier telephone conversation. "You're twenty-nine, unattached, with three years service in the Navy, most of it on LCIs, right?"

"I was executive officer on one for awhile."

"Any family?"

"A father and mother out in Michigan."

"Are you well acquainted in Miami?"

"As a matter of fact, I'm not. I've been down here about three months. Sort of a vacation."

"Do you know Mr. Perry Noland? Or his boat? . . . Ever hear of him?"

Randall shook his head. Gifford said it did not matter and leaned back in his chair while he fitted a cigarette into an ebony holder. He did this with a certain air, as though impressed not only by himself but by his position and surroundings.

Randall was attentive but not impressed. The bronzed face with its blond mustache was a little too handsome for his taste, the sport coat and slacks too close to the *Esquire* pattern. To him the mouth seemed weak and sensuous and he was wondering why he should think so when the lawyer glanced up and spoke.

"You've made this inland trip before, of course?"

"Several times," lied Randall, who had sailed it but once. "Also I know navigation—not that you need it on that route—and I know how to handle boats."

"But you don't make it a business?"

Randall shook his head. He said he was just an amateur but he was experienced. He said he was in the advertising business and if Gifford cared to wire Olsen and Farley, his New York agency, they could testify as to his responsibility.

Gifford waved the cigarette holder. "Time enough for that when and if Mr. Noland approves. As I told you, I'm only acting for him. If we can get together I'll make an appointment for you. If Noland agrees why then"—the toothy smile flashed—"I guess you're in."

"Fine," said Randall, not liking Gifford any better but wanting the job. "What is it you and I have to get together on?"

"I was coming to that." Gifford leaned forward. "As you know it's an expensive proposition taking a boat of that size north. The hull isn't overpowered but the two Hall-Scotts will probably take better than six hundred dollars worth of gas getting to Falmouth, on the Cape, where you're to deliver it. In addition to that you'll need help. You'll have to find a mate somewhere. There'll be your salary, the mate's, and expenses—food and one thing or another—for two weeks or more. Naturally Mr. Noland would like to cut down somewhere if possible."

Randall sighed inaudibly and his hopes wavered. *Here it comes,* he thought. *Some gimmick that will louse everything up.*

"So?" he said.

Gifford's light brown eyes were watchful, the one sharp thing in his otherwise smooth, bronzed face.

"So we have an idea that should be good for both you and Mr. Noland. If you're from New York you've seen these summer cruises advertised sailing out of Maine. You know, the kind where you live aboard some schooner, and help work, and get your vacation for a nominal sum? Well, why not do the same thing on the Inland Waterway?"

"Oh," said Randall, recovering some of his lost interest.

"Exactly. In addition to the crew's quarters forward the *Julia* has three double staterooms and a single, all pretty comfortable except the single. You could take seven passengers. Say you take six at a hundred and fifty apiece, which would be cheap for a two-week trip like that. That's nine hundred. You eat ashore every night and plan your stops so you can. Explain that to the passengers so all you'll have to feed them is breakfast and lunch. A hundred and fifty dollars should more than cover your food, and you wind up with seven hundred and fifty to split with your mate, or steward, or whoever you get to help you. Maybe a third for him and two thirds for you."

Randall relaxed and new interest flickered in his dark gaze. Having been trained in a business that dealt in ideas he was equipped to recognize a good one when he heard it—or so he thought—and he saw at once the possibilities in Gifford's suggestion.

"It might work out," he said, not wanting to appear too eager.

"Of course it will work out." Gifford stood up and began to pace the room, his own enthusiasm adding arguments. "You'll get twice what you could expect in wages and Mr. Noland'll save himself several hundred dollars in expenses that he would otherwise have to pay for a crew and supplies. Thousands of people want to make that trip and only a few get the chance. You put the right ad in the paper and you'll be turning them away." He stopped to glance at Randall. "Providing you can sell yourself to Mr. Noland."

"How do I stand with you?"

"I think you'll do and I like your attitude."

"Where's the boat?"

"At Fort Lauderdale."

"Anybody aboard?"

Gifford pinched the cigarette from the holder. "Not now. Not for the last couple of weeks. But you'll find her sound enough."

"Okay," Randall said. "How do I get to see Mr. Noland?"

"I'll phone him," Gifford said. "How would two o'clock suit you?" He went back to the desk and wrote down an address. "He's not in the telephone book," he

said, "but it will be all right for you to go right out there.
I've weeded out a couple of applicants already and I
can stall any others that show up until I hear from Mr.
Noland."

Randall hauled himself out of the chair and accepted
the address. Somehow he felt no real liking for the
lawyer. He was just a little too smooth for Randall's
taste, impressing him as one who had never had to work
too hard for whatever success he had achieved, who had
never done much fighting, either physically or morally,
and had never been a real front-line guy. And yet, he
asked himself, what possible difference could it make?
He was highly pleased with the results of the conference and now he said so.

Gifford looked pleased too. He stroked his blond
mustache lightly and his gestures were expansive. They
shook hands, Randall in his gabardine slacks and seer-
sucker jacket, his dark hair starting to curl in the mid-
day heat, and Gifford in his impeccable jacket and doe-
skins.

"Good luck, Randall," he said. "I hope you put it
over."

Randall thanked him as Gifford opened the door, he
thanked the bespectacled secretary in the anteroom;
he went out already phrasing in his mind the advertisement he would write to entice the necessary paying
passengers.

2

THE street where Perry Noland lived proved to be a
dead-end affair on the north side of town and not far
from the bay. There were two houses on either side, a

turnaround for cars at the end, and beyond this two
stone gateposts with a heavy chain stretched between.
A sign which said: *Private Road,* hung there, and as
Randall made the turn he could see the red roof of a
house above the palms and shrubbery and, at one side,
a glimpse of blue waters.

It was quiet here as he got out of the car and checked
the address. He saw then that Noland had the last house
on the right, a one-story rambling affair with pink stucco
walls, less pretentious than its two-storied neighbors
but still not for wage slaves or white collar workers. The
grass was well clipped, the shrubs and foundation plant-
ing neat and orderly, the driveway which led to a side
door well kept. From the looks of the other houses he
decided they were closed, the owners already having
gone north, but here an expensive coupe stood in the
driveway opposite the door, a heavy stained-oak affair
with wrought iron straps and studdings.

Randall walked up two steps and pressed the white
button at one side, whereupon the sound of chimes
came faintly from somewhere inside. Presently the door
opened and a man in a natty tan suit peered at him
through thin-rimmed glasses.

"Yes," he said.

"I'm Knox Randall, Mr. Noland," Randall said. "I
think Mr. Gifford phoned you about me."

"Oh, yes. Yes, indeed. Come in."

Randall stepped into a gloomy hall and the closing of
the door made it gloomier. On the left a living room
faced the front of the house, its outlines vague because
of the drawn curtains; on the right, its French doors
overlooking the driveway, was a smaller and somewhat
brighter room, its maple furniture and leather chairs
suggesting it was used for a library or study. It was

cool here. The air was faintly blue with cigarette smoke, but mingled with it was a lingering musty smell, as though the windows had not yet been opened that day.

"We're getting ready to close up," Noland said, indicating a chair, "as you can see. That's why I'm anxious to get the *Julia* north as soon as possible."

"Sunday, the ad said," Randall offered.

"If possible. That way I can get a plane either Sunday or Monday and be out of here without having to worry about the boat."

Noland walked back and forth as he spoke, his movement jerky like his voice, his thin lips moving only slightly when he talked. Randall put his age in the late thirties and noticed now the exaggerated shoulders and slim waist that had been tailored into the tan suit. A loud, hand-painted tie lay against a blue-striped shirt, the complete picture intimating that Perry Noland was a city dweller by instinct and inclination. About Randall's height but slimmer, he had straight brown hair and, when presently he removed the glasses and used them to gesture with, bright blue eyes that were quick and restless, like the Broadway flavor of his accent. He kept moving while Randall went over the story of his background, and finally he nodded and sat down to light another cigarette.

"Anyway, you know the pitch," he said, "and I think it should work out if you write the right kind of ad. The *Julia's* a good boat, not new—I've had her three years but she was built in '28—and not fast either."

"How fast?"

Noland rubbed a pointed chin that seemed a little small for his face. His nose was pointed too, so that the overall impression reminded Randall of a weasel.

"Eleven knots all day long, if you've got water enough

under her, and a couple more if you push her."

He went on to give other details and Randall, watching him, began to speculate on yacht owners and where they got their money. Noland, for instance, did not look like the owner of a 74 footer, though at the moment Randall didn't know why he should think so. Most yachtsmen didn't look like yachtsmen when you got them ashore and into a change of clothes, and as he pursued the thought it occurred to him that what he really had in mind was that Noland did not look like a man of any great background, nor one who had inherited either wealth or social position. That meant he had made his money on his own, and only when Randall remembered the war and the easy money boys who had cashed in by black markets and sharp practice, did he find the explanation for Noland and his kind. Now, apparently, the man was pinched for cash, and even as he thought this Noland confirmed the hunch.

"I want to get out from under," he said. "I want to get her up to Falmouth so I can sell her this spring or summer, and I want to do it as cheap as I can. I've got a credit card with United Oil," he said. "You'll find their marinas in most of the places you stop, but I'll give you a couple hundred in cash so you won't have to depend on them. You can get sales slips and we can check up when you get north. There's just one thing I want to be sure of."

He leaned forward. He put on his glasses, giving his angular, bony face an owlish look. He was twisting a large signet ring on the little finger of his left hand as he watched Randall.

"Suppose you don't get six passengers to sign on," he said.

Randall knew what he meant, and as he began to do

some mental figuring Noland said: "The thing is, I don't want to hang around here next week waiting for you to get a load. What happens if you get four by Saturday? That's six hundred bucks. Figure a hundred for food and expenses. That's not so much for you and the steward, or whoever you get to help you. Will you agree to shove off on Sunday with four?"

To Randall this would still be a good deal but for effect he gave the matter some visible thought. Then he nodded. "Why not?" he said. "I don't expect to get rich."

Noland seemed relieved. He leaned back and for the first time his thin lips fashioned a smile.

"It's a deal," he said. "You're my boy." He stood up quickly, his voice clipped. "Today's Wednesday. Your ad will come out tomorrow morning, and you've got Thursday and Friday to get your customers. Saturday too, while you're laying in your supplies. Four or more and it's your problem. Under four I'll kick in with some extra cash so you can still make a few bucks."

He moved to a kneehole desk and picked up three keys on a chain. "The padlock key," he said, handing them to Randall, "is for the hatch up forward. The other two are for the port door of the deckhouse and the door that goes from the cockpit to the master's stateroom. Take a run out and look her over," he said, and went on to explain where the boat was berthed.

"I'll get that ad written first," Randall said.

"Good idea." Noland took out a pigskin wallet and extracted a card. He peered at it a moment and then replaced it. "Maybe I'd better give you this credit card and the money later," he said. "Give Gifford a ring if everything is all right. Give him a ring anyway."

"How would it be if I stopped by here Saturday for the card?"

"Well"—Noland rubbed his palms a moment—"the
trouble is I'm away most of the time. Tell you what," he
said. "Suppose I drive out Sunday morning around nine
—I don't think you'll be starting too early your first day
—and see you then?"

He looked pleased when Randall said that would be
all right with him. He rubbed his hands again as he
started for the hall, slipped on a scatter rug, and cursed
abruptly.

"I'll be looking for your ad," he said when he had re-
adjusted his padded shoulders. He opened the door.
"I hope you get a load and make yourself some dough."
He gestured a signal of good-bye but made no effort to
shake hands, and Randall stepped across the narrow
porch and went down the steps into the afternoon sunshine.

Randall was quite proud of the advertisement he
handed in at the classified counter of the *Journal* that
afternoon. It was a six-line item which not only gave the
essential facts but also gave sufficient color to make the
proposition sound attractive. He figured that one insertion, properly phrased, would do the job if it could
be done at all, and because his money was paying for
it he put the same care into its making that he would
have used on a client's full-page layout. As a result he
did not get to see the *Julia*. For it was then four o'clock
and he decided that his inspection tour could wait until
the morning, and that a swim—possibly his last one—
would be more to the point.

He spent the rest of the afternoon in lazy self indul-
gence, giving his imagination free rein about the trip
north, and by seven o'clock he was at Lenore Calvert's
place clad in his custom-made gabardine, his hair neatly

combed and his dark face beaming. Lenore took one
look at him and nodded.

"So you got the job?"

"I think so," he said. "Come on."

Lenore looked very fetching in her print dress and
spectator pumps, and her thick auburn hair was piled
high in some complicated design that, on her, looked
good. She always wore stockings when she went out
because, she said, she hated bare white legs and hers
were always white because she always burned and
peeled, and she wanted therefore, no part of the beach
and its much celebrated ultra-violet and infra-red rays.
Now, getting into the car, she pulled her skirts up to
readjust the seams, and asked for details. Randall said
no. He said they must wait until they had a drink, and
so he drove in comparative silence to this place on the
Beach where the cocktails were moderately generous
and the roast beef really good.

It was small, this place, narrow but deep, without
entertainment except for a piano which was placed far
back and played by a portly colored man who stayed
away from the loud pedal and played with harmony in
mind instead of arpeggios. The things he did were
pleasant, and you could talk without shouting, and presently Lenore was sipping her Martini and listening to
Randall's account of his conquest. He spoke with enthusiasm as he gave her the details but when he finished,
her green eyes were thoughtful and remote, and, realizing now that her reaction was not quite what he had
expected, he asked her about it.

"You say this fellow's name is Noland?" she asked
finally.

"Perry Noland. Why?"

Lenore took a cigarette from the pack he had put on

the table. "I don't know," she said. "I think he's the one
somebody took a few shots at a week or so ago."

Randall supplied a light, not saying anything for a
few seconds, but watching Lenore. When she did not
elaborate he said:

"What about it? Who says so? Was it in the papers?"

Lenore finished her cocktail and spoke without enthusiasm. She said she didn't know if it was in the papers
or not. She said she heard someone talking.

"In Sylvester's," she said, mentioning a bar down
the street from her apartment where they sometimes
went for a quick drink. "I was sitting there one afternoon—and I'm in and out of there quite often and they
don't pay too much attention to me—and Sylvester was
telling some fellow about it. I think Noland leases the
place to Sylvester, or owns it or something, and maybe
that's how Sylvester knew. Anyway the way I got it
somebody opened up on Noland from a passing car—
and missed."

Randall's recent feeling of accomplishment and well-
being began to deteriorate. He had an old scar on one
brow, put there by a football cleat some years ago. It
made the brow irregular and when he frowned it
twisted oddly; it was well twisted now as he remembered his recent interview with Perry Noland.

"I wondered about him when I talked to him," he
said.

"Wondered? How?" Lenore said.

"The way he looked, the way he talked." He went on
to describe Noland when Lenore questioned him. "Had
a pointed chin and a lot of angles in his face," he said.
"Reminded me of a weasel, just like his padded
shoulders reminded me of Broadway. He knew something about boats all right and that one in particular,

but he didn't talk like a man who'd been around them long." He hesitated and then thought of something else.

"But what the hell. Plenty of sharpshooters have been cleaning up the last few years in one racket or another. So he cleaned up and he's got a boat he wants taken north. I'm his boy." He beckoned for the waiter, some of his good nature returning. "What do I care about his private life? . . . Who is supposed to have shot at him?" he added as a new thought occurred to him. "Or didn't Sylvester say?"

"He thought Ernie Mondello."

Somewhere in Randall's consciousness there was a fusion of nebulous processes and he decided the name was vaguely familiar. "A gambler?" he said. "Here on the Beach?"

"Something like that," Lenore said. "He used to run a nightclub. You know the one—*The Surfside*. I think Noland was his partner, or put up the money or something. Anyway, from what I heard, Noland sold it out from under Mondello, or took it over and—"

She stopped and her glance went beyond Randall, steadied, then narrowed as a sudden stiffness came about her red, mobile mouth. She reached out, still not looking at him, and touched his hand.

"Excuse me a minute," she said. "Tell the waiter I'll have the same, only with lemon peel."

Randall stood up. Their table was on the right side, about half way down, and he waited until he was seated and had ordered the drinks before he glanced over his shoulder. Lenore was standing at the bar, a semi-circular affair to the left of the entrance, and with her was a swart, thin-faced man in a powder-blue sport coat.

Randall had seen him before, though he did not know

his name. In the month that he had been taking Lenore around—and he had been seeing her nearly every day —he had seen the fellow perhaps once a week, each time either here, where they so often ate, or in Sylvester's Bar. In every instance Lenore had gone to speak to the man for a minute or two, after which he usually finished his drink and left. The last time it happened Randall had asked who it was.

Lenore had dismissed the subject as unimportant, saying he was a character she had known in New York but now, thinking back, Randall realized how little he knew about this girl who had been his companion these past weeks. What little he did know he liked, for she was the sort of girl he needed under the circumstances; yet he had no real knowledge of her past or background, and such information as he had was sketchy.

He had met her in Sylvester's at a time when he was taking a dim view of the world and all its people. Behind him he had two months of drinking and idleness, and girls who could be picked up at bars and beaches by anyone who was moderately presentable and had money to spend. He had, finally, enough of such affairs and he was still brooding about this girl in New York who had decided to marry someone else, and he was gloomily nursing a highball when he noticed Lenore having a drink and minding her own business at the other end of the bar.

He liked her looks then, though he did nothing about it. There was a sexiness about her and the way she carried herself that had a certain distinction, but such attributes she apparently took for granted; she made no attempt then or in the following days to attract attention, nor would she notice the others who came in to sit closer, watching from the corners of their eyes and finally asking for a match, a gambit which got them nowhere since she simply called the bartender and told him that the gentleman wanted a light.

She told Randall this later, but even at first he admired her technique, and it was this as much as anything else that finally inspired him to offer—through the good offices of the bartender—to buy her a drink. By this time he knew she was aware of him, and it pleased him when she accepted and nodded casually towards him to lift her glass in thanks.

Randall let it go at that on that particular afternoon, but the following day when he came in before dinner and found the stool next to her unoccupied, he asked if she minded. She said hello, and no, she didn't mind at all, and before the evening was over they'd had a pleasant dinner and a few laughs, and he had a date for the following evening.

Again they had dinner, this time followed by dancing and several drinks in which she matched him drink for drink. But when, coming home, he made his passes, she parried expertly so that after it was over and he kissed her good-night at her door their understanding was such that they could both laugh at what had happened. That was how it started, and it had been fun for Randall because she was easy to be with, demanding little attention and quite content, it seemed, whether the fare was dogs and beer or breast of guinea hen and twelve-year-old Scotch. She liked to drink and so did he when he was with her, and once, when he'd had too much, she put him to bed at her place on the studio couch, making no fuss about it then or in the morning when he apologized.

He found her green eyes wise and experienced in human behavior, and he discovered that she looked more

sexy than she was. But still he knew very little about
her background. She was from New York. She was on
a little vacation. She mentioned once that she had come
from around Boston, from a large family, but more recently she had worked in a New York nightclub, one of
the more gaudy establishments with shows which featured a line of girls. With her looks and her full blown
figure she had done all right—

"Until," she said, "I discovered I could make twice
as much money selling cigarettes, and wear more clothes,
not that I'm particularly modest."

He had never questioned her beyond this, accepting
their relationship for what it was and knowing that
when, and if, she wanted to confide further, she would
do so. . . .

He stood up, his thoughts suspended, as she stopped
beside the table. When she sat down she took another
cigarette and gulped half of her Martini, her eyes avoid-
ing him. After a few seconds of this she reached out
and covered his hand with her own, and he twisted his
so that he could hold her fingers. Finally she looked at
him, a disturbed darkness in her eyes that he had not
seen before.

"I think I'll go with you," she said.

He blinked, aware at once that she was serious but
unable at first to put down his surprise. When he was
quite sure she meant what she said, he grinned.

"Okay," he said. "We'll share the master's stateroom."

"No we won't," she said, and now she laughed with
him. "You'll stay where the crew stays and I'll travel in
style. How much is it going to cost me?" She reached
for her bag, and he said with some alarm:

"Hey! Not here."

"All right. But tell the truth. I'll find out anyway."

"A hundred and fifty for the two weeks," he said, not understanding what prompted her decision but well satisfied that she had made it. "Seventy-five a week."

"You've got a passenger, but no discounts. I've got some money. You've been buying me four or five dinners a week and furnishing all the liquor—"

"Dinners are not included," he cut in, explaining that only breakfast and lunch would be supplied. "From now on," he added, jokingly, "you buy your own."

"Hah!" she said. "Are there going to be any men passengers? I'll find someone to buy dinners."

Randall laughed and said all right. He said she could go, and though he knew that they had no common future and realized that once in New York their paths would seldom if ever cross, he was really pleased to think that she would come. He asked her if she was ready to eat, and she said: "In a minute," and hesitated. "Will you take good care of me, Knox?" she said. "I mean, until we get to New York."

Her tone was suddenly wistful and he saw that her smile was gone, choking off the obvious crack that had occurred to him.

"I mean"—she stumbled on the words and tried again —"I mean I don't know much about boats and if something should happen—"

She stopped again and he saw that deep down there was something akin to fear in her eyes. He said of course he'd take care of her, and wondered as he spoke if the man in the powder-blue coat was responsible for the change that had come over her.

3

THE optimism that Knox Randall had felt the previous afternoon was soon justified the following morning, not only by the speed with which he got his first applicant, but by the cruiser itself. Driving out from Miami his optimism had been tempered somewhat by certain doubts about the boat, but when he parked his car at nine o'clock and looked her over, from a distance first to get the overall picture, he was more than pleased with what he saw.

She lay against a concrete bulkhead a hundred yards or so west of the railroad bridge, just beyond a slight bend in the New River. There was quite a stretch of this bulkhead, with its extensions for water, but most of the boats that had wintered there had gone north and the *Julia* was quite alone on her side of the river, the mistress not only of the bulkhead but of the adjacent sandy plaza which had been cleared of trees and brush.

Randall looked her over fore and aft before going aboard and what he saw coincided with Noland's description. She did not look fast but she did look comfortable, with plenty of beam and pleasing if conservative lines. She had none of the modern streamlining, but neither did she look topheavy, and he was delighted when he saw she had a flying bridge. He made his way there first and stripped the covers from the wheel and controls, knowing that though there would be wet days ahead he would at least have the visibility he wanted when the weather was thick and the deckhouse windows had a tendency to steam up.

He was below, looking over the interior layout, when he was hailed from the shore, and presently he was talking to his first applicant, a brown-skinned, slow-spoken man with the build of a blacksmith. . . .

By eleven o'clock Randall had signed on four passengers and collected half of the fare. The first man, whose name was Oliver Dalton, had a small-town look about him, both in his clothes and mannerisms, that made Randall wonder why he should be interested in such a trip; he seemed to be out of place aboard a boat, and yet there was something about him that promised to wear well on a cruise of this length, and Randall could think of no good reason for refusing him passage.

The couple who came next with the foreign-sounding name and accents to match, were polite and well-mannered, old enough to know what they wanted—Randall put them in their late forties—but not so old as to be crotchety. The fourth passenger, a tall, gray-haired man, close to sixty by the looks of him, was mild-mannered and pleasant, his conversation indicating that he not only liked boats but also knew quite a lot about them. His name, he said, was John Barnard, and he seemed very pleased indeed when Randall said he could come.

He had also turned down another couple: a plump, red-faced man of forty-five or so, and a platinum blonde half his age. Mr. and Mrs. Something-or-other the man said, a statement that Randall did not believe but which made no difference to him anyway. Married or not he did not like the man's looks nor his brash aggressiveness; the blonde—buxom, bold-eyed, and gushing—was a type he had seen before, and together they made a com-

bination which to Randall added up to a two-week-long
party with a lot of liquor and noise and late hours, and
no peace and quiet for anyone else aboard.

Then, shortly before noon, while Randall was still
congratulating himself over his handling of this couple
and his general good fortune, business picked up.

She was dark and luscious-looking—he could tell this
much the moment she stepped from the taxi—with a
low contralto voice and a figure that, if not exactly perfect in its contours, was worth a second look in any company. As she walked across the sandy stretch on her
high heels he saw that her legs were on the heavy side,
though nicely shaped and well-tanned, and even in the
simple linen dress he could see that she was deep-
breasted and sturdily built. Then, as he stepped to the
bulkhead to meet her he had a close-up of her face, and
he promptly forgot about her other attributes.

"Am I at the right place?" she asked, holding the
paper. "And am I in time?" she added.

He realized he was staring. He colored before her
amused glance; finally he found his voice.

"Yes," he said. "Come aboard."

She took his outstretched hand and stepped on tip-
toe to the deck. When she came forward and let her
heels down she slipped slightly on the varnished surface
and he caught her arm to steady her. She said: "Thank
you," smiling up at him, and he saw that she was shorter
than he had thought, with smooth olive skin, almost clas-
sically regular features, and black eyes set deeply behind tapering lids which gave them an elongated intimate look.

He let go of her arm. He said they could sit in the
deckhouse and she said she had no business wearing
high heels aboard a boat like this. Then, before he could

stop her, she reached down and slipped off her pumps.

"That's better," she said, and padded ahead of him alongside the deckhouse and through the open door. "Now," she said when they were seated, "tell me about the trip."

Randall found it hard to keep his eyes off her as he explained how the cruise would operate. He said it was his plan to take it reasonably easy, tying up each night at a place where they could have dinner ashore. He said that this should be the only additional expense, since breakfast and lunch would be served aboard.

"It sounds like fun," she said. "A hundred and fifty dollars, the ad said. Payable when?"

"Well, seventy-five now, to keep your place." He smiled back at her. "So you won't say you'll go and then back out and leave me with an empty berth, and the other seventy-five Sunday morning when we push off."

"Could I see where I'm to sleep?"

He said sure and she put her shoes back on. "I'll show you around," he said, and crossed the deckhouse to the companionway ladder forward.

He went down the four steps and turned to give her his hand, a gesture that somehow seemed necessary under the circumstances, and she held on a moment as they stood in the doorway to the galley. When she had expressed approval of its compact efficiency he indicated the toilet and lavatory opposite, and then led her two steps forward to the double stateroom.

"In here?" she asked. "Oh, this is nice."

She inspected the two curtained ports on each side, felt the inner-spring mattresses, noted the drawers underneath and the lockers above.

While she voiced her admiration of the quarters he

told her that another girl would share the cabin with
her and now, as he stood close to her, her nearness and
the fragrance of her perfume doing strange things to his
stomach, he began to wonder how she would get along,
not so much with Lenore Calvert but with the men
aboard. He was glad now that among the present passengers there were no obvious wolves. He wondered
about the steward, not yet engaged, and then he wondered about himself.

There was something exciting about this woman
whose name he did not yet know, a fascination that he
had felt from the instant he touched her hand. He did
not know what it was, or how he knew, but it seemed
to him that here was a woman—he put her age at
twenty-seven or eight—who would always fascinate
men. A possessive woman perhaps, demanding comfort
and physical pleasures, but always aware of the subtle
power she possessed to charm and influence those who
interested her. Somewhere behind the olive softness of
her features he felt there was a determination and
singleness of purpose that, quite unafraid of anything
that life might offer, might be both rewarding and exciting if properly explored.

These and other things passed through his mind in
the few moments he stood there and then, as she looked
up at him again, he turned away.

"I'll show you the rest of it," he said, and helped her
back to the deckhouse and down a similar ladder aft on
the starboard side.

On the immediate right as they faced aft, along the
narrow passageway which led to the after stateroom,
was a single cabin, not all of which had full headroom;
next to it was a compact double cabin, its bunks one
above the other but comfortable, and beyond was a

toilet, lavatory and enclosed shower. At the end of
the passageway and just forward of the cockpit was the
wide master's stateroom and when the girl saw it she
was impressed.

"Why, this is wonderful."

"I gave it to a man and his wife who came earlier,"
Randall said with some reluctance.

"Oh, I didn't mean I wanted it. I think my quarters
are very nice indeed."

She closed the door and he drew back to let her pass.
Out in the middle of the river a boat went past, apparently traveling a little too fast; for a moment later,
when the girl was opposite Randall, the wash rocked
the *Julia* violently, throwing her against him so that he
had to brace himself. For a long second he had her by
the arms, the softness of her body hard against him;
then the deck steadied and he let go, and she said:

"I'm sorry. The next time I come aboard I'll wear
sneakers."

Her hand was hot inside his own as he helped her to
the deckhouse; as they sat down there was a film of
moisture on his tanned forehead, and his dark hair had
begun to curl. Then she was taking out some bills and
counting out seventy-five dollars.

"I'll give you a receipt," he said, and then he chuckled.
"I don't even know your name. I'm Knox Randall."

She smiled and said hello in her low voice. "I don't
need a receipt," she said, "but the name is Kelly."

"Miss?"

"Miss."

She stood up then, and closed her bag. She asked
when she had to be aboard and he said he planned to
start around ten Sunday morning, taking it easy the
first day and spending the next night at Palm Beach.

"You can come Sunday morning before ten," he said, "or you can sleep aboard the night before if you like."

She said she would let him know, and he helped her ashore, and then he stepped back into the deckhouse to watch her walk on her high heels to the waiting cab.

The next taxi to circle onto the sandy plaza and pull to a stop did not come until after four o'clock. Like the one preceding it, it contained a woman, but Randall could not get a good look at her because she did not get out; instead the door opened and a slender, wiry man stepped down and headed for the boat.

A long-visored fishing cap sat jauntily atop the newcomer's sandy hair. Khaki trousers, a faded army shirt, and dirty sneakers completed his attire, and he walked confidently, with the lithe, springy stride of a fast lightweight. His glance took in the boat from stem to stern as he advanced, and when he was ready he said:

"Mr. Randall? I'm Alan Harding. I understand you're looking for some help."

Randall said that was right and who told him.

"The fellow on the party boat down the river. They said you were asking around this morning."

Randall shook hands and asked him aboard. The first thing he had done that morning when he arrived in Lauderdale was to make some inquiries along the riverfront boats as to where he might find a competent mate and steward. At one of these, a diesel-powered fishing boat which was berthed between the highway and railroad bridges, a leather-skinned veteran heard him out, spoke briefly to his companions and they said: "Young Harding ain't doing anything; wasn't the last we heard."

Randall asked where he could find Harding and they

said they didn't know but he generally stopped by during the day. He was, they said, a fair cook and steward. He had worked aboard several other boats from time to time, though never for too long. As to the reason for the constant changes, they refused to speculate.

Now, examining Harding at close range, Randall found that he liked the fellow's looks. He was perhaps twenty-six or so, his snub-nose face sunburned and freckled, his eyebrows bleached by sun and weather. Without resembling one in the least, he reminded Randall of a terrier.

"I need a steward."

"What are the duties?"

"Cook breakfast and get lunch for six or seven passengers." Randall hesitated, and when there was no reaction he said: "Relieve me at the wheel and make yourself generally useful . . . I understand you've worked around quite a bit but never for long. Why is that?"

Harding had light-blue eyes and there was a smile behind them as they centered on Randall. "Some say I'm a snoop," he said. "I don't always mind my own business . . . Yeah, I've worked around," he said. "I was skipper of this one for a while."

"The *Julia*?" said Randall. "When?"

"Last year. For seven or eight months."

"What happened?"

"Well, Mr. Noland—he's still the owner, isn't he?— never used her much but he always had a good supply of expensive cigars aboard and his liquor cabinet was stocked with the best. He used to go two or three weeks without coming aboard and it got so I was drinking more of his liquor than he was. He warned me once and then the next time, well—"

He let the sentence dangle, his smile quizzical, his eyes challenging, as though to say: Well, there it is. If you don't want me, say so.

Randall didn't know whether to laugh or not. Such frankness impressed him and he found himself liking the little man because of his confession. He had an idea Harding would work out. He did not look like a trouble-maker and Randall was confident that he could personally handle any such incidents that might arise. Yet he continued to wonder about the other because something about his assurance and manner suggested a type of background and breeding quite different from that usually found among waterfront characters. He also thought of Lenore Calvert and Miss Kelly, and he decided to speak of them.

"There'll be a couple of good-looking unattached women aboard," he said. "I wouldn't want any trouble with you."

Harding massaged the side of his snub-nose with one knuckle. He examined the inside of his cap.

"You won't have any trouble with me," he said. "Unless they ask for it. And anyway"—he grinned again—"it's going to be kind of crowded for that sort of thing, isn't it? Mind telling me what the job pays and how far we're going?"

Randall stepped over to the built-in sideboard and found the morning paper. He showed Harding the ad and said he already had six signed on.

"Say, that's all right," Harding said. "Noland gets the boat taken up a lot cheaper—does he buy the gas?—and you make a nice stake."

Randall said even if he didn't get a seventh passenger he would collect nine hundred dollars. "A hundred and fifty should cover food and beer and cokes, which leaves seven-fifty. Five for me and two-fifty for you." He sat down and said: "I figure two weeks to New York and then two days for you and me to Falmouth after we dump the passengers."

Harding stood up and adjusted his cap. "I'd like to go," he said. "It sounds interesting. When will you let me know about it?"

Randall had already made up his mind. He had been a good judge of men in the Navy, and although he seemed to sense an instability about Harding that he could not put his finger on, he felt sure that in so short a trip it would not matter.

"If you start," he said, "you go all the way. I'm not going to get hung up half way there. Also, what liquor you drink you buy yourself."

Harding shrugged indifferently. "It still sounds good."

"Then be here around nine thirty in the morning," Randall said. "We've got things to do."

Harding gave him a casual, two-fingered salute, ducked out the door and jumped nimbly ashore. He walked quickly to the waiting taxi and when it pulled out a few seconds later Randall still did not know what the girl in the back seat looked like.

4

KNOX RANDALL packed his bags and moved out of his room the following morning. He breakfasted hurriedly at the corner drug store and then he telephoned Gifford, the lawyer, who offered his compliments when he heard what had been accomplished and told Randall not to worry about the cash and credit card for the

United Oil marinas, adding that if Noland did not come
to the boat before then, he would surely be there Sunday morning.

Alan Harding, unencumbered by any baggage, was
sitting on the bulkhead next to the *Julia* when Randall
parked his coupe, and he gave a hand with Randall's
bags, unlocking the padlock on the hatch and helping
stow them below. Randall told him to start sweeping out
the staterooms while he changed to ducks and T-shirt,
and when he was ready he moved the ladder from the
after deckhouse companionway and started to work on
the generator. As though a good omen for what was to
follow the motor started with the third spin of the fly-
wheel, stuttered a few times, and settled down to a
cheerful drone.

Randall saluted it, knowing from past experience
about the contrariness of some generators. He put the
ladder back, found paper and pencil in a deckhouse
locker and began to make a list of things to be done that
day. Before very long he came to the subject of provisions and as he began to list the things he needed an idea
came to him and he called Alan from his work.

"How about getting a ham and a turkey roasted?" he
asked.

"Sure," Harding said. "Keep us in lunches for nearly
a week."

"Do you know any place that'll do it for us and have
them ready by tomorrow afternoon? Take the car," he
said when Alan nodded, "load it with some of this
canned stuff." He handed the other a list and added:
"Get three cases of canned beer and as much coke as
you can."

He gave Harding some money and the keys to the
car, and when the coupe swung into the road and out of

sight, he began to move the wicker furniture out of the
deckhouse. It was possible to rearrange the pieces so
that part of the rug could be lifted and the engine-room
hatches raised, but now he wanted to give the house a
thorough cleaning first. He was just taking up the car-
pet when he heard a car and glanced up to see a taxi
pull to a stop fifty feet away.

The girl who got out was tall and blond and slender.
Her legs and arms were bare, and the peasant-skirted
sport dress she wore had a halter-like top so that in the
back there was very little of anything from the waist
up. He noticed this much as she got out of the cab; as
she started towards him he saw that her legs were slim
and straight—but not too straight—her carriage erect
and easy. After that he had no further impression at the
time because she was looking at him, her smile friendly,
and saying with unaffected cheerfulness:

"Good morning. Is this the boat that was advertised
in the *Journal*? I mean, about the cruise? Have you any
room left?"

Knox Randall hesitated, an odd excitement stirring
in him. Without knowing anything about this girl except that she was young and fresh-looking, he found
himself assigning her a category that had once been
familiar to him. He had known girls like this in college,
and later, and he had seen a few in Florida, though
never alone or unattended. Now, thinking about the
small remaining cabin, he was afraid.

The others making the trip, Lenore Calvert excepted,
were only people who had a hundred and fifty dollars to
spend. Here, suddenly, was a girl he would have been
happy to have aboard just for the sake of her company.
He knew instinctively that she would be fun to have
along, and although in looks and mannerisms she was

the exact opposite of the luscious Miss Kelly, she already seemed important in his eyes.

He thought of Lenore, who did not yet know where she was to sleep. He thought of giving this girl Lenore's berth in the forward cabin, and then he was ashamed of his disloyalty.

"One," he said finally, pushing his hair back from his forehead. "I'm afraid it's pretty small."

"May I see it?" the girl asked, and then she was aboard unaided, ducking through the deckhouse door and pivoting gracefully to look about and express her approval.

Randall moved aft to the passageway below and opened the first door, still afraid but not knowing what else he could do except stand there with his fingers crossed.

She stepped inside and what she saw was a cabin the same length as the bunk, which, fortunately, had a good mattress and looked comfortable. There was a three-foot space beside this, offering room to move about and dress, but of the length, only three-fourths of it had full headroom. There was a jog at the forward end made by the engine-room bulkhead and the deckhouse, so that in effect the last eighteen inches of the bunk were tucked into this niche, leaving a two-foot upward clearance for the occupant's feet.

Randall waited while she explored the cabin, aware of the subtle fragrance she had brought to it. A hidden dry-cell somewhere inside him had suddenly come to life and was shooting strange currents through his chest and when, finally, she turned and her smile was still there, he felt wonderful.

"What's wrong with this?" she said. "There's plenty of room for me. I'll only sleep here anyway."

They went topside and out to the wicker chairs he had moved to the sand. She said her name was Nora Graham. He explained about the trip and its cost, making things sound as attractive as he could. She produced seventy-five dollars from a billfold and now, as he sat there wanting to spend some time with her and get better acquainted, an odd urgency had come over her and it was clear that she wanted to get away. He did not understand this at first because he was being as charming as he knew how in the hope that she would like him. Then he saw the waiting taxi and knew this must be the reason for her restlessness.

He told her she could come aboard Saturday night if she liked, but she said she didn't think so. She'd be there around nine Sunday morning, she said, and then, giving him the same unaffected smile she greeted him with, she climbed into the taxi and was gone.

Randall went back to the nearest wicker chair and sat down, stretching his legs luxuriously and spending the next few minutes in a blissful contemplation of the days ahead. For a while he could think of nothing but Nora Graham, knowing already the kind of girl she was, but speculating on her background and the reasons why she might be taking a trip of that sort. It occurred to him that a nice girl—and she was certainly that by his standards—might well have asked more questions about who else would be aboard; she might have asked questions about him so that she would have a better idea of exactly what she was getting into. The fact that she had not done so bothered him just a little and led presently to the further consideration of Miss Kelly and Lenore Calvert.

He remembered his promise to take care of Lenore, though he still wasn't sure what it all meant, and this sobered him a little. "Three dames aboard," he said softly, "not counting the husband and wife."

And now he was concerned, though he didn't know why, as to whether three such different women could get along in close quarters for two weeks, and if there would be any trouble. He was still wondering about this when Alan Harding came back with the coupe and the supplies. . . .

They worked all afternoon around the boat. They swept, and cleaned, and polished. They swabbed down the deck and sides, they started the motors and let them run. They checked the tanks and got out all the charts and arranged them in order, laying out a rough itinerary as they did so. Later they sat a while with cans of beer and talked of things while Randall made out another list of supplies that had been forgotten.

He went into Miami for dinner that evening but he left Lenore early after promising he would pick her up between eight thirty and nine the following evening, since she wanted to spend the last night aboard. He was more tired than he had thought when he got back, and after a quick nightcap, he went to bed and slept soundly.

He was up at eight, and after a quick shave and shower he drove into the center for breakfast. Alan Harding was waiting when he returned, and there were still many things to be done before Harding took the coupe to town to pick up the ham and turkey which had been ordered.

By lunch time they were about finished and Randall told Harding to take the rest of the day off. He wanted to know if Harding expected to spend the night aboard and the little man grinned and said no. He said he had certain unfinished business to take care of. He said there were a couple of girls to say good-bye to, and how were chances of a little advance.

Randall gave him twenty dollars. The things that Harding said and did continued to amuse him but with the twenty dollars went a sober warning.

"Hangover or not," he said, "you be here at eight in the morning with your gear."

"Sure," said Harding. "Eight o'clock it'll be, Skipper."

Randall took it easy that afternoon. Occasionally a passing craft would rock the *Julia* gently in her berth, and the double-decked sightseeing boat, its wide, street-car-like seats crowded as usual, made its scheduled round trip up the river. But for the most part the water was quiet, there was little to attract his attention, and as the afternoon wore on he had plenty of time to think. With his thoughts came a new understanding of the responsibility that would soon be his.

Until now he had been too busy getting ready, and too pleased with the opportunity, to consider the other aspects of the job. It was a long way to New York. Some of the days would be tedious and hard. Things got pretty strenuous on a trip of this sort and he could only hope that the weather would be generally good, and that his passengers would slip into the routine without clashes of personality and temper. He went over the list in his mind, sizing them up as best he could, and it was then that the taxi swung out of the tree-lined road and circled close to the boat.

He saw at once that the passenger was Miss Kelly but he was not prepared for the bags that the driver started to unload. A little dismayed but trying not to show it, he went to give a hand.

Miss Kelly wore a white sharkskin suit which made a striking contrast to her smooth olive skin and tanned legs. Her dark, elongated eyes were amused as she studied him, and apparently he had not been too successful in masking his original surprise for she said:

"Don't look so alarmed, Captain. I'm not going to stay."

Randall was fussed. He had been fussed when she first came aboard and he hadn't been able to overcome the feeling of disturbance she created. He stammered and said it was all right, that he just hadn't expected her.

He took the hatbox and pullman case below and she called down to him from the deckhouse, telling him to put them on one of the bunks.

"I'm not going to unpack now but I would like to come back later," she said when he returned. "You said it would be all right."

"Yes," Randall said. "Only—well, I didn't expect you and I have to be in town this evening." He thought about Lenore Calvert and his promise to call for her. "I'll be back by ten though."

"That will be perfectly all right." She hesitated, her head tipped as she considered him, her eyes obscure. She worried her lower lip with the tips of her teeth and then, having made up her mind, she said: "Could we sit down a minute. There's something I'd like to tell you."

She chose the settee and motioned him beside her. She pushed her hair back, her gaze sliding past him to the river. "I thought I'd better explain something," she said. "I'm not Miss Kelly, really. That was my maiden name. My name is Julia. This boat was named after me."

Randall was nodding politely, paying attention to what she said. He heard every word distinctly but the mental mechanism which registered those words must

have been faulty at the time for his reaction was de-
layed.

He said: "I beg your pardon." And then it hit, and the
shock came, and in his disbelief he said: "Julia? You're
Mrs. Noland?"

She looked at him and spoke quietly. "Yes," she said.
"I'm Mrs. Noland."

"But does he know that—"

"No. I left him after I found out the day before yesterday that I could make this trip." She took a breath
and her mouth tightened. She had a short upper lip, a
slight tilt to her nose so that the nostrils were somewhat
prominent. Randall saw them flare as her lips grew
thin, and then she relaxed and her tone was matter of
fact.

"It's a long story." She glanced at the waiting taxi.
"Much too long while that meter is running, even if you
were interested. Do you know anything about Mr.
Noland?"

"A little."

"He's not going to like it. He doesn't like anybody
who crosses him. I'm at a hotel but he doesn't know
which one. I have an idea he'll have someone watch
the railroad station and the airport." She shrugged and
said: "Oh, I know it sounds melodramatic, but it's nothing I can go to the police about; not until he does something to me. I'd much rather not give him the chance."

She hesitated and when Randall did not speak she
continued: "I'm sure it would never occur to him to look
for me here and that's why I want to stay aboard
tonight. I've been worrying about it. I've been afraid
that he might come tomorrow, not for me but to see you
off, and it would be my luck to run into him. Once I'm
aboard I can stay below until we've started."

Randall was about to say that Mr. Noland intended to do exactly as his wife had feared, but he didn't. There was no point in scaring her. If Noland came and she stayed below—

"I thought I ought to tell you," she said. "I got to thinking about this trip you worked up, and the other people who are counting on it, and I thought if you knew about me—why then you'd be sure that nothing happened to spoil things."

Randall exhaled slowly. He glanced at the cigarette in his hand and found his fingers trembling. He snapped the butt through the open door and now he knew that what he had just heard was not going to make any difference. Julia Noland was old enough to know what she was doing and the rest of it was none of his business.

"I'm glad you told me," he said as she rose, "so long as we forget that you told me. You signed on as Miss Kelly and it can stay that way as long as you like."

She stood close to him, mouth curving, her dark eyes satisfied with what they found in his face. "Thank you," she said. "I'll see you a little after ten."

When she had gone, Randall made himself a stiff highball. It had very little effect on his mood and later, after he had changed and driven out to the beach, the Martinis and the solitary dinner cheered him not at all. The steak, which was tender and cooked as he liked it, was just so much food, because he kept thinking of Julia Noland and her husband.

He was still thinking the same thoughts as he drove into Miami, still worrying, his uneasiness growing even though it seemed unlikely that Noland would find out what his wife planned to do. Then, as he approached the section of town in which Noland lived, an idea came to him. He slowed down, glancing at street signs to find out where he was; after a few blocks he turned left, towards the bay.

He hadn't too much hope that he would be successful in finding his man at home, but it was a thing he had to try. For if he were lucky in finding Noland he thought he might be able to collect the money and the credit card now, thus forestalling any visit to the boat in the morning. If he could see Noland now that would be the end of the matter, and it was with this thought in mind that he made the last turn and coasted into the darkened, quiet street.

His headlights told him that there was no car parked in the block. The houses on either side were black and indistinct in the shadows but he drove on, seeing now the turnaround with its gates and chain, and coming finally to Noland's house. Like the street, the driveway was empty, and he was about to go on when he thought he saw a crack of light at the study, as though curtains had been pulled across the French doors leaving a thin strip of glass uncovered.

He stopped at once but he had already reached the front of the house and from where he got out he could see no light at all. For a moment then he stood there undecided, but the compulsion he felt to see Noland if possible was still strong, and in the end he moved back to the driveway and went along it as he had the other afternoon, looking hard for that crack of light but seeing nothing in the windows but the reflections of the night.

Nothing at all showed behind the French doors. The night was all about him. Back on the cross street a car went by and somewhere in the distance he heard a bus accelerate; here it was quiet and nothing moved but the soft, evening breeze.

There was no explanation, either then or later, for

what he did then. Having come this far, having thought
he had seen a light, some stubborn streak inside him
urged him to make sure that no one was inside, and so
he went up the steps, ignoring the growing tension
which had begun to creep along his thighs and back.

He pushed the bell button resolutely, and again there
was that distant sound of chimes. He pushed again and
stepped back, turning as he waited, to glance along the
narrow porch and the line of the house. That was how
he happened to notice the crack in the French doors.

There was no light behind that crack but it was there
nonetheless, a one-inch opening left by someone who
had been careless or indifferent in the closing of those
doors. Randall moved towards that crack, his gaze
fixed. He made as much noise with his shoes as he could.
He knocked on the glass pane as loud as he dared, annoyed now and feeling like a house-to-house salesman
who is denied entrance while someone watched from
behind a window shade.

"Mr. Noland!" he said.

He widened the crack.

"Mr. Noland! It's Knox Randall, Mr. Noland."

He put his hand forward and knew now that a cur-
tain had been drawn. He pushed it aside and then he
stopped, half in and half out of the door.

The skin was tight across his shoulders now and the
back of his neck was cold. Some latent, atavistic instinct
warned him that something was wrong and suddenly,
realizing his position, he was afraid.

With breath held he waited. The seconds ticked by,
part of his brain telling him he was a damn fool while
the other part nagged him, reminding him that he was a
coward, that if something was wrong he should find out

about it. In the end his shame proved stronger than his
fear, for he was young and he had a lot of pride.

Quickly then, no longer hesitating, he stepped inside. He called again, loudly, to identify himself, and
now he was groping for his cigarette lighter, striking
flame, and holding it up against the blackness.

The corners of the room were fathomless and it had
no shape, but on his right, no more than a step away, he
saw the outline of a desk and the lamp which stood
there. Sidling towards it, he reached for it, and as he
touched the warm surface of the metal shade he knew
he had been right about the light he had seen. A second
later the room was bright, and he was blinking against
this brightness and turning, and then he saw this thing
on the floor.

It lay beside an overturned maple chair and Randall
started towards it, knowing somehow that this was Perry
Noland but not knowing what had happened until he
had taken another step. Words formed in his throat as
he started to speak and then he stopped and stiffened
there, his gaze wide with shock and horror when he
realized that the sprawled figure had no face.

The nausea and sickness came almost at once but he
fought it, his brain still numb and unable to correlate
the welter of thoughts which sought recognition. For in
that first moment Randall knew only that Noland was
dead, that he had been shot at close range with a heavy
charge, and that of the face he remembered there was
nothing left but the line of cheek and jaw, a blue eye,
open and staring, the twisted frames of what had once
been thin-rimmed glasses.

5

KNOX RANDALL was never sure how long he stood there. In all probability it was not more than a minute, if that, for the ghastliness of the bloody, shattered face was more than he could take, and his nausea was overwhelming him. It was not the disfigurement, as such, that gave him trouble, for he had seen men like this before and knew what explosive charges did to flesh and bone; rather it was the circumstances surrounding the murder that unnerved him, the fact that this was peacetime and the victim a civilian.

He could not bring himself to look at the shattered face again but he did glance at the hands, and on the left little finger he noticed the signet ring he had seen Noland twist before. Then, swallowing fast as he started to back away, he saw the sawed-off shotgun lying beyond the overturned chair and knew for sure how death had come.

He moved automatically then, unable now to think but reaching with sweaty hands for the lamp and grateful for the darkness that swept through the room. He groped past the curtains and went down the porch steps, sucking deeply of the night air, weaving a little as he hurried along the driveway. He reached his car and stood a moment before getting in, his body wet with perspiration, not knowing yet whether he would be sick or not. Behind him, in the next block, he heard a car

start and followed with his ear the sound of its motor
until it was gone; by then his nausea was better, and his
mind began to function.

Even as he started the car and his headlights slashed
a bright semi-circle over lawns and shrubbery some inner voice, feeble now though it struggled to be heard,
told him that his flight was a mistake, but it was not until he had driven six blocks to a neighborhood tavern
that he was able to think sanely about the consequences
of his act.

He ordered a straight Bourbon and felt it burn going
down. He took another with water and now his breathing was regular and the perspiration had stopped. His
hand still shook when he lit a cigarette, and when he
started the car again he drove slowly, moving farther
and farther from the scene, knowing it was wrong but
arguing now, defending himself, forgetting the ethics of
the case in his effort to be practical.

He remembered, as a youngster, how he and his
friends would sometimes talk about imaginary situations, usually heroic. "What," someone would say,
"would you do if you woke up and found the house next
door was on fire?" "What if you were riding your bike
across Main Street bridge and you saw a woman drown-
ing?"

There were always answers when you were a kid, and
in your mind's eye you were the hero, moving unfail-
ingly to do the proper and accepted thing. Later, he
could remember discussing murder with various people,
and in such hypothetical cases the course of action
seemed quite simple and obvious. He could remember
walking out of movie theaters and criticising the action
of the hero or heroine whenever he—or she—would run
away from murder, or try in some way to cover up the

crime and thereby hinder the official investigation. For
to Randall, his duty as a citizen always seemed clear beyond question: should he ever be unfortunate enough to
discover a murder, the first and only thing to do would
be to telephone the police and wait until they came, always remembering to touch nothing in the room.

He still believed in the theory and it amazed him a
little to find that what he had done, what he was, in fact,
doing at the moment, was the exact opposite.

He attached no blame to his flight from the room. It
had been a mistake even to get out of his car. He had no
business knocking at the French door, much less opening it because it was ajar. He had been tense and a little
afraid when he entered, and the shock of his discovery
made it impossible to remain without being sick all over
the floor.

So he had hurried outside. That was all right. He
should have stayed right there until he had control of
himself, not turning off the light but just waiting, and
then moving back into the house to telephone the police.

Well, he could still call them.

Or could he? Would they believe him when he explained why he had run away?

Whether they believed him or not he would be a witness of some kind, most likely harangued and questioned for God knows how long. And what about the
Julia, and the trip, and the money he had taken and
spent for provisions and couldn't give back?

He considered all these details and once started it was
impossible not to consider them again. Like a merry-go-
round, his thoughts made the circuit, going nowhere,
adding nothing but a slight dizziness to his confusion.
He was still at it when he pulled up in front of Lenore
Calvert's apartment, and as he sat there before turning

off the ignition he knew now that he was not going back, nor was he going to call the police.

From the standpoint of one who had been brought up to do the right thing, his decision was all wrong. He admitted his weakness and was ashamed of it, but he clung stubbornly to the practical aspects of the matter and it was these which influenced him in the end. He could not, he told himself, help Mr. Noland now. There was no possible way the police could connect him with the case, since he had not been seen and had no intention of going to the house in the first place. Maybe the murder would be discovered by morning. If so, and if the police came to Fort Lauderdale to stop the trip, there was nothing he could do. But so long as there was a chance of his getting started, of giving his passengers a day or two of the cruise for the expended portion of their money which he would be unable to return, he would be satisfied.

He got out of the car and walked on, head down, mouth set grimly. He was still wrong and he knew it, but he kept going, stubbornly, through the court and up the stairs, knocking, watching the door open and finally moving forward to receive Lenore's welcome kiss.

They had driven no more than five blocks before Randall noticed that Lenore was squirming on the seat, and turning now and then to glance out through the rear window. He gave her three more blocks and when she kept it up he spoke about it.

"What's the matter?" he said, his voice curt because his nerves were still on edge. "Sit still, can't you?"

"Well, for Heaven's sake," Lenore said, unused to such tones from him. "What's got into you?"

He did not bother to answer. He kept his eyes on the

evening traffic, his jaw set and the tightness still in his face. She sat reasonably quiet after that and presently she said:

"Where are we going? This isn't the way to Lauderdale."

"It is the way we're going."

"Really?" said Lenore.

"I have to take this car back." Randall paused, making an effort to be pleasant. "I got some money coming on my deposit. I'll get somebody to drive us out . . . I didn't mean to snap at you. I've had a tough couple of days."

Mollified, Lenore moved closer and sat that way until he turned into a corner parking lot filled with shining cars and dominated by a small building at one side, over which a lighted sign proclaimed: HONEST JAKE.

Jake came out on the steps to take a look, a plump sunburned man with a genial exterior and the mind of a loan shark. He listened to Randall's story, consulted a black notebook, checked the speedometer.

"Yep," he said. "Twenty-two dollars you got coming. Be sorry to lose your trade."

Randall said he was sorry too. He said he had to get someone to drive him to Fort Lauderdale and what would it cost. Whereupon Jake peered at the gasoline gage and said:

"You've got six or seven gallons left; you've been a good customer for twelve weeks. Go ahead and use it— on me." He yelled for a colored boy who was polishing a car and said: "All it will cost you is what you want to give the boy."

They rearranged Lenore's bags on the little seat in the back and the boy climbed in. They rode in silence for twenty minutes but presently Lenore began again

to sneak an occasional backward glance. Randall was
aware of this, and he looked in the rear view mirror each
time she did so, seeing nothing but the line of headlights
behind him. Finally, when they had left Hollywood behind, he could stand it no longer. He leaned towards
her, spoke quietly.

"Just what the hell is your trouble?"

"I think we're being followed," Lenore said just as
quietly.

"Nuts! . . . Why?" he asked when she made no reply. "You running away from something?"

She said of course not and suddenly he was no longer
concerned with her but with the disturbing alternative
that somehow, someone had followed him from Noland's house. He scoffed inwardly even as the thought
occurred to him but he was nervous now, and when he
saw a Neon sign ahead he made up his mind.

"We'll turn in here for a quick drink and find out," he
said. "Boy!" he added to the dozing Negro. "We're stopping here for a drink. If any car pulls in right after we
do, point it out to me when we come out."

He swung into the parking space and stopped. By the
time he and Lenore were at the tavern's entrance no car
had followed them in and he felt better. They had a
drink at the bar, and when he glanced at the wall clock
and saw it was a quarter of ten, he remembered Julia
Noland and knew he had to get back to the boat.

Outside, the boy said no car had stopped since they
had left. Lenore said she was sorry but by now Randall
was thinking of other things. He was thinking about
Julia Noland and the earlier estimate he had made. He
recalled her dark, exciting beauty, the fascinating
power of her personality. He had felt then that she was a
strong-willed and possessive woman and it occurred to

him that such a woman could kill a man if she hated him
enough, just as other women had killed their husbands
under the right provocation.

But even as he considered such a possibility his mind
rebelled as he probed on. One thing he was sure of:
Julia Noland was a smart woman, far too smart to murder her husband and run away without an alibi. With
her, such a theory just did not make sense. A wife would
always be suspect until cleared. The police would look
for her at once, and if guilty, flight would serve only to
increase the suspicion of the authorities. Sooner or later
Gifford, the lawyer, would be called in to identify the
body, and Gifford knew of Randall's proposed trip. The
police would want to question him as a matter of course.
Even if he were lucky enough to get started they would
stop him somewhere along the route and so discover
Julia's presence. If guilty, she must know that this
would happen.

No, he told himself. His trouble was simply that he already had a guilt complex of his own and his logic was
faulty. The sawed-off shotgun, a gangster's weapon
since prohibition, indicated a far simpler explanation:
The odds had caught up with Noland and he had been
eliminated by someone a little tougher than he was. . . .

The *Julia* was dark as the coupe rolled out on the
sandy plaza and Randall kept its headlights focused on
the deckhouse until he had unlocked the door and carried Lenore's bags aboard. He gave the boy two dollars,
and when he came back inside he found Lenore
pleased and surprised with her surroundings and eager
to tell him so. She had taken off the short flannel jacket
she had worn, and in her thin summer dress her full,
well-rounded figure was pleasant to contemplate. She
looked quite pretty as she explored the drawers and

lockers in the room, and when he realized how grouchy and difficult he had been and how calmly she had accepted his mood, he felt a little ashamed and wanted to make up for it.

"Would you like a drink?"

"A small one, please. To sort of celebrate my being here."

He went below to the galley to chop some ice and it was then that he heard her call to him, an undertone of alarm in her voice.

"Knox!" she said. "A car's coming."

He went topside at once, nerves jumping because of her tone. He saw the car and knew at once that it was a taxi. As he stepped to the doorway it pulled away and then Julia Noland was coming forward, an overnight case in her hand.

"Hello," she said. "I hoped I wouldn't be too early."

He said they had just arrived, and introduced her to Lenore. He said they were to be roommates and that he was just making a drink. Julia said, yes, she'd like one, and he went below to make them, giving the two women time to look each other over and form the necessary opinions.

They sat around with their drinks for fifteen minutes, talking of this and that, and then Julia put her glass aside and said she guessed she would do a little unpacking and go to bed. Lenore said she would be down shortly and when she finished her drink she stood up. Randall was leaning on the sideboard, and she came to him and stood close as he straightened.

"I'm a little tired too," she said. "You don't mind if I go to bed, do you, Knox?"

He said certainly not. He said it was a good idea and he was sorry he'd been out of line. She put her arms around his waist and pressed her body lightly against him.

"You weren't really. You never are. You're sweet."

She kissed him on the mouth before he could reply, inspected his face with her green eyes and kissed him again before she stepped back. "Good-night, Knox," she said. "I think it's going to be fun."

He sat for awhile after she had gone. He had made himself a tall, double highball and he took his time with it because he wanted to be sure the women were settled before he turned out the lights. He gave them a half hour, so that it was about eleven thirty when he went forward along the deck to the hatch and his quarters.

He did not undress at once but rearranged some of his things to be in readiness for Alan Harding. He took off his shoes and shirt and was about ready to wash when he felt the deck tip slightly and straighten.

He turned instantly, reaching for his flashlight, knowing by the feel of the boat that someone had stepped aboard. Above him the hatch was still open and he went quickly up the ladder. He started aft, snapping on his light, and as he did so another flashlight focused on him from the deckhouse windows, canceling his momentary advantage.

Seeing very little now, and nothing at all in the deckhouse, he continued aft; he stepped through the doorway and snapped on the overhead lights. Then he was face to face with two men, one of whom he had seen before: a swart, slender fellow in a powder-blue coat, the one Lenore had spoken to from time to time, the lad from New York she had known. The other man was heavier, older, more important looking, with little eyes that looked mean in the shadows.

Randall found his flashlight still on and snapped it

off. He thought of Lenore and knew now how right she had been. He had no idea what these men wanted, but however he added things they spelled trouble.

"What's the idea?" he said.

The heavy man was the spokesman.

"We want to see Miss Calvert."

"What makes you think she's aboard?" Randall circled casually, getting his back into the corner nearest the shore.

"She told us she'd be."

"You mean you followed us. And waited at the end of the road until you thought I'd gone to bed."

"Have it your way, Mac." The heavy man glanced down the forward companionway. "But get her up here."

"She's gone to bed," Randall said, stalling. "She's sleeping aboard. Anything you want to say to Miss Calvert you can say in the morning."

"We want to see her now."

Randall measured the fellow lazily. He looked at Powder-blue coat, finding a suspicious bulge under the left arm and wondering if it was a gun.

"You'd better shove off," he said.

"When we're ready," said Powder-blue.

As he spoke his eyes flicked past Randall and his hand moved upward towards the V of his coat. At the same time the boat tipped gently and a voice said:

"Good evening, all."

Randall jerked his head about, his gaze startled and then incredulous when he saw Alan Harding on the deck outside the doorway. For Harding had a .45 automatic in his hand and it covered adequately the two intruders. At least they must have thought so because Powder-blue's hand was still in the V of his coat and he moved it back carefully and put it slowly at his side.

Harding came in and now Randall saw the camera in
Harding's other hand. Harding's face was flushed and
his light-blue eyes were not too clear. Randall had an
idea Harding was a little drunk. He was sweating pro-
fusely, his breath spasmodic as though from some recent
exertion. He was a different Harding, too, from the one
Randall remembered.

This man's hair was neatly combed and his clothes
were neat. The flannels and the Shetland sport coat
looked well worn, but they were beautifully cut and
had been expensive when new. Now Harding said, his
voice pleasant though a little thick:

"Why don't you gentlemen do what the Captain
says?"

For another moment the two men seemed undecided.
Finally the heavy one shrugged and jerked his head at
his companion. "Okay," he said.

"But first," Harding said. "Just for the record—" He
moved up to Randall and handed him the gun. "Anyone who breaks and enters—and a boat is the same as a
house—takes his chances on getting shot. And now that
we understand that—"

He broke off again and began to focus the camera
which had a flash-unit attached. The heavy man's face
got red and he opened his mouth, apparently thought
better of it when he saw the leveled automatic, closed it
savagely. The flashbulb went off and Harding bowed.

"That's in case you decide to come back," he said.
"It's always nice to have something to give the authorities." He put the camera aside and took the gun
from Randall. "I'll see you to your car. This way,
please."

He backed off, the gun still pointed. He fell in behind

the two as they stepped ashore. Then the three of them
marched off into the night and Randall stood there shaking his head, too bewildered now by all that had happened to him to speculate further.

Close by the bulkhead he saw the bulging flight-bag,
packed almost beyond capacity; he saw the open mu-
sette bag and knew where the gun and camera had
come from when Harding, approaching without a
sound, had looked into the lighted deckhouse and
quickly assessed the situation.

In the distance he heard a car start and saw the headlights flash on through the trees. Presently Harding
came trudging through the darkness and Randall,
standing there, realized that there was another enigma
which he had been unable to understand. Seeing Harding dressed up for the first time he was reminded of
young men one saw in smart New York supper clubs,
the kind that made the good fraternities at college and
were accustomed to the best. And yet— He gave up,
sighed, and wrestled the flight-bag into the deckhouse,
wondering how Harding could possibly have carried
it from town.

"Thanks," said the little man. "Who were those guys?"

"I don't know, but I was very glad you decided to
stay aboard."

Harding chuckled. He said his plans hadn't quite
worked out. "I gave up my room and got a little drunk
and spent all my dough. I damn near died slugging
those bags . . . What did they want?" he asked
abruptly.

"They wanted to see one of our passengers."

"Some passengers we've got."

"A girl," Randall said. "Come on, let's go to bed."

They went forward and as they undressed Harding said: "Don't worry about those lads coming back. If they do I'm a light sleeper. I just hope you don't snore."

6

KNOX RANDALL was too busy the next morning to give much thought to what had happened the night before. At first, when he awakened to the sound of Alan Harding's ablutions the things he had seen and done seemed remote and unreal, and what bothered him most just then was the practical matter of how far he could get and what he was going to do without the cash and credit card which Noland had promised and could no longer deliver.

Harding, hearing him sit up, said good-morning and asked how many there would be for breakfast. Randall said there would be four and right then, with the rest of his worries pressed far back in his mind and temporarily under control, he got another jolt. He swung his feet to the deck and sat on the edge of the bunk, rumpling his hair, his dark eyes brooding while he wondered how he could have failed to connect two obvious facts, both of which had been known to him two days previous:

Alan Harding had worked aboard this boat. Julia Noland had been married to the owner. Therefore Harding would recognize Julia and the Miss Kelly myth would soon be at an end.

He groaned inwardly and stood up as Harding climbed through the hatch, aware that there was nothing he could do about it but hopeful of putting off the

meeting until later in the day. Then, remembering that
Julia had said she would stay below until after their
start, an idea came to him; that is why, when breakfast
was nearly ready, he knocked on the forward cabin
door to tell Lenore that if she and Miss Kelly wanted to
stay in bed he could bring in a tray.

"You're a darling," Lenore said sleepily when the tray
was ready and she opened the door.

"It's a special Sunday service," Randall said. "For this
Sunday only. From now on—"

Lenore tossed her hair back and belted her robe. "I
know," she said. "We get up and eat breakfast or we go
without."

Randall closed the door, happy that this problem was
postponed but wondering what he had done to deserve
such troubles. He continued to wonder as he breakfasted with Harding on orange juice, boiled eggs, toast
and coffee. Still wondering, he helped clear the table
and gave a hand with the dishes. By then the third passenger was ready to come aboard.

It was the thick-browed, plain-looking man with the
build of a blacksmith, the first one to answer the advertisement. Randall remembered that his name was Oliver
Dalton, and as he introduced Harding and gave a hand
with the inexpensive but new-looking bags he wondered
again why this man and his country clothes should be
making such a trip. This time, however, Randall had
little chance to speculate, because he had no more than
got Dalton installed in his cabin when another taxi had
arrived, its occupants the foreign-looking couple. Fournier, their name was, the man plump-bodied, with thin-
ning black hair, a mustache, and glasses; his wife small
and dark, like her husband, also with a mustache,
though very faint, on her upper lip. Both were polite,

precise in movements and speech, and most appreciative of the help Randall gave them in getting settled.

The sixth passenger came a few minutes later, the tall, gray-haired man whose name was John Barnard. He, of all the others, seemed most at home as he followed Randall down the ladder to the cabin he was to share with Dalton, and when Randall had made the introductions he stopped for a few moments to talk with them and see that conversational ice was properly broken.

He excused himself when he again heard the sound of an approaching car but he was not at all prepared for what he saw when he stepped from the deckhouse door. He was, in fact, so confused and bewildered by the argument that was taking place beside the taxi that he could only stand there and gape, the words he heard meaning practically nothing at the time.

The principals were Nora Graham and Alan Harding, and neither was giving an inch. They both talked at the same time, Alan gesturing angrily, the girl shaking her blonde head, and now and then stamping her foot.

"Hey!" Randall finally got under way. "Knock it off!" he said, addressing Harding as he stepped across the bulkhead to the sand. "What goes on?"

Harding glared at him, looking more than ever like the terrier he was. "Is she making this trip?" he demanded. "Did you sign her on without telling me?"

"Without telling you what? Certainly she's making the trip."

"Not with me, she's not," Harding said.

"Oh, stop it!" the girl said hotly. "Who cares if you go? I'm a better steward than you are anyway. At least I won't be having hangovers every other morning."

Randall got in between them, still not knowing what

it was all about. He took Harding's arm, shook him a little.

"Take it easy!" he said. "Why shouldn't she go? What's it to you?"

"She's my sister."

Randall peered at him, unable to believe his ears. Then the meaning of the statement struck home and he thought: *Oh, my God! What next?* Aloud he said: "All right, so she's your sister. She paid her money and she—"

"Then why didn't you tell me?"

"Because," the girl said, "I used my middle name. I told him I was Nora Graham."

"You would," Harding said and then, to Randall: "Well, I'm damned if I'll go with her along."

Randall looked right back at him. He wasn't smiling now and his gaze was steady and intent. For another moment their eyes remained locked; then Harding looked away. Randall said: "Relax . . . Both of you."

He glanced at the girl. She wore the same backless dress. Her blonde hair was radiant in the sunlight and her level gray eyes had sparks in them. She looked flushed and defiant; she looked lovely.

"It's all right," he said. "If you pulled a fast one it's still all right." He turned back to Harding. "You're not going to back out on me now. We shook hands on it, remember? All the way or nothing, wasn't it?"

He saw the other weaken. Anger still smoldered behind the freckled, sun-burned face but there was a chink in Harding's armor now, put there by Randall's simple argument.

"Take her bags, will you?" he said as though the matter was settled. Then he grinned. "You're the crew,

Alan," he said. "You and me. Don't annoy the paying customers."

Harding muttered something under his breath but he picked up the bags. Nora Harding was watching Randall and he felt again the pleasurable stimulus of her presence. Her gray eyes thanked him as she turned to follow her brother, and then an automobile horn beeped once and Randall saw the car at the edge of the clearing.

When the man behind the wheel signaled with one hand, Randall started towards it. It stood perhaps sixty feet away and he covered half of that distance before his mind began to function. When it did the thought that followed shocked him strangely. For suddenly it came to him that he had seen this car before—or one exactly like it. A maroon convertible, a '49 model. In the driveway of Perry Noland's house.

He knew it could not be but he went on, heart beginning to pound, seeing now the man behind the wheel. The man wore a light suit and Panama hat. He had dark glasses, but even so there was something familiar in the line of cheek and jaw.

Then, everything in his being protesting, all reason telling him that this could not be, Randall watched the man remove the glasses and knew that the impossible had happened.

"Hello," Perry Noland said affably. "Everything all right?"

Randall stumbled on, his mouth dry and slack. The situation was now beyond all belief and he could only stare, and try not to, and somehow find his voice.

He started to speak and found he couldn't until he had swallowed to clear his throat. He put one hand on the edge of the lowered window in order to combat the odd feeling of weakness that had come over him.

"What's the matter?" Noland asked. "You look a little pale."

"I'm okay," Randall said at last.

"Got a full load?"

Randall nodded. "Seven."

Noland lit a cigarette from the one he was smoking and flipped the butt from the window. He took an envelope from the seat and opened it. As he counted the bills inside Randall took a deep breath and stood back from the car, glancing about as he did so, as though to make sure that everything was as he remembered it and that he was not being victimized by some hallucination.

He discovered then that Harding was watching him. Harding was moving slowly towards him across the sand and now Randall was scared by the suddenly realized potentialities of impending disaster. Shaking his head violently, he turned; he made his shoulders as broad as possible so that he blocked off the open window; he put one hand behind him and waved for Harding to back up and stay away.

"Two hundred even," Noland said. "And the credit card. Also a card with my New York address and telephone number. Call me when you get in and if I'm not there I'll be in Falmouth."

He handed Randall the envelope, put on his glasses and stepped on the starter. Randall began to breathe again. He did not know where Alan Harding was but he was certain now that Noland had not recognized his ex-employee and could not, therefore, make any trouble or question Randall's choice in stewards.

Noland was saying the usual things one said under the circumstances and Randall was replying automatically without knowing what he said. Then the car lurched forward, gathering momentum and bouncing off through the trees.

When Harding came up beside him, Randall said: "I didn't want Mr. Noland to see you. I was afraid he might make a fuss when he found out you were going with me."

"I thought there was some reason you didn't want me around." Harding stepped on the smoldering cigarette butt. "I didn't know who it was at first," he said, and looked up. "But I told you why he fired me. That happened to be the truth."

Randall had already started for the *Julia*, his intelligence bruised and his brain as yet too numb to accept the facts. Noland was alive, but someone else was dead. What had happened to the man with but half a face Randall did not even bother to speculate. In the days that followed the victim became a Mr. X, but right now he had but one thing in mind: to get away—and as quickly as possible.

"I'll get the motors started," he said. "Get the lines in. Let's get the hell out of here before I go nuts."

It did not take long. The motors started without delay and by the time Randall had them idling smoothly, Harding had all the lines and fenders in but one and was holding the *Julia* off by the bow with a boathook. With the exception of Julia Noland all the passengers were topside to witness the departure, and Nora Harding, in sneakers now, called to the bridge to ask what she could do.

Randall was headed up river and he told her to hold a fender on the port quarter. He said there wasn't much water here but he thought he could go forward and make his turn, and as the bow began to swing Harding ran back to cast off the stern line, then came aboard, boathook in hand.

The *Julia* inched forward under her port motor and began to swing. She came into the middle of the river nicely and as Randall reached the bend, he blew for the railroad bridge. The attendant came out and started the gasoline motor which supplied power for the lift and when Randall saw the bridge start to move he shoved his controls to "Ahead."

Muddy water boiled briefly under the *Julia's* stern and she nosed down river, sliding under the railroad bridge as the Las Olas bridge began to lift. Ahead of them was Tenth Street Bridge and then the palm-lined river with the homes of the wealthy, which flanked it with green lawns and private docks. What lay beyond was something Knox Randall refused even to guess.

7

IT HAD been announced earlier that the first day's run would be short. A sort of shake-down run, Randall called it, to give him a chance to feel out the boat and see what, if anything, needed adjustment. West Palm Beach was the announced destination, a cruise which, even under reduced throttle, should take no more than five hours, including the fifteen or more bridges which had to be opened to allow them to pass.

By the time they left Lauderdale behind them and got straightened out in the canal which paralleled the beach for some miles, most of the passengers had finished their explorations and were making use of the cockpit cushions. Presently Alan Harding came to the bridge and glanced at the chart.

"When it comes to picking passengers," he said, "you do all right. That Miss Calvert is nice . . . Also," he said, "I got a look at Miss Kelly. Some babe. Miss Bedroom-eyes herself."

"Yes," Randall said, waiting for what came next.

"Only she wasn't called Kelly when I knew her. Her name was—"

"Noland," said Randall. "Julia Noland. She used the same approach as your sister." And then he related the story Julia had told him, including her reason for making the trip. "I forgot you knew her until this morning."

Harding thought it over. "Running away from the husband, huh?" he said finally. "It doesn't surprise me much." He studied the mangrove swamp off the port bow thoughtfully for a few seconds. "There were times when he could be a mean son-of-a-bitch . . . What do you want to do about lunch?"

Randall made some suggestions. Then he said if Julia was still below to ask her if she wanted to be known as Kelly or Noland, and when Harding found out to take her around and introduce her to the others.

Harding waited until everyone had a good look at Boca Raton before he served lunch, and when everything was ready he came to the bridge to relieve Randall. The drop-leaf table had been set so that three people could use the settee, with three places opposite and a chair at each end. The lunch was good but simple— sliced ham and turkey, lettuce and tomato salad, rolls, and a choice of milk, coca-cola, or beer—and when they had finished Randall made a little speech.

He announced it as such with some embarrassment because, he said, he wanted to be sure that everyone understood the way things worked on a cruise of this kind. They gave him their attention, Dalton, Barnard, and Lenore on the settee, the Fourniers and Nora on the other side, with Julia Noland opposite him. Already he could tell which of the passengers had adjusted themselves. Nora and Julia were in sunsuits and Lenore wore slacks and a sport shirt; all wore sneakers, as did Barnard, along with cotton slacks and a faded denim jacket. The Fourniers, dark, polite and retiring, were too dressed up, while Dalton was neither one nor the other with his business-suit trousers and striped shirt.

"As you can see," Randall began, "the food is not going to be fancy, but it should be good and there is plenty of it. We can't give you too much variety but we can give you all you can eat. When you eat out each evening you may be able to get the variety that we lack aboard. Also," he said, "we have to more or less eat at the same time."

He went on to explain that with only one man to get the meals it would be impossible to cater to individual habits. The hours might vary somewhat, according to what time they got under weigh each day. If they liked they could take a vote as to what time they wanted breakfast but, once served, those who missed it would have to wait until lunch.

Barnard inclined his gray head and said that was fair enough. The others nodded approval.

"We should always have fruit juice in the morning, and eggs, bacon, cold cereal for those who want it," Randall went on. "We won't always have milk but we'll have coffee, as well as some sort of soft drink, and we'll have beer." He smiled and said: "Though I'd like to make one rule about the beer. For every can you take out of the ice box I wish you'd put a warm can in its place." He told them where the beer was kept and where to find the Coca-Cola. "If you'll just remember that there will always be cold drinks."

He hesitated and said: "As for duties you have only one—to take care of your own cabin. Make your bunk or not, as you like. No one will touch it or pick up if you don't. Dress as you like, do as you like, and if everyone is moderately considerate of the others aboard we should have a good time. You can give a hand with the lines and fenders if you like, and if you want to do a little steering we can show you how."

He said that was about all, except for one thing. "The shower," he said. "We can fill our tanks every night—though in some ports the water tastes of sulphur. If you're making a drink you'd better try to get ice from the box that you know is all right. But we can only hold so much and I'm afraid you'll have to limit yourself to one shower a day—unless you can talk someone out of his turn."

He asked if there were any questions and there were none, so he thanked them, winked at Lenore, and went back to the wheel.

For the next half hour Randall was alone on the bridge and his thoughts turned inevitably to Noland and the murder victim he called Mr. X. He still shivered inwardly when he remembered his last meeting with Noland, and even now he recalled the shock and incredulity that had swept over him when he recognized that car and the man who was driving it. There was something else too, that scared him a little in retrospect, for as his mind went back over the details he realized how very close he had come to walking in on the murderer.

He was sure now that he had seen a light when he

drove past Noland's house the night before. In the time it had taken him to park his car and walk up the driveway the killer had fled—or had he? Could he have still been in the house? Had he been waiting somewhere in the darkness to see what he, Randall, intended to do?

That he might have been recognized increased his uneasiness; he remembered the things that had been said about Noland—Lenore's doubts when she found out who owned the boat, Julia's concern about what her husband would do when he found she had left; even Harding's recent remark helped to shape his opinion. A man had been murdered. It was not Noland though what was left of the face resembled him as did his general height and build. The ring and glasses had obviously been planted to confirm identification, all of which added up to—

To what? Randall did not know, but he could not stop thinking now. A man had been killed in Noland's house, apparently by Noland; a man who would be identified as Noland. If this were true then the only reasonable solution was that Noland had one thought in mind—to disappear.

The answer to this came quickly when he remembered that an attempt had been made to murder the man a week or two before. Lenore had said so. Some fellow named Ernie Mondello, whom Noland had double-crossed. Sure. Why not? If you knew you were going to be killed and could arrange a phony death before that, you could be safe. You'd need money, a lot of money. But that could be done. With a little time a man could convert his holdings—some of them at least—into cash and deposit it under a fictitious name.

But if this hunch was right it meant that he, Randall, would not be seeing Noland in New York, or in Falmouth either. Mr. X, as Noland, was dead. Julia would inherit Noland's remaining estate. Or would she? . . .

He got that far when someone moved beside him. "Hello," said Nora Harding. "Need a navigator?"

Randall's troubles departed and his tanned, rugged face eased into a smile. "Hi," he said, and stood up to point out their position on the chart. "We're just coming up to this black marker."

In good weather he did not use the glass chart case but kept the charts, folded to manageable size, on top, weighing them down with the binoculars, ashtray, rule and dividers, the points of which he moved along the chart as they progressed so that he could tell at a glance just where he was and which of the red and black markers he was approaching.

"How do you take them going north?" she asked.

"Black on the starboard all the way. Except when we're using main shipping channels handling ocean traffic."

She glanced at the number on the marker they were passing, moved the points of the dividers up. "A black coming up," she said, "and then two reds."

"You've sailed before."

"When I was a little girl. My father had a small ketch . . . Pretty, isn't it," she said, nodding towards Delray, where the modern, pink and white houses fronting on the waterway reminded him of Bermuda.

He said it was one of the prettiest, and cut his throttles so that the *Julia's* wash would not rock too violently the cruisers tied up in the yacht club slips. From ashore someone waved and they waved back. In the cockpit Dalton stood up and took a picture with his folding camera while Lenore watched him and Julia, stretched out on the cushions, took a sun bath.

"I'm sorry I had to trick you," Nora said when he re-sumed speed.

"You were the girl in the taxi the first time Alan came."

"Yes. He told me he thought he had a job, so I got this idea and—" She left the thought unfinished and said, soberly: "If I have to be a shrew I will, not that it will do much good. Nothing ever has with Alan. I don't im-agine anything ever will but—I thought I'd try once more."

She moved the dividers and Randall remained silent, not understanding what she was driving at but knowing she wanted to talk. She went on matter-of-factly, unbur-dening herself of this problem of hers rather than asking for sympathy.

"We're like strangers now," she said. "Have been since before the war. When we were children—he's three years older than I am—it was different, but once he started to grow up something happened. Maybe that was the trouble, that he never did grow up. I guess he doesn't want to, actually. It's like some sort of neurosis, as if something had been left out of his makeup."

She went on in the same tone, and gradually there grew in Randall's mind a picture of Harding that bore out in part some of the things he had already suspected. He had sensed the man's instability and lack of purpose almost from the first, just as he sensed last night that Harding had had the advantages of background and opportunity. He had come from a good family, not wealthy but well off. He had been to three prep schools and two colleges before going off to war.

"I thought that might change him," Nora said. "So did Dad. Mother died when Alan was fifteen and it took him a long time to get over it. Sometimes I think that may have been the beginning of his trouble but—well, the war changed nothing. He was a gunner on a B-29. For a year or more after he came back he did absolutely nothing. Dad died while he was in the service and there was a small income for Alan."

She moved the dividers again and said: "What home we have now is in Connecticut with my aunt and uncle— I work in New York—and there's an insurance business that practically runs itself. Uncle Jack got Alan two or three jobs but he never lasted more than a month or two. He came down here about a year and a half ago. We never hear from him, and the reason I came down was to try once more to talk some sense into him. Uncle Jack has to take it easy now and he has to get someone in the office who can eventually take over the business. I thought maybe Alan had had enough of his beachcombing, that maybe he had started to grow up. Well he was having no part of that. It was silly, I guess, to think I could do any good."

She glanced at Randall and her mouth curved. "He made me furious, damn him! I made up my mind I'd take this trip just to spite him, so I phoned the office and they gave me another two weeks. From now on he can do as he pleases because we both know our dislike of each other is mutual . . . What did you do before you took this job?"

Randall said he wrote copy for an advertising agency. He mentioned the name and she said she had heard of it. She asked him if it was time to turn the chart over, and when he checked his position he said yes.

"Then this is just kind of a vacation," she said. "You're taking the boat up for a friend of yours?"

"Not exactly." Randall hesitated and then, because he

liked this girl so much, he thought: *What the hell! Tell her and start straight.*

"I was engaged to a girl in New York. I thought I was in love with her. I guess I was at the time. The trouble was her family didn't have as much money as they liked people to think they had, and I guess either she or they thought she'd have more security if she married someone with something besides a seventy-five-hundred-a-year salary to fall back on. The trouble was, I didn't realize what was happening until she told me she'd made a mistake. So I got a leave of absence and came to Florida."

"To play the field?"

He had to smile because she was so right.

"Something like that. For a while at least. Also," he said, "to do some serious drinking, waste my time, and feel as sorry for myself as possible."

She was watching him now, her mouth still curved, her eyes hidden behind the dark glasses. "At least you're honest about it. And did it work out? Playing the field, I mean?"

"It worked all right, everything considered."

"I was talking to Miss Calvert. She said she was a friend of yours."

He said Lenore was one of the best and decided to explore another subject. They were in South Worth now, and with no traffic ahead and no immediate anchorages to worry about, he advanced both throttles.

"I want to rev her up and see how she acts," he said when her glance questioned him.

He found out presently that the port motor acted fine but that the starboard one developed a pronounced "ping" when it approached 2100 R.P.M. He let it run that way for a few seconds, brought it back to 1950 and kept it there while he studied the girl.

She was standing erect now, a tennis cap cocked on her two-tone blond hair, the wind which whipped over the top of the screen tugging at the sun-bleached edges. She wore shorts and a strapless bandeau; her skin lay smooth and soft upon the firm young body and he liked the fine line of her profile as she let the breeze beat against her face.

And now he felt again a mild stir of excitement in his blood stream. It had been a long time since he had been with a girl like this, and it made him feel awkward and clumsy because he was not quite sure how to act. With girls like Lenore you knew very quickly, if you knew anything at all, and they were fun to be with—for awhile. There a kiss or a caress was given or accepted without much thought. This, he knew, was something else.

"We'll be in around three," he said, and cut back on his throttle when he blew for the Lake Worth Bridge.

"Before that, won't we?" she asked.

He shook his head. He said he wanted to take a look at the starboard motor. "There's a boatyard and docks up beyond the Flagler Bridge," he said. "I think we'll tie up there. It's farther from the center of town but we'll be that much ahead in the morning."

"What do you want me to do when we come in?"

"Grab a fender and stand by." She started to turn away and he said, hesitantly: "And—"

"Yes?"

"I was thinking about dinner. We'll have to telephone for taxis and I don't know where everybody's going but I thought perhaps we could eat together."

"I'd like that," she said simply. "If you can work it out."

8

IT WAS John Barnard who had the idea about dinner and talked it up among the passengers. A place called the Maison LaFitte which served an excellent meal; not cheap but really good.

"Everyone likes the idea but the Fourniers," he said as he jackknifed his spare, tall frame beside the upraised engine-room hatch while Randall was tinkering with a distributor. "They think they'd rather stay aboard."

"I'll speak to them," Randall said. "But count me in—and Miss Harding."

"There's a phone booth down by the end of the yard. I'll order two cabs for, say around six thirty."

Randall said that would be fine and then he thought of something else. "You seem to know your way around boats," he said. "Have you been here before?"

Barnard straightened, his gray-thatched weathered face lost to Randall's sight. "I made the trip a couple of times. That was some years ago though." . . .

By the time Randall had finished with the motor it was five o'clock and the boat was quiet. When he came out on the deck he found Alan sitting on a stringpiece talking with the mate of another cruiser moored across the way. He went over and asked where the others were and Harding said he thought they were looking over the other boats, thirty or forty of which lay nosed-in on either side of the main jetty.

"All except the Fourniers," he said. "They're in their cabin."

Randall washed his hands and face, and went aft to knock at the Fourniers' door which presently opened a crack to reveal part of Mr. Fournier's face. When he saw who it was he slipped through the opening and closed the door, his manner apologetic.

"We could perhaps talk in the salon," he said. "Mrs. Fournier is resting."

Randall said he was sorry, smiling at the term "salon" and adding that he wondered if there was anything wrong. "I understand you don't want to go ashore for dinner."

"I meant to speak to you." Fournier settled himself in a wicker chair. "If you will permit it, we would prefer to remain aboard. I could speak to the steward and he could purchase sandwiches for us when he returns."

Randall ran his fingers through his hair and took his time answering. He had been both amused and intrigued by this couple when they answered his advertisement. He had agreed to take them because he had an idea they would stay more or less by themselves. The very way they conducted themselves during that interview suggested that they would be quiet and well mannered, but now he found himself wondering what had prompted such a trip in the first place.

The name, Fournier, sounded French to him but he did not think this was the case. The man's dark features might have come from Spanish ancestry, but his accent, now that Randall had become accustomed to it, had more of the cadence of some mid-European country. It was, however, none of his business and when he realized the man was waiting he said:

"That won't be necessary. We can always give you sandwiches."

"Please." Fournier was shocked and he put up his

hand, palm forward. "The understanding was that we supply our own dinners. That was the agreement." He smiled, his eyes questioning behind the glasses. "Is that not so?"

Randall sighed and stood up. "Whatever you want to do, Mr. Fournier."

"If it is no trouble."

"It's no trouble. I'll speak to Harding and you can tell him what you'd like."

Fournier said thank you and bowed slightly from the waist.

When Knox Randall came aft along the deck shortly before six thirty he saw that Julia Noland, Barnard, and Dalton were dressed and waiting on the dock. He had left Harding struggling into a clean shirt, and now as he swung through the deckhouse he met Lenore coming up the ladder.

"Knox, honey," she said. "I've hardly seen you all day." Her auburn hair was piled high, her green eyes were artfully shadowed, and her mouth was inviting when she smiled. "You've neglected me."

"On account of my days of leisure are over."

"Yes," said Lenore, "and I don't like it." She took his arms in her hands and pulled him closer. "Remember what you promised," she said, and gave him a small shake to punctuate the reminder.

Randall heard the tap of steps on the after companionway ladder but he couldn't do anything about it. Lenore was already talking.

"I want to ride with you," she said. "You said you'd take care of me . . . Oh, hello," she added, not at all confused when she saw Nora, but stepping back and smiling.

Randall wanted to brain her. He fumbled for some-

thing to say but Nora saved him the trouble. Her smile
was radiant but superficial, a model's smile; her glance
was cool

"Let's just swap seats," she said. "That will solve
everything."

Lenore was a little mystified by such directness. "I
didn't mean—" she began.

"No, really," Nora said. "It makes much more sense.
I couldn't possibly ride with Alan." She stopped in the
doorway. "You two can go with him and I'll ride with
the others."

Then she was gone, saying something to the others on
the deck, and Randall was standing there crushed and
speechless because he had wanted so much to be with
Nora.

But he could not be angry with Lenore. Her easy
ways and pleasant manners were the things he had most
liked about her, and he could tell by looking at her that
she had not acted from maliciousness or spite. He remembered, too, the incident the night before when the
two men came for her, and now his promise took on
added meaning, becoming an obligation that he could
no longer ignore.

She was watching him closely, a frown working at the
bridge of her nose. "Did I do something wrong?"

"No."

She believed him.

"Then let's have a drink before we go," she said. "We
don't have to hurry, do we?"

They had a drink. Harding joined them and they had
another. Then, during a lull in the conversation, the
little man said:

"Who were those two characters that came looking for
you last night?"

"What two characters?" said Lenore.

Harding and Randall exchanged glances. Harding arched his sun-bleached brows. "Didn't you hear them?"

Randall saw at once that she didn't know what they were talking about so he explained. "One of them was your friend from New York in the powder-blue coat. The other was huskier, older."

Lenore's eyes lost their sparkle. Beneath her makeup an odd paleness grew and her voice was guarded.

"They wanted to see me?"

"And they got a little tough about it," Harding said. "What did they want?"

Lenore gave it a try. She said without conviction, she couldn't imagine what they wanted, and was saved from further explanation by the arrival of a taxi driver who squatted down to peer through the door.

"You the party that wanted the cab?"

They finished their drinks and followed him down the dock. They rode into town and across the bridge to a spot on Worth Avenue, not far from the ocean. They had trouble finding the Maison LaFitte because it did not front on the street and was reached only after an exploratory mission that took them through an alley-like arcade, but when they were finally served they all agreed with Barnard's choice.

For Randall, however, the excellence of the food and the pleasant surroundings were hardly enough to make the occasion a happy one. The foursome from the *Julia* was at a table far enough removed so that he could not see Nora, and since she occupied much of his thoughts his conversation was something less than scintillating. Lenore on the other hand, was gay and talkative, and Harding, when he put his mind to it, had a lot of charm.

He and Lenore carried the conversational ball, waved to the others as they left, and thoroughly enjoyed their dinner. Later, when Randall paid the check, Lenore nudged him and winked.

"I told you I'd find somebody to buy my dinners."

Harding liked that. He chuckled and slipped his arm through Lenore's as they left, and Randall, remembering the things that Nora had told him about her brother, was somehow more discouraged than before.

They found another taxi after they had window shopped for awhile, and started back to the boat. Randall, still occupied with his thoughts, paid little attention to where they were going. He was not even sure where it was that they stopped so Harding could get the sandwiches for the Fourniers, so that when it happened he only knew that they had crossed the bridge and were going north, quite far out, along a darkened residential street, now deserted.

The heavy sedan came alongside as if to pass. For a second it hung there, as though the occupants wanted to make sure who was in the taxi, then shot forward at an angle, slowing quickly as it did so and forcing the taxi to the curb.

The driver leaned out and cursed angrily as he stood on the brake pedal. A man dropped from the open door of the sedan and spun about while the sedan rolled on a few more feet.

They all saw the gun, and in the taxi's headlights the powder-blue coat was unmistakable. Beside him Randall felt Lenore stiffen, heard her frightened gasp; then the man was at the window waving the gun.

"Out with those lights!" he ordered. "Now hand me those keys."

The driver, thoroughly intimidated now, obeyed and

saw the keys tossed onto the pavement; then the gunman was ready for the others.

"Out!" he said. "You in the back."

Harding's reply was flat and defiant. "Suppose you
come and get us, junior."

"Take it easy," Randall said.

The man opened the door and backed away, the gun
leveled. They got out one by one and stood waiting. Up
ahead the lights of the sedan were still on. The door on
the driver's side had opened and a second man was
moving back.

The gunman took Lenore by the wrist. "Come on,
baby!"

"Let go!" Lenore said, her voice strident. "Let me go!"

"Behave!" the man said.

Randall moved up a step, angling to one side. He
could see Lenore struggling, and now the second man
had her by the arms and was telling her to get wise before someone got hurt.

The things that were said did not register with Randall. He was aware of only one thing: that he had failed
miserably to do the thing he had promised to do. He was
angry with Lenore for not telling him the truth in the
first place, angry with himself for letting such a thing
happen. Already she was halfway to the sedan, and he
was standing there doing nothing. In another few seconds it would be too late to help and the thought galled
him beyond endurance.

"Look," he said, and took another step. "This is kid-
napping, chump."

"Stand still."

Randall hesitated, balancing his weight. The light
was bad and he could not be sure about the gun. He
took another half step, wondering if he could dive in

before it went off, and in his calculations he forgot about Harding. So, apparently, did the gunman. Which was a mistake.

For even as Randall made up his mind Harding moved. Off to one side and about the same distance away as Randall, he struck out with lightning swiftness, his attack so explosive that when the lad in the powder-blue coat swung the gun from Randall there was no time to use it.

Harding cuffed it aside as his compact, wiry body catapulted forward. He swung from behind him with his right as he moved and in the darkness Randall was not sure what happened next. He heard the gun clatter to the pavement, heard the gunman's stifled curse and saw him reel backward, struggling to keep his feet, turning as he did so.

Harding, carried off balance by his rush, went down to one knee and had trouble regaining his feet. Randall, stopping to grope for the gun, pawed blindly over the pavement and finally came up with it. Even the taxi driver was busy, intent not upon the struggle but upon an endeavor of his own as he leaned inside the cab and snapped on the headlights.

It was all over in another second or two.

The erstwhile gunman was halfway to the sedan and running hard. He called: "They've got my gun," and that was enough for his companion.

He let go of the struggling Lenore and slapped her aside. He jumped in behind the wheel and rammed the gearshift into second. An instant later the car bucked forward with a roar while the fellow in the powder-blue coat clung to the right-front door and Harding, who had nearly reached it in his sprint, slowed down and stopped.

Randall lowered the gun, unwilling now to start shooting. He saw Harding turn to help Lenore and then he heard another car approaching from the rear. He swung towards it as it began to slow down. It turned out to be another taxi, and as it stopped opposite him John Barnard stuck his head out and said:

"Anything wrong?"

Randall put the gun in his pocket. He said some car had forced them to the curb but he didn't know why unless it was an attempted stick-up.

His driver had found the keys with the help of the other cab's lights and now he climbed in and started the motor. "Stick-up hell!" he said disgustedly. "Those guys wanted that dame and you know it. Might've got her too, if it hadn't been for the little guy."

Lenore got into the back seat. She said she was all right. "Thanks, Knox," she said.

"Thank Alan," he said.

"Those were the same two thugs that came aboard last night," Harding said thoughtfully. "Followed us up by car."

He let it go at that. He asked no questions and nothing more was said as they rode the remaining blocks to the boatyard. When they got out the driver asked if anyone had seen the license number of the sedan and should he report the incident to the police. Randall tipped him generously and told him to forget it.

The others were aboard when they got back. They said they had done a little sightseeing which explained why they were late. They asked a few questions without adding much to what they already knew and presently some of them went below.

Harding delivered the sandwiches to the Fourniers and Randall got out the charts for the next day's run. He

said they'd get an early start and put in at Eau Gallie
the next afternoon, and Harding said in that case he
thought he'd turn in.

Lenore came up from her cabin as Randall was putting his charts aside. She wore the green housecoat he
knew so well, but the overhead light was not kind to her;
her face was lined with weariness, and her eyes were
somber.

"I'm sorry I caused so much trouble," she said.

He let her move closer. "It's all right, baby. But I
think maybe you'd better tell me about it."

"I will, Knox. But please, not tonight."

"Tomorrow then.

"Yes," she said. She kissed him in her customary
fashion and turned away. "Good-night, Knox. And
thanks."

He watched her go and now he was alone, turning off
the overhead light and leaving the one on beside the
door until he made sure that no one else was topside.
Out on deck the night was soft and starlit, the water
flat and black as it stretched to the east. Here and there
a channel marker pinpointed the darkness, and as he
turned towards the dock other lights glowed cozily from
the snug cabins of other craft which lay motionless in
their slips.

He saw Nora Harding as he started to light a cigarette. She was perched on a pile almost opposite him.
She had made no move to attract attention, but now
that she knew he had seen her she stood up and started
back along the wharf towards the deckhouse door.

He wanted to go to her. He knew she must have witnessed the little scene with Lenore and he wanted to
talk and try to make her understand. Instead he stood
quite still, knowing there was no explanation he could

make, aware that from now on it was his job to keep an
eye on Lenore, to go ashore each evening when she
went and see that no harm came to her. There would be
no time for dinners with Nora nor any chance for fun or
an understanding until the trip was over; by then he was
desperately afraid it would be too late.

He called good-night to her as she stepped down
from the dock, and she answered him. Then she was in
the deckhouse, moving down the companionway ladder
and out of sight.

9

THE alarm clock woke Randall at a quarter of six the
next morning and as he turned over and yawned, Harding reached out and silenced the offending clock. The
little man slept raw and now he went naked halfway up
the ladder to take a quick look at the weather.

"Okay," he said. "No fog. When do you want to eat?"

"I'll have some coffee after we get started. Eat when
you want to and have breakfast for the others at eight.
I'll eat then."

Nora came out of the deckhouse as Randall got ready
to back off. She wore slacks and a sweater, her blond
hair was tousled, and sleep lay softly in her gray eyes.
She rubbed them with the back of her hand. Without a
word she climbed up on the dock to give her brother a
hand with the lines, though she got no thanks from him.

"Why didn't you stay in bed?" he said. "You paid
your fare."

She did not bother to answer him. She understood

that tides were sometimes tricky and that with a boat of that size two or three hands were far better than one. She tossed her line aboard, followed it to the deck and then stood by the waist with a fender as Randall jockeyed the *Julia* away from the dock. When he was clear she put the fender away and began to coil the bow and spring lines, paying no attention to Randall or her brother.

Her job done, she straightened and stood watching the Riviera Bridge as Randall blew for the bridge tender. Her hair stirred in the morning air and she brushed it back from her face. She waited until they went through the bridge, until she had waved to the bridge tender, and then she started below.

Randall called to her. He said: "Thanks, Nora," and there was a fine warm glow inside him when she waved back. He could not tell whether she smiled at him or not but he thought she did, and when Harding came past, clinging to the guard rail as he moved forward, Randall said:

"Leave her alone. If she wants to help, let her."

Harding grinned. "She likes boats. She'll probably be up every morning. She always was a good kid that way."

Lenore joined Randall on the bridge after breakfast. She had knotted a scarf about her auburn hair and she wore another one around her neck to keep the sun off. She asked questions about the charts, the markers, the compass; she tried the binoculars and pointed to a pure white bird perched on the bank.

"An egret," Randall said.

All of this was preliminary to the things she had in mind, and after about ten minutes she sat down on the cushioned seat. This put her to one side and behind

Randall, who sat on the jump seat behind the wheel and was unable to watch her expression.

"That was Mondello last night," she said at last. "I should have told you before."

"The gambler? The one who took the shots at Mr. Noland a couple of weeks ago?"

"That's the way I heard it."

Randall was impressed. He remembered now the things she had told him back in Miami. He turned to look at her but she was gazing over the starboard quarter at the sea, visible now through St. Lucie inlet.

"Mondello didn't follow you because of anything that had to do with Noland, did he?"

"No."

He waited, thinking, watching the wide brown waters of Indian River open up before him. He asked if Mondello was the one with the blue coat and she said no. "The other one," she said. "I used to work in his night-club in New York. They had some trouble there one night and he told me to get out of town. He's been paying me a hundred dollars a week to stay out. The times you saw me talking to Manny—he's the one in the blue coat—he was paying off." She turned to look at him, her mouth twisted as though from some inner taste she found displeasing. "You didn't think I was just down here on a vacation, did you?"

Randall shrugged to indicate that what he thought was unimportant. He said he had not concerned him-self with why she was in Miami, though he had won-dered more than once about this very thing.

"I liked you," he said, "and we had fun. The rest of it was none of my business. . . . What kind of trouble?"

"A couple of rich dames got to hanging around the club. In their forties, bored and looking for excitement, coming in with different escorts every couple of weeks and always loaded down with diamond bracelets clear up to here. I guess they got a kick out of sitting around after the place closed and talking with Mondello and the boys in the orchestra."

She took a breath and said: "So one night when things weren't going too good for Mondello he had the place knocked off. I didn't know it at the time it happened. I'd changed my clothes and was getting ready to come downstairs when these two guys came in with guns. They had handkerchiefs over their faces, and dark glasses, and they lined everybody up and cleaned them out, Mondello included, to make it look good. They came running through the foyer as I came down the stairs, and as they got outside they pulled off the handkerchiefs, not wanting anyone on the street to know it was a stick-up, and I got a look at one of them."

She said: "I didn't know it was a phony at the time but I recognized one of the men. They ran down the street and I went out and yelled, and a cop tried to stop them. They shot him in the leg and got away. Later the plain-clothes men came around and took my name and questioned me, and when they left Mondello came to see me. He told me to get out of town or else. He said I could come down here and take it easy until things blew over and—well, when you've been around like I have, never getting anywhere and knowing mostly men who think you're a pushover and try their damnedest to prove it, you forget a lot of things the rule books tell you. I couldn't feel sorry for the women—they could afford it —and the cop wasn't hurt bad." She laughed abruptly and said: "Also I was a little scared, so I did what I was told."

Randall nodded, slowly digesting what he had heard.

He understood Lenore's decision and found that he liked her none the less because of it. It was not always easy to fight alone, especially when the odds were bad, even when you had a cause.

"How long ago was that?" he asked.

"About four months ago."

"You didn't tell Mondello you were going back?"

"No, but the day I left Manny came up and saw I'd packed one of my bags. He didn't say anything but I guess he watched me after that. That's why we got tailed Saturday night."

Randall thought it over and there was still one thing he did not understand. "Why?" he said, and Lenore knew that what he meant had nothing to do with Manny.

"A week or so ago," she said, "I found out that another fellow had been arrested for the job. I don't know if he was framed or where the cops got the idea, but they took him down and booked him. That was a couple of months ago. He's out on bail and I understand he'll probably have to take the rap. That makes it a little different. I've been thinking about it, telling myself I'm a chump because I don't even know the guy." She grunted softly. "I guess I would have stayed right there, kept right on being a heel if it hadn't been for you making this trip."

"Because you thought you could make it without Mondello knowing where you were." Randall examined the premise and found it was not enough. "But that doesn't explain why you wanted to go back."

Lenore stood up and leaned against the windshield, her glance resigned, a little embarrassed. "I guess I wanted to be like you," she said simply.

Randall started to speak, he started to make a crack,

and some instinct warned him not to. Some quality of understanding that was an integral part of his character made him realize that Lenore was serious, and what she was about to say was not an easy thing to do.

"You're honest," she said, as if to answer him. She was looking past him now and her voice soft. "And clean. You do the right things because that's the way you are. . . . Oh, I'm not talking about this girl trouble and feeling sorry for yourself and wasting your time and money because you were hurt and trying to forget. I guess people react differently to things like that and I know you're not very proud of yourself. That's what I mean. You woke up one day and found out you'd been a fool; the point is when you found it out you did something about it."

She sighed again and said: "I guess if you had stayed on I would have stayed on too because I have a lot of respect for you and the way you do things. When you decided to go back and knuckle down again I thought I might as well give it a try and see if I couldn't start clean. When you get back you'll have your friends, and your way of living, and I guess you know what you want. My way is different but it's still all right for me. I've got a little money and I'm going to tell my story to the D.A. and when it's over I'm getting out of town. But I'll do it my way. I can always make a living and I know I'll like myself a lot better when it's over."

Randall had nothing to say. He felt touched and humble before the simple honesty of her confession. There was nothing cultured or erudite about her words, but the meaning behind them was clear and convincing, and he knew that somehow he'd never had a nicer tribute. Thinking back over the past three months he was ashamed, and a little proud that she had put her trust in him.

When she started off the bridge there was still nothing he could say so he put his hand on her arm and pressed it. She smiled and turned away, and then Harding appeared to help her aft to the cockpit.

John Barnard had followed Harding, and when the little man came back he said: "I'll relieve you for a while. Mr. Barnard would like to do a little steering. Where are we?"

Randall indicated their position on the chart and Harding nodded. Barnard settled his spare frame on the jump seat and glanced at the instrument panel. He wore a T-shirt now instead of the denim jacket, but the sun held no threat to him since his neck and face were already darkly tanned.

Randall stood for a moment watching the older man and presently Barnard reached behind him to lift the top of the seat which ran from one bridge rail to the other. He fumbled there with his hand, still watching his course, and presently he came up with a round cushion that fitted exactly the jump seat's perimeter. As he slid it under his buttocks, Randall grinned and went away; not until some time later did it occur to him to wonder how John Barnard had known the cushion was there.

After lunch Randall took the wheel again, and as the afternoon wore on his hopes that Nora would join him began to wane. Nora had other plans. She had a book and she sat reading in one corner of the cockpit while Lenore sat talking with the taciturn, broad-faced Dalton, who looked ill at ease in his shore clothes. The Fourniers had been out briefly and retired again. Bar-

nard and Harding were playing gin rummy in the deckhouse, according to Julia Noland who came presently to
keep Randall company.

She wore slacks and a halter and dark glasses. She
was, Randall thought, a little hippy for slacks, but there
were other things you were apt to notice more, especially
when she wore halters. He asked her if she would like to
steer and she said yes. "How does it work?" she asked.

"Steer the way you want to go—like a car. . . . You
mean you never steered this boat before?"

She shook her head. She tested the wheel. "This is
fun," she said in her low contralto voice. "I'm glad I
came."

Randall wondered how she'd feel when she found out
what had happened to Mr. X. He had managed for most
of the day to keep his thoughts on other things, but now
the truth was back to haunt him and he wondered how
long his luck would last. He wondered if he had been
wrong in his assumption that it was Noland's plan to
disappear. With the wish fathering the thought he considered the possibility that Noland had arranged a murder and had somehow disposed of the body—until he
remembered how the glasses and the telltale signet ring
had been left on the victim.

"I beg your pardon," he said, aware that Julia had
spoken.

"I said this was more fun than I ever had before on
this boat."

"Oh?"

"Mr. Noland hardly ever went out unless he had business to transact. I had to be the hostess and I didn't like
his friends. Men mostly, who chewed cigars and made
passes. Sharp-eyed men who talked from the corners of
their mouths and undressed you with their stares. What

women there were were usually cheap and loud, and
mostly a little drunk. As for Perry"—she paused and her
shrug was expressive—"he insisted that I come and then
ignored me."

Randall might have contested the statement under
other circumstances, for it was a little hard for him to
believe that any man, octogenarians and upwards excepted, could long ignore this woman's dark seductive
beauty. There was something so vital and fundamentally fascinating that her very nearness brought on a
strange awareness of her physical attractiveness. One
might, he thought, become surfeited, or wearied in the
struggle to match her intensity, but one could hardly
ignore her unless one was equally strong-willed and
determined.

"How long have you been married?" he asked finally.

"Nearly four years this time." She paused and said,
"I was married once before when I was eighteen. It
turned out to be rather a ghastly mistake and I thought
that this time it would be for keeps."

He offered her a cigarette and she asked him to light
it for her. They talked then of the Indian River and the
passing countryside, and after a while he said he'd better take the wheel because they were about ready to
turn off for Eau Gallie.

She moved aside and presently he made his turn,
heading for Elbow Creek towards the Eau Gallie docks
and boatyard, a snug, protected little harbor so hidden
from sight that not until one had swung past the angle of
the creek did the elbow open and present the masts and
deckhouses of the craft already tied up there.

It looked crowded to Randall, and he thought at first
he might have to anchor out, but now a man had come
to life on the nearest dock, a portly, well-aged man who

waved them on, his gestures pointing out a berth just big enough for the *Julia* along the vertical inner edge of the U-shaped docks.

There was no current here to bother Randall and he went in very slowly, with Harding, Barnard, and Nora placed strategically to toss the lines and fend off the cruisers already moored fore and aft of the opening while the owners came out to watch and to lend a hand in case of an emergency.

Intent as he was upon the job at hand, Randall took no notice of the others on the dock. He got to a point where he could be warped in, and cut his motors, Julia still at his side. It was then that he heard someone call her name.

"*Julia!*" the voice said, a surprised urgency in its cadence. "Good God! Why didn't you tell me. We had no idea what had happened to you."

Randall had heard the voice before and now he looked at the owner while his heart sank. Tall, blond and still immaculate, Eaton Gifford stood on the dock while Randall helped Julia from the bridge deck. She moved alongside the deckhouse and the lawyer held out his hand and helped her ashore. Behind him two men stood watchfully alert; sturdy, conservatively dressed men in city clothes.

There was little in their looks or manner to indicate their profession but in Randall's mind there was no room for doubt. That Gifford was here at all told him that his companions represented the law, and the hollowness grew inside him as he began to fold his charts and get out the canvas covers.

Now it comes, he thought, certain now that this was the end of the trip, but thankful that he had been able to salvage two days by his silence.

10

THERE was a white-painted, elongated structure, part
house and part shops, flanking the outer edge of this
portion of the dock. Here under roofs of varying height
—the building was three-storied in front and two-storied
in the rear—were gas tanks and water lines, the oil
drums, the marine supplies, the sail maker's shop. At the
front, the second and third stories apparently served as
living quarters, but underneath was an office or waiting
room of sorts in which there was an ancient roll-top
desk, a scarred oak table well littered with newspapers
and magazines, a few chairs. It was through this doorway that Julia had gone with Gifford and his two companions, and it was to this room that Randall was summoned a half hour later.

The man who came for him, a rusty-haired fellow
with a thin, straight mouth, said his name was Carney,
from the Miami police. He said they wanted to ask
Randall a few questions, and when he entered the room
he glanced first at Julia, who was staring out the window, her dark beauty as striking as ever, but paler somehow, the mouth drawn.

"There's been a murder, Mr. Randall," Carney said
without naming names, "and I'd like you to tell me
about this deal you made with Mr. Noland to bring this
boat north."

Randall lit a cigarette and took his time. He started
with the advertisement he answered and progressed
from there to his interview with Gifford, noting that
while the lawyer could still be classified as handsome he

did not seem as assured as before. What Randall had
once thought was a weakness around the mouth was
more pronounced now; the toothy smile wasn't working
and there were traces of anxiety in his light-brown eyes.
He kept working on his blond mustache and nodding
from time to time, as though impatient for Randall to get
on with his story.

Randall gave his account exactly as he remembered it,
leaving out only his discovery of the body, and when
he finished Carney said:

"When did you see him last?"

"Sunday morning. He came to the boat to give me
some money and a credit card so I could charge gas
along the way."

"When Sunday morning?"

"I don't know exactly. I didn't look at my watch. I'd
say it was somewhere between nine thirty and ten."

"You're sure of that?"

"Positive."

Carney puffed his cheeks and let his breath out. He
glanced at his companion who shrugged resignedly.
Gifford shifted in his chair and said, "*Whew*," in what
sounded like an expression of relief.

Carney eyed him aslant. "No one accused you, did
they?"

"You did some thinking along those lines though,"
Gifford said. "When you found out Mrs. Noland was
missing you were all set to accuse *her* of murder."

"Let's say she was a suspect," Carney said evenly. "In
a brutal murder like that a wife is always a suspect,
especially when she stands to inherit a sizable estate."

"We don't know how much she'll inherit," Gifford
countered. "I handled a lot of Noland's business but

until I find out what debts are outstanding no one will
know how much he was worth."

"We sometimes suspect the victim's lawyer," Carney
said, as though he had not heard. "It depends on a lot of
things." He turned to Randall, his voice still even and
unemphasized. "I don't want to try to change your
story," he said, "but I want you to think back while I try
to show you how important your testimony is."

He leaned back in his chair and said: "Somebody
blew off half of Mr. Noland's face with a sawed-off shotgun. Mr. Gifford here found the body this noon and the
medical examiner looked it over at one o'clock. He said
the man had been dead more than twenty-four hours
but probably not more than thirty-six—that was close as
he wanted to guess."

Randall decided the medical examiner was pretty
good. By his own figuring he knew that Mr. X had been
dead about thirty-two hours at the time the examination
was made.

"Mrs. Noland says she came aboard the boat Saturday night a little after ten. She says she did not leave
her cabin until after you left Lauderdale."

"Several people will testify to that," Randall said.

"Mr. Gifford was at the Miami Airport at eight thirty
Sunday morning. He took the plane to Havana with a
friend and spent the day there, returning around midnight last night. So if you saw Mr. Noland around nine
thirty or ten Sunday morning it means he was killed
between then and one P.M.—if the medical examiner is
right about the twenty-four hours." He paused and
said: "That's why we hustled up here to locate the boat
and talk to you." He glanced at Julia. "We didn't expect
to find Mrs. Noland."

She turned then, her chin up. "I told you why I came along, and why I left my husband."

"If you're worried about my story," Randall said to Carney, "my steward can verify it." He told about Harding and his former job with Noland, and Carney asked that Harding be called in.

Randall went and got him. "What time was it when you saw me talking to Mr. Noland yesterday morning?" he said when they returned.

Harding looked the room over with his light-blue eyes. "A little before ten."

"Did Noland see you?" Carney asked.

Harding said he didn't think so and explained how Randall had waved him off.

"But you know it was Noland?"

Harding cocked his head and looked back at the detective. "Sure," he said.

Carney dismissed him. He rubbed his chin and did not seem particularly disappointed. He had, apparently, several theories, and now that one was thoroughly exploded he turned to another.

"That narrows it down a little," he said. "Someone tried to kill Noland a couple of weeks ago. Ernie Mondello, maybe, or some of those Beach gamblers. There were marks on Noland's wrists and ankles, as though he had been tied up before he was killed. Maybe he wouldn't stand still for a pay-off and they caught up with him. It looks as though someone put the pressure on—probably more than one man was in on it from the looks of things—and Noland wouldn't play and got shot for his stubbornness. Either that or it was along revenge lines and the killers taunted him some before they blasted him. He had business dealings with Mondello, didn't he?" he asked of Gifford.

"They owned a night club," the lawyer said, "until
Mr. Noland took it over. But it wouldn't have to be
Mondello. Noland had trouble with a lot of people. I
understand he had a couple of small factories during
the war and afterwards he bought some boats and
planes from the War Assets Administration. He did
some business with one or two South American groups
and he had a finger in some deal that was supposed to
supply planes for that crowd in Cuba that was going to
attack the Dominican Republic or some such place.
Later he made arrangements with some ex-Army flyers
to take a few planes to some Central or South American
country. I don't know the details but I know there were
some arrests made. Not Mr. Noland, though. He got his,
and legally his skirts were clean."

Gifford went on to elaborate, and from what he
said Knox Randall was ready to accept Julia's expressed
opinion of her husband. The picture he had was of a
man who was shrewd, ruthless in his business dealing,
and without ethics of any sort. Yet this was of small
concern to Randall at the moment. What he wanted to
know was where he stood.

"I'd like to finish this trip," he said, and explained to
Carney his obligations.

The detective wasn't sure. "Mrs. Noland will have to
go back with us, at least for a few days. I suppose it's up
to her what she wants to do with the boat."

"My husband wanted it taken to Falmouth so he
could sell it," Julia said. "I certainly have no use for it.
Do I have anything to say about it, Eaton?"

Gifford pushed his lips out. "The will will have to be
probated but the boat is part of the estate. I can't see
that it matters whether it's in Falmouth or tied up here.
I'd suggest you go ahead, Randall. If there's any objec-

tion later I'll wire you and you'll have to leave it wherever you are."

Carney was appreciative of Randall's problems and obligations. "If we can get someone to type out a statement from you and have your signature witnessed," he said, "I have no objection."

He got out his notebook and asked where Randall worked, took down his New York address, requested two or three references. Randall's spirits rose and he said he'd find out if anyone aboard could do the typing. He thanked Julia and she said she would speak to him before she left.

As it turned out Nora Harding was the only one aboard who professed any expert knowledge of a typewriter. The manager of the dock produced a machine together with paper and carbons, and Nora typed out the statement with Carney standing by to see that it was properly done and properly signed. With this much accomplished, the detective was quite willing to wait until Julia and Gifford were ready for the return trip to Miami.

It was seven o'clock before Julia had completed the preparations for her departure and by that time most of the others had started for the center of the little town, once again led by Barnard, who knew a little restaurant where they could eat. Randall paced back and forth in the gathering dusk, and in the deckhouse he could see Gifford and Dalton sitting there in silence on opposite sides.

Julia came up at last, followed by Lenore, and she carried but one small bag which Gifford immediately took from her. He held her arm and helped her to the deck; he helped her from there to the dock. When she saw Randall she said:

"Will you wait for me, Eaton? I want to talk to Mr. Randall."

Gifford leaned against the building and Randall moved towards the front of the dock with Julia at his side.

"You're going to leave the rest of your things aboard?" he asked when they were alone.

She nodded. She watched him for a moment with her long, narrowly tapered eyes. "I want to come back," she said. "I've been happy since I've been aboard and maybe I can be happy again." She glanced down at the water, her voice controlled. "There's nothing to keep me in Miami, once the funeral is over and they have finished with their questions. What's to be done can be done by Mr. Gifford. I knew nothing of my husband's business affairs—and very little about his private ones."

She poked at the stringpiece with the toe of her shoe. "I suppose it sounds pretty cold-blooded, putting things that way, wanting to come back and go right on as if nothing happened. But—well, I guess that's how I feel. To do anything else would be hypocritical, because there's been nothing between us for nearly two years and when I walked out the other day I put the whole thing behind me. There's simply nothing there any more."

She put her hand on her breast. "I don't feel anything. Maybe a little numbness from the suddenness of it all, a little shocked that such a thing could happen to anyone I've lived with for four years. Oh, I don't know how to say it, but I want to come back and sit in the sun and rest."

Randall could understand her reaction. She had made it clear the other day when she explained why she was leaving Noland. Yet it was not this which occupied his mind at the moment. He kept thinking of the man he called X. For Noland was alive and he, Randall, was the only one who knew it. Gifford had obviously made the identification and had come to the same conclusion Randall made. Julia might not even be called in to verify Gifford's identification; even if she were called, she could take no more than a glance at that mutilated face.

And all the time Noland was walking around somewhere. Apparently he preferred to remain dead, but what if Julia knew the truth? What would happen if she should run into him some time by accident. He shook off the morbid overtones of his thoughts and took another tack.

"What will you do now?" he said. "I mean when you get to New York."

Julia said she did not know. She had no plans. There was an apartment in New York and she would stay there awhile until she could decide what she wanted to do.

"But this is what I wanted to speak to you about," she said. "I wondered if you would re-arrange your schedule a little. Could you make short trips the next two days and perhaps make it up later on."

"Why—"

"You could go to Daytona tomorrow. The next day you could go to St. Augustine, and the others could do some sightseeing. That will give me two days and a chance to join you there. If I can't make it you can go on and do as you like."

He hesitated. He tried to adjust his plans to the unexpectedness of her request. "After all," he said, "it's your boat now."

"Please." She put her hand on his arm and he could feel the soft warmth of it through his sleeve. "Let's not put it on that basis."

Her sudden earnestness embarrassed him. "I didn't mean it that way," he said. "Of course we can."

"Oh, good." She stepped back. "Now I'll have something I can look forward to." She paused for a word of caution. "But if I shouldn't be there, you're to go on and forget about me."

Gifford came forward to meet them. He took her arm as she said good-bye, and they walked along the dock and up the path towards the road.

Lenore had been watching from the doorway of the deckhouse, and now she moved out on the dock followed by Dalton.

"Isn't he pretty?" she said dryly.

"Who?" said Randall.

"Mr. Gifford. Very attentive too."

Randall laughed. "Why shouldn't he be? She's the boss now. He's working for her."

"Are you ready to eat?" Lenore said. "Mr. Dalton's coming with us."

"If it's agreeable to you, Mr. Randall," Dalton said.

Randall smiled. He had spoken hardly a dozen times in two days to this quiet, powerfully built man with his small town clothes, and he was glad that the other was beginning to come out of his shell. He wanted to say so but he didn't.

"Glad to have you," he said. "You two go ahead while I get a jacket. I'll catch up with you in a minute."

Dalton stood there uncertainly, as though undecided

as to the next move. Then Lenore tucked her arm inside
his. "Come on, Oliver," she prodded. "You heard what
the captain said."

11

THE schedule for the following day was a compara-
tively easy one and Randall slept until seven o'clock.
Harding lit the stove and put some water on while
Randall got the motors started, and again as they got
ready to move out from the dock, Nora came hurrying
up to give a hand while she rubbed the sleep from her
eyes.

"I hear the motors," she said when Randall asked her
how she knew they were getting ready to shove off.
"You're late this morning."

He said they had an easy day ahead, and explained
that they were only going to Daytona. He did not state
his reasons for the change and she did not ask, but at
breakfast he told everyone that Mrs. Noland hoped to
rejoin them in St. Augustine. He said this accounted for
the change in schedule, and since the news had already
gone around as to why Julia had left the night before
his explanations were accepted with but little comment.

"That way," said Barnard, "we'll have plenty of time
to look around St. Augustine tomorrow afternoon." He
glanced at the others. "You'll find it an interesting town
if you've never had a chance to look it over," he added.

Later in the morning, as they approached Hallover
Canal, Barnard came to the bridge to keep Randall
company. This narrow strip of land, no more than a mile
in width, which separated Indian River from Mosquito

Lagoon, was neatly cut by a narrow canal over which there was one bridge, and Barnard had something to say about the history of the place.

"They used to have a kind of marine railway here," he said. "Or at least some method of hauling boats out and dragging them overland by mules. Some difference now, huh?"

Randall said it certainly was, and with the canal behind them he asked if Barnard would like to take the wheel. The older man nodded, and Randall rose and stretched before he lit a cigarette.

He had noticed the change in the country as they moved steadily northward up Indian River. The mangrove swamps had given way to gravel and sandy banks, interspersed here and there with roots, and what mangrove trees there were, were short and forlorn-looking. There had been a lot of ducks farther back and now he watched a long-necked, black-looking bird swimming off to one side and ducking occasionally for fish.

"A cormorant," Barnard said. "Like they use to fish with in Japan."

They watched in silence for a while, Barnard at the wheel and Randall checking the chart and markers. They spoke of the weather and how fortunate they had been so far. Barnard said it was generally pretty good at this time of year but that as they got farther up they could expect some rain. Randall, aware that he was not really equipped for wet weather, having nothing in his gear but a rain coat, said he hoped Mr. Noland had a rain suit or two aboard.

"Maybe in that locker just beyond the generator," Barnard said.

Randall started to say something, then stopped to examine the gray-haired man at the wheel. His mind

106   INLAND PASSAGE

went back to the previous day when Barnard had found
the jump-seat cushion without even hunting for it.

"Why would the rain suits be there?"

"Oh—seems like a likely place."

"You knew there was a cushion for that jump-seat too.
You know more about this boat than I do."

Barnard was silent for a moment, his brown, weathered face impassive. "I ought to," he said finally. "I
owned it once."

Randall stared at him a moment. He took a deep
breath and looked out across the lagoon. He thought:
Now I've heard everything. He watched Barnard take a
pipe and tobacco pouch from a hip pocket. He said:

"Noland buy it from you?"

"It was part of a deal."

Barnard filled the pipe with loving care. He asked if
Randall would watch the wheel while he got a light. He
sucked flame into the bowl until he was satisfied that the
tobacco was fired evenly. When he was ready he said:

"I called her the *Marie;* after my wife. She was built
in '28 and I got her in '34 for about one sixth of what
she cost. Noland took her off my hands in '45." He
glanced at the chart and settled the pipestem solidly
between his bicuspids.

"I'm retired now. Got a little income, and a place just
outside of Lauderdale. I knew the boat was down here
and when I saw your ad I had a hunch. There aren't too
many seventy-four-footers around Lauderdale, so I
thought I'd take a look. The minute I talked with you I
knew I was coming along. Be my last trip on a boat like
this, I guess; anyway it'll be the cheapest trip I ever
had."

Randall digested the information and now he asked if
Barnard knew Noland very well.

"We were partners once."

Randall waited, having no further capacity for surprise. Barnard went on matter-of-factly, quite unaware of the effect his words had on his listener.

"I was in the novelty jewelry business up in Rhode Island. Just a little factory that my father started. I kept it going somehow through the depression years but when the war came along and everything was rationed I was about finished. I figured I might tool over here and there and make some little metal gadget for the Army or Navy, but I wasn't much of a hand at sitting it out in Washington and wangling contracts."

"That's where Noland came in?"

"He'd got a couple of contracts—don't ask me how— and was looking for a place to manufacture these things. Well, to make a long story short we made a deal. By then I needed capital and he arranged it for a half interest, along with the contracts. As it turned out I wasn't very smart."

"You mean you trusted him?"

"Yes. We made money but we needed more to expand and we both put up some stock for the loan. Like a fool I let him arrange this, and what he did, though I didn't know it at the time, was to put up the money himself through a dummy. Anyway, in the end he wound up with control, and after the Germans surrendered he saw a chance to sell out and there wasn't anything I could do about it. I got enough out of it to retire. I can live fairly comfortably even with interest rates the way they are, and my children are all grown up and married. Time we wound things up I couldn't afford a boat like this anyway so Noland took it over."

"At his price."

"Sort of."

Barnard told all this casually and without any outward sign of bitterness. The impression he gave was that
of a man who had been cheated but had in the end
decided to accept the situation with calmness and equa-
nimity. Yet for all of this Randall could not help feel
that, deep-down, there must have been great bitterness
in Barnard's heart. To Randall, never free from the
problem of murder nor able to understand all of its ram-
ifications, what he heard added up to a rather good
motive for such violence, had Noland really been the
victim instead of Mr. X. He was still thinking about this
when Harding came up to relieve him and announce
that luncheon was being served.

Shortly after they had finished eating and while
Harding was washing the dishes, they passed Ponce de
Leon Inlet and presently they were moving up the Hali-
fax River towards the skyline of Daytona Beach. Here,
as they turned into the modern, well laid-out boatyard
and yacht basin, the dock master waved them into a
sheltered spot not far from the marine railways.

As Randall remembered it, this was one of the best
spots on the entire trip, with tall boat sheds and green
lawns across the way, a loud speaker in the main office
which boomed forth from time to time to summon an
owner or a yard workman to the telephone. By the time
he had gassed up and checked the motors most of the
others were ready to go ashore. Barnard had already
ordered cars but because Randall was hot and dirty he
said he'd stay aboard, take a turn at the shower, and see
what was needed in the way of provisions.

When he was clean he stretched out on his bunk for
an hour and then went about making his list. He
ordered a car at the office and went into the center of
town to do his shopping, buying the necessary groceries

and vegetables as well as a carton of shrimp for a salad
the following noon. The others were back when he
returned, and he had no chance to talk to Nora until just
before dinner. It was then that Lenore came to him and
said, with a burlesqued rolling of her eyes, that she had
a date for dinner.

"Mr. Dalton?" he asked.

"Mr. Dalton."

Randall's first eager thought was of Nora; his second
of Lenore. "Does he know about Mondello?"

"No."

"Well?"

"Oliver can take care of me, Knox. I'll be careful." She
was so serious, so much like a little girl asking her
mother for permission to go out, that he had to smile at
her.

"Okay," he said. "If you come back early and don't go
riding around the country-side."

"Yes, dear," said Lenore. "Thank you, dear."

She tripped off and Randall stepped ashore and sat
on a piling until Nora appeared in the deckhouse. She
stood talking to Barnard and the Fourniers until he
caught her eye and beckoned, not wanting to talk in
front of the others. He thought she looked wonderfully
slender and desirable in her gabardine skirt and sweater
but he found no enthusiasm in her face as she moved
towards him.

"Could we have dinner together?" he asked.

She examined him closely, nothing showing in her
gray eyes.

"What about Lenore?"

He laughed lightly, pretending that her question was
amusing but irrelevant. "What about her?" he said eva-
sively.

"I thought there was some mutual arrangement about dinners with her."

Her tone was casually indifferent but he refused to let it irritate him.

"She had a date with Mr. Dalton."

"Oh?" Nora let her brows climb. "Well, I'm sorry but I've already said I'd go with Mr. Barnard and the Fourniers." Apparently she saw the disappointment in his face for she said, politely, but with no great warmth: "But you could go with us. There should be room. Why don't you speak to Mr. Barnard?"

Randall spoke to Mr. Barnard, not wanting to go but refusing to sulk in front of Nora. He went to dinner with the others, and so did Alan Harding. Afterwards Barnard suggested a movie and they attended en masse. By the time they got back to the boat everyone felt like going to bed and when Randall climbed into his bunk he was a thoroughly disgusted young man.

Along about the middle of the following morning Nora came to the bridge and stood looking at the chart. Randall, who had given her a polite good-morning earlier and was still grumpy from his group treatment the night before, kept his eyes on the canal ahead. For some time now, and for some distance ahead, he had the boring job of what he called ditch plowing, following the thin red line on the chart which indicated the deepest water, looking uninterestedly at the surrounding country which had changed to high banks on either side, badly eroded here and there from the wash of passing boats. Ashore there were cabbage palms now, many of them short, with here and there some stately live-oak trees with their beards of gray-green moss. There were still plenty of egrets—or were they heron? He never was quite sure—but he had seen it all before and he made up his mind that this time Nora would speak first. Presently she did.

"I've been talking to Lenore."

He waited while five seconds ticked off. "Oh?"

"She was telling me about you."

"Me?"

"Not just you—though I guess most of it was about you at that—but about the two of you, and what good friends you've been." She paused, and when she continued her voice was soft but clear. "I guess I didn't understand how it was."

"Sure." Randall adjusted the visor of his cap, his dark eyes sultry. "I told you I'd been running around and you figured Lenore was my latest flame."

She made no reply to this and nothing changed in her voice. "She thinks you're wonderful," she said. "She told me why you promised to look out for her."

"How much did she tell you?" Randall asked, interested now in spite of himself.

"Just that she was going to New York to be a witness in some case; that there were a couple of men who were trying to prevent her from testifying. She told me what really happened that night she was with you and Alan." She smoothed the chart out and said: "I'm sorry I jumped to conclusions."

"You couldn't give me the benefit of the doubt, hunh?"

She straightened, spots of color showing under the even tan of her cheekbones. He thought for a moment he had crowded her too far with his boorish stubbornness and he became a little panicky. Then, still not looking at him, she said:

"I told you I was sorry."

"How sorry?" Randall's smile broke through as his spirits bubbled, his teeth flashing whitely against the deep tan of his face. "Sorry enough," he said when she glanced round, "to have dinner with me tonight? Assuming that Dalton promises to look after Lenore?"

Her laugh was a lovely sound and there was nothing coy about her answer. "I'd like that, Knox," she said, sounding as if she meant it.

"And maybe a movie?"

"Maybe even a movie."

She turned then as someone moved into sight beyond the deckhouse corner and then Oliver Dalton was standing there, looking up, the expression on his broad, blunt-nosed face suggesting some new embarrassment.

"Oh—I—" He stopped and tried again. "Hello, Miss Harding. I didn't know anyone else was here," he said. "I wondered if I could talk to you a minute, Mr. Randall."

"Sure," Randall said heartily. "Come up and sit down."

Dalton climbed up in his dark worsted trousers and striped shirt with its turned-up sleeves and turned-down neckband. Nora said: "A red and two black, coming up. That must be the Matanzas River up ahead." She swung past Dalton and through the opening in the rail. "I'll see how lunch is coming," she said.

Dalton took his time. He was, it seemed, a man who seldom wasted words and now he apparently had trouble finding the right ones.

"I don't like to cause any trouble," he said finally, "or make complaints."

"Why not? That's the only way we have of knowing when things are wrong. What's on your mind?"

"Someone's been going through my things."

Randall stiffened inwardly, his mind racing on ahead and disturbed by the idea it picked up.

"It wasn't Mr. Barnard," Dalton went on. "I spoke to him. He said no and I believe him."

"Have you any ideas?"

"I don't like to say. I thought if I told you—"

"I'm glad you did. I'll speak to Mr. Harding."

Dalton sounded rather miserable about what he had done. "I don't like to cause trouble."

"It's all right," Randall said, his anger smoldering but controlled. "I'm glad you told me. It won't happen again."

Dalton sighed. He stood up, hesitating as though reluctant to have the matter end that way. Finally he turned away and Randall watched him, wondering again as his thoughts slid off on a tangent, why this stolid, slow-spoken man had ever signed on for such a trip.

He spoke to Harding when the little man came up to relieve him at lunch time. He was still angry, but he had his temper in hand and, like Dalton, he didn't want any trouble at this stage of the trip.

"I thought we had an understanding," he said evenly.

"About what?"

"About your keeping out of the passengers' quarters."

Harding blinked sun-bleached brows and, as though an invisible shade had been drawn over them, something happened to his light-blue eyes.

"Who says I was in anybody's quarters?"

"Dalton."

"Nuts!"

Randall turned. He eyed Harding steadily and the other met his gaze. "Why don't you grow up?" he said with mild disgust. "You were honest about telling me you were a snoop and a little light fingered—in a small way, of course—so why can't you be honest now?"

It was, apparently, the right approach to use. Harding was not ashamed, but he had been challenged and now he straightened his wiry body and met the challenge.

"All right," he said, "so I took a look around. Why don't you ask Dalton what he's doing with the thirty thousand dollars he's got in one of those bags he forgot to lock?"

"What?" Randall stared at him. "What?" he said again.

"You think I'm kidding?"

Somehow Randall knew Harding was telling the truth. He swallowed, lips tightening. "You counted it, I suppose."

"No, but it's damn close to thirty thousand. In new bills."

Randall thought it over, accomplishing exactly nothing by the effort. "All right, so he's got thirty thousand. He's not bothering anyone, is he? He minds his own business, doesn't he?"

"Sure but—"

"Then suppose you mind yours. What are you, an F.B.I. agent in disguise?" He stood up and motioned Harding behind the wheel. "You stay the hell out of those cabins from now on. I mean it."

Harding sat down, his freckled face flushed. Randall watched him a moment, not wanting any further argument but giving the other a chance. When nothing more was said he turned and went below.

12

THE *Julia* came into the St. Augustine Municipal Wharf in the early afternoon. Here, along the T-shaped structure, were tied boats of all shapes and sizes: sailboats, cruisers both large and small, a houseboat which carried a crew of seven and was a hundred and twenty-five feet overall. Tourists with cameras walked the docks to inspect the new arrivals, and habitues in shorts and sneakers moved about to give advice and lend a hand with the lines.

There was a seven or eight-foot tide here and Randall consulted with Barnard while he got his spring lines out and satisfied himself that the *Julia* would not hang herself on the dock, or on her neighbor, before the night was over. He was too busy for a while to worry about his passengers but when, finally, he had finished his duties and changed his clothes, Nora was waiting.

The land-end of the dock came out on a street which paralleled the shore, and tasseled carriages with Negro drivers in high hats clop-clopped along in search of paying customers. Randall signaled a single seater.

"A carriage, Madame?" he said with a bow.

"If you so wish, sire."

They went first to Fort Marion—Castillo de San Marcos, the sign outside said—and left the driver while they walked across the moat. They inspected each inner room and read each sign, discovering that the fort had been built in the sixteenth century, destroyed, and rebuilt in 1675. They learned that this fort had never been taken;

that Oglethorpe laid siege for twenty-seven days from
the islands across the inlet but finally gave up when
some supplies arrived from Cuba because his cannon
could not breach the walls.

They climbed the ramparts and stood for awhile in
the sunshine watching the fishing boats come in from
the sea through the wide inlet and past the drawbridge
as they went upriver. And when they had enough of
this they rode slowly through flower-decked narrow
streets, going for awhile along the length of the main
avenue with its little park in the center, and then moving crosstown to visit the oldest schoolhouse in the
United States, and, so the sign said, the oldest house.

"1599," the driver said. "And just like she was made,
'cept for a new roof."

For Knox Randall it was a perfect two hours. They
talked with a naturalness heretofore undiscovered, were
impressed by the same things, and shared some of their
thoughts with a spontaneity that was good for his soul.
Even as they walked back along the dock he found cause
for rejoicing, because in a little while they would go
forth again, this time for dinner.

At least that is what he thought. He even thought so
when he stepped through the deckhouse door and
found Julia Noland sitting there with a magazine, smiling lazily at Randall and saying hello to Nora.

"You made it," Randall said, trying to simulate a
heartiness he did not entirely feel.

"I told you I would."

Her elongated eyes surveyed him, then moved to include Nora, who seemed a little embarrassed as she said
it was nice that Julia could make the rest of the trip. It
was hard to know what to say to a woman whose husband—to all intents and purposes—had recently been

murdered and after a moment of awkward silence, Nora gave up, saying something about seeing Randall later before she excused herself and went below.

Julia continued to smile, her glance studied as she waited for Randall to speak. "Are you glad to see me?" she asked in her low intimate voice.

"Of course," Randall said, and then, seeing her glance go beyond him, he turned to find the rest of the passengers coming along the dock.

"I'd like to talk to you," Julia said. "I was wondering if you might take me to dinner."

Randall flinched inwardly. He thought of the two hours just spent with Nora. He had looked forward to the evening ever since that morning and he wondered just what the extent of his obligation to Julia—as the new owner of the boat—might be.

"I—I'd like to," he said, "but I've already asked Nora. We were going to dinner, and then to the movies."

Julia watched impatiently as the others started to jump down from the dock. "Take Nora to the movies," she said, "and have dinner with me. I'm sure she'll understand. There'll be lots of other evenings, you know. Or would you rather I spoke to her."

Randall gave up. "All right," he said, trying to sound as gracious as possible under the circumstances. "Say, in an hour?"

He went below as the others scrambled into the deckhouse, and knocked on Nora's door. He took a breath when she opened it. "Julia wants to talk to me," he said. "She wants me to have dinner with her. I told her about you and she said it would only be for this once."

He paused, seeing the smile that she had started fade away. Some of the brightness went out of her gray eyes.

"We can still go to the movies," he said quickly.

"You'd better go with Julia." She stepped back, her tone reserved, indifferent. "It's quite all right," she said. "There'll be other times."

There was a restaurant about a hundred yards up the shore from the Municipal Wharf, a boxlike structure built on piles and extending out over the water. A large, electrically lighted sign proclaimed the name and the character of its fare—namely seafood—and according to Barnard it was well worth a try.

His party was already seated when Randall arrived with Julia and was shown to a corner table for two. The others waved, all but Nora, and something of what he felt must have shown on Randall's face because after he had ordered drinks Julia put out her hand and pressed his briefly.

"I'm sorry," she said. She studied Nora a moment and digressed. "She's really quite lovely, isn't she?" She came back to the subject. "But I really did want to talk to you."

Randall offered a cigarette and a light, then settled back, resigned but determined to be pleasant and attentive.

"Though if you asked me why," she said, "I'm not sure I could tell you."

Randall was a little slow. "Why what?"

"Why I wanted to talk to you. I think probably it's because I want you to understand why I wanted to come in the first place and why, after what happened, I wanted to come back."

"I think I do understand," Randall said. "I've heard some other things about Noland, none of them flattering. He must have been pretty tough to live with."

"I didn't think so when I married him."

Randall asked if she would have another drink and she said she would, absently, as though she were no longer aware of him or her surroundings. Distance grew in her shadowed eyes and he felt the things they saw were not in this room but in the past.

"I ran away from home when I was eighteen," she said. "From a little cross-roads town where the wind blew most of the time and there was nothing to do but work and wait for a future that would never come. One day I decided to do something about it. I'd saved a little money and St. Louis was my first stop. I found a furnished room. Within a week I had a job as a waitress, and after that it wasn't long before I could tell, from the way men looked at me, that I had something they wanted. I couldn't help that; I was even pleased about it, because I was smart enough to realize that it could be an advantage."

She took some of her cocktail and her mouth was twisted. "I was very smart," she said wryly. "I married a man ten years older than I was because he was a smooth talker and wore good clothes—at least good by comparison. He had money to spend and big ideas. He was a salesman. He traveled through the middle west and travel was something I wanted very much just then." She made a wet circle with the bottom of her glass and her mouth remained twisted.

"Also," she said, "he was a bit of a forger on the side. Not an important one, but clever enough in his way, and because he kept moving it was a long time before they caught up with him. Two years nearly, and part of that time I was passing checks for him; checks he said had been given him to pay for the device he sold." She glanced up, her smile crooked. "Do you know what it was? One of those little check-protecting gadgets. He sold them on commission, out of a suitcase."

She finished her drink and said: "I will say this for him: when they caught him he told the truth and they let me go. I told him then that I'd had enough, that I'd divorce him. And I did. I worked as a waitress again and went to night school. I got a job as a demonstrator for a food company—I always had plenty of nerve and confidence, and I could talk to people—going around to department stores, and the larger grocery stores, and showing the women how to make puddings, or whatever it was I was demonstrating. I did all right too. I made some money and saved some of it. I came to Florida for a vacation and ran into a man at a party who offered me a job in his real estate office."

She said: "It was a renting office mostly, and that's how I met Perry Noland. He wanted a house and after I found him one he wanted to take me out. I went, naturally, and I liked the way he did things. We got along well and when he asked me to marry him I said yes. He had money, at least enough, and enough importance to impress the sort of people he associated with. I thought I loved him and I thought along with it I would get some security, an advantage which might not seem too essential to someone like Nora Harding but which was tremendously important to me. What I got of course, was someone not too different from my first husband, just more impressive."

Randall considered everything she said. He found that his original opinion of her remained unchanged, but now he understood some of the elements which had gone into her character and made her the woman she was. He asked if she would like to order and she said yes, if she could have one more drink.

"So now I'm alone," she said thoughtfully. "I'll have plenty of time to think on this trip and nothing to worry about. I'll stay in New York for a while and after that I'm not sure what I'll do. I do know that if I get the chance to marry again it won't have to be for money or security. I should know enough by now to tell the genuine from the spurious. Maybe next time," she added quietly, "I will really be in love."

She said other things after Randall had ordered but his thoughts remained on the statement she had just made. To him, the idea that she now had a little money and some security was no sinecure, and before he put the thought from his mind it occurred to him that her chances of getting the right man were even less, now that she had something besides herself to offer, than they were before.

"What happened in Miami?" he said finally.

"Nothing much. There were more questions, and pieces in the paper about how the police expected to make an arrest, but I still don't think they know who did it. Mr. Gifford is taking care of things for me, and what I want most now is to forget everything that happened."

The rest of the passengers had long since left the restaurant by the time Julia and Randall were ready to go but when they got back to the boat there was no one in sight, though light streamed from the fo'c'sle hatch, suggesting that Harding might be below. The main deck, which had been only slightly below dockside level when Randall tied up, was now about three feet lower and he jumped down first to help Julia.

He got hold of both of her hands and she squealed as

she jumped, knocking him off balance so that they had
to grab each other to stay upright. They swayed,
straightened while Julia clung to him, her body firm and
warm against his own. She looked up at him in the darkness, her mouth close to his; then she released him and
laughed softly.

To Randall that laugh had overtones of mockery and
he knew why. She had expected something more and he
had been unsure of himself, perhaps a little afraid. She
had sensed this instinctively, and the thought left him
hot and embarrassed. He could feel her eyes upon him
as he moved forward to call to Harding and ask where
everyone was.

When he came back with the information that the
Fourniers had turned in and the others were still seeing
the sights, Julia was still watching him, and now light
from the deckhouse fell upon her face and he could see
the amusement in her tapered eyes. She let him help her
aft and into the deckhouse. He said he'd better get out
the charts for tomorrow and she said she'd help him.

He became increasingly aware of her nearness as
they spread the charts out on the floor and checked dis-
tances. He could feel the warmth of her, though nothing touched but their shoulders. He felt uncomfortable
and awkward in her presence and wondered why. A
week ago he would have been grateful for the opportunity and eager to explore its possibilities; a month ago he
might even have become infatuated with her. Now,
thinking about these things, the spell she had recently
cast began to fade and he found his mind turning to
Nora. Yet when she came in a little later to find him still
on the floor with Julia and his charts, it was hard to meet
her glance; he was glad that there were others about to
demand information about the next day's run.

The days that followed were pleasant and uneventful. The weather was generally fine, with only one squall to wet things down, and because the days were full and long everyone seemed ready to go to bed fairly early.

From St. Augustine they went steadily northward, across the St. John's River, across Nassau Sound, and on up past Cumberland Sound and Ft. Clinch to the river and St. Andrews Sound. Here Randall asked his passengers to take a vote on where they wanted to spend the night. He said he had planned to go on to St. Simon, but he remembered that the Jekyll Island Club, once the exclusive haunt of millionaires, had been taken over by the state and was now public property. He said he thought they could tie up right there and eat at what used to be the club, whereas if they went on to St. Simon they would have to phone for a car and drive to the Cloisters for dinner. He cautioned them however, that should they choose Jekyll Island it meant that the next day's run to Beaufort would be long and hard.

When they saw Jekyll Island they settled for that, and the next morning Randall was up early and under weigh by six o'clock, helped as usual by Harding and his sister. For Nora, regardless of what she thought about the episode with Julia, gave no outward sign of resentment. She spent much time on the bridge when Randall was there, helping with the charts and picking up buoys with the binoculars when they crossed some of the wider sounds. She commented on the passing countryside when there was anything interesting to note, pointed out that the palms had given way to stands of tall pines, their trunks gashed slantwise by the knives of the turpentine workers.

She took delight in the names of the waterways they traveled, calling them out from time to time lest he miss them. Little Mud River with its flat, marshy background, Old Teakettle Creek; St. Catherine's Sound, Bear River, and Skidaway Narrows.

They stopped at Thunderbolt and its floating docks for gas and to mail letters, and then pressed on, slowing down near Isle of Hope because of the skiffs and playing children who swam unafraid out from the jetties on the high banks off the port side.

Randall had figured the distance at better than a hundred and thirty nautical miles, and because he was a little late and there was no one ready to take a line, he had trouble getting docked at Beaufort. There was a lot of tide, moving strongly now, and it caught him as he came in too slow. For a time then he thought he might have to settle for a berth next to some tie-up dolphins, and he might have done so had he not realized that there was no easy way of getting ashore for dinner. Finally, not wanting to serve everyone aboard, he pushed off with the help of Harding, Nora, and Barnard, backed safely away to make another, more determined pass at the dock, this time successful.

The weather held the next day. The azaleas were in bloom, and when they came through Middle Ground approaching Charleston, Dalton and Harding got out their cameras. They were too far away to do much with Forts Johnson, Sumter, and Moultrie but they passed fairly close to a sizable mine-layer which lay in the stream, and both got shots of the high bridge at Sullivan's Island. Farther on they were held up for a while by a primitive ferry operated by cables which, when slack, lay safely underwater, but even so they were tied up at Georgetown before six, and after the experience of the night before the docking arrangements seemed pleasant indeed.

By now the Lenore-Dalton combination was a steady twosome. There had been no sign of the sedan which had followed her to Palm Beach, and even the murder of Mr. X had receded in Randall's thoughts, diminishing steadily as Nora became more important to him. Each day she helped him on the bridge and each evening they had dinner together at a table for two. For Julia had made no further demands on his time or affections, and was, apparently, quite content to have Barnard as an escort.

In Georgetown the pattern was repeated. Nora and Randall ate well at a place called Deason's and afterwards walked slowly along the quiet main street. At Wrightsville Beach the following evening they dined on steamed clams and lobster at a busy restaurant not far from where the *Julia* was tied up. This time, however, there was no post-dinner stroll because it had turned cool and the sky was overcast and threatening, a warning reminder that the days could not all be pleasant, an omen, though none recognized it as such, of the trouble that lay ahead.

13

THE weather caught up with them during the night and Randall awoke early because he was cold. Unable to get warm in bed he dressed hurriedly, teeth chattering, and then went up the ladder to open the hatch and have a look around.

"How is it?" Harding asked, shivering aloud from his bunk.

"Cold."

"Which way's the wind?"

"Northeast."

"Oh-oh. The old Neuse River's going to be tough to-day."

"Maybe too tough," Randall said. "Put plenty of clothes on. We can get started and later I'll have a talk with Barnard."

Harding chuckled. "He'll know. He knows more about this boat than you and I put together."

"He ought to," Randall said. "He used to own it."

Harding muttered something that sounded like: "The hell you say," but he was putting on a sweater and Randall was not sure as he went topside to start the motors.

They gave him no trouble and he let them idle while he took the covers off the wheel and seats. By then he knew he'd need warmer clothing and he went back below to get it. He put on woolen slacks that were a little dressy for the job, but warm; he added another sweater and a wind breaker and hoped Barnard had been right when he said there might be rain suits in the locker near the generator. The suits were there as the old gentleman had prophesied, but once under weigh Randall was soon cold again, and the rain that came presently served only to make matters worse.

After breakfast, when Harding relieved him at the wheel, Randall sought out Barnard and asked him what he thought. Barnard rubbed a weathered jaw and shook his head.

"I wouldn't try it if it was me. You get a sixty-five-mile sweep down Pamlico Sound when the wind's northeast, and by the time it hits the Neuse River you've got yourself some weather. Twenty miles of that? Un-unh."

"The trouble is," Randall said, "we're likely to get a couple of days of this."

"True enough."

Randall found the thought disturbing but he knew that Barnard was right. Here, in the canal above New River Inlet, there was shelter enough but his common sense told him that unless there was a sudden and definite moderation in the next two or three hours he would have to stop at Neuse City and wait for a change, even though it meant wasting most of an afternoon.

As it was, he was quite ready to pull into the nearest Neuse City marina at one o'clock and call it a day. So, it seemed, were his passengers. For Bogue Sound, wide, windy, and separated from the Atlantic by a beach no more than a quarter of a mile wide in places, was far from smooth and the last twenty miles were enough to verify the wisdom of Randall's decision.

Harding held up lunch until everything was secure, and by the time they had finished eating the rain had practically stopped. For an hour or so thereafter they sat around the deckhouse watching other craft come in to tie up close by or at one of the other marinas a short distance away. They talked about the weather and listened to the snorting of the locomotive that was engaged in switching operations behind the station a few hundred yards away; they turned on the radio; finally they dispersed.

The Fourniers went below for a nap. Harding had some things to mail and he went off, accompanied by Barnard. Julia and Nora had letters to write, and when Lenore went below to change her clothes—she had promised to look over the town with Dalton—Randall found himself alone with this man who turned out to be almost as much of an enigma as the Fourniers.

"Having a good time?" he asked.

"Fine time," Dalton said.

There was no elaboration on this and Randall offered a cigarette.

"No, thanks. I don't smoke."

"You don't drink either, do you?"

The brown, blunt face experimented with a smile. "Never have."

"Saves a lot of money." Randall hesitated and tried again. "No more trouble in your room?"

"Nope."

"You haven't been around boats much, have you?"

"Never. Thought I'd like to try it."

Randall let things stay that way while he surreptitiously studied the man. He was not, he admitted, bad looking in a plain-faced sort of way. His brows were thick, his hair a nondescript brown, like his eyes. His jaw was a little heavy but it seemed to go with the deep-chested bulk of his torso.

"You live around Miami?" Randall said, trying again and wondering how a man like this could be carrying around thirty thousand dollars in new bills.

"South of there. Down Homestead way." Dalton opened up a little. "Moved out from Illinois with my sisters almost twenty years ago."

He gestured idly and the hand caught Randall's eye. It was a broad-backed hand, hard, calloused. The nails on two fingers were broken and dark.

"Harding and I have been wondering what your business was," Randall said, making it up as he went along. "I said you were a mechanic, or maybe ran a garage."

Dalton's smile came slowly and it did a lot for the plainness of his face. His teeth were strong and well shaped and his eyes became alive.

"Have my own garage," he said. "How'd you guess?"

Randall did not have to go into that because Dalton saw Lenore coming up the ladder and was on his feet, his interest in Randall a thing of the past.

Lenore wore a green woolen suit and a scarf was tied about her auburn hair. Her mouth was a painted red and her eyes were shadowed. She looked happy and her smile, when she saw Dalton, was quick and genuine.

"We're going sightseeing," she announced. "Want to come along, Knox?"

Randall said he guessed not and grinned inwardly at Dalton's relief. He said he had some things to do. He watched them walk across the dock, understanding why a man like Dalton would be pleased and flattered by the company of a girl like Lenore, but wondering, too, just what she had in mind.

Randall knew nothing at all of the trouble between Fournier and Harding until he and Nora were having dinner that evening. Fournier had said nothing to him and neither did Harding, though Randall noticed a discolored bruise on the little man's cheekbone as they dressed for dinner.

According to Nora, it happened just before that while Randall was shaving. Lenore and Dalton were still doing the town; Barnard had not returned and Julia had gone for a walk. The Fourniers had also gone for a walk after their nap, but their walk was a short one, and when Fournier went below, quietly as was his custom, he surprised Harding in his room. Nora, in her own cabin at the time, heard the argument and witnessed the end of the incident.

"I heard Mr. Fournier accuse Alan of spying on him," she said, "and when I came out they were fighting." She paused, her gray eyes troubled as her mind went back. "I grabbed Alan's arm and pulled," she said. "I was furious. I don't know what I said but they stopped. Fournier bowed and apologized—you know how he is —and stepped back into his stateroom. By that time Mrs. Fournier had come down, and she walked right in without a word. I didn't say anything to Alan; I was too angry with him. I just shut my door in his face and left him standing there."

Randall glanced at his wrist watch. It was nine o'clock and he remembered they had come here at a quarter of eight. They had not come with the others but had sat in the deckhouse with cocktails he had made after they had been left alone.

"Why didn't you tell me before?"

"I wasn't sure whether you knew about it or not. And then, well"—she smiled shyly and dropped her glance —"Mother used to tell us not to talk over our troubles with Dad when he came home from work. She said to wait until he'd had dinner and had a chance to recover from his day at the office."

Randall was pleased by the simple honesty of her statement. For a moment his heart was full and he wanted to tell her how he felt; then his thoughts moved on to Harding and the moment passed. The scarred brow bent crookedly over one eye as he frowned, and a grimness came about his mouth as he told her about Dalton's earlier complaint.

"It sounds just like Alan." Nora's tone was hopeless and resigned. "And it doesn't do any good to talk to him. I made up my mind I wouldn't. It was a mistake to think that I could do any good making this trip with him. We're like strangers to each other but at least we

haven't had any trouble, and I'm still hoping to get him
to go to Connecticut and talk to Uncle Jack when he's
finished with you. After that I'm definitely through trying."

Randall paid the check and they went outside to
stand for a moment while they looked at the sky. The
stars were out now but the wind was still brisk. They
discussed it, wondering aloud if it had lessened any and
whether they would be able to leave in the morning.

The docks alongside which the *Julia* lay were two
hundred yards or more to their left and the street on
which they stood was the last paved thoroughfare on the
shoreside. Between this and the waterfront was the
restaurant and another like it, the docks and yacht
basins, the ship chandlers' shops. To their right the
pavement led past boatsheds and warehouses to curve
out of sight in the darkness, and up ahead was the station where a three-coach train puffed impatiently and
blew white clouds of steam against the night.

They walked this way, as though by mutual consent,
Randall's right arm locked with Nora's left one, their
hands clasped. They circled the station and read the
words on the tender—Atlantic & Eastern Carolina R. R.
—wondering aloud where the train was going and
where it had come from. They waited a while but nothing happened and Randall said he guessed the train
wasn't going anywhere right now. They gave up finally,
turning left and walking on until they came to the cross
street which ended in their dock. There was a lighted
office at the near end of this, currently occupied by three
men in work clothes who were listening to a radio program; they glanced up and nodded to Randall and Nora
as they strolled past.

Lights from the master's stateroom suggested that the Fourniers were aboard, as was Julia, whose dark head could be seen through one of the forward ports. She stepped to the companionway to see who it was when Randall came into the deckhouse, and Nora asked her where everyone was.

"Lenore and Oliver Dalton are at the movies," Julia said. "So was I until I couldn't stand it any longer."

Randall chuckled. "A little stinker?"

"In technicolor. . . . I was supposed to go with Alan," she added, "but he saw a car on the main street and told me to go on ahead and he'd join me. Only he didn't."

"A car?" Randall said, a sudden uneasiness stirring in his brain. "What kind of a car?"

"Why—I don't know. Just a car—with a Florida license. None of it made any sense to me. There was no one in it that I could see, but Alan said he wanted to wait and find out whose it was. Don't ask me why."

Randall glanced at his watch. It was ten minutes of ten and the uneasiness was growing in him as he thought, not of Harding, but of Lenore, and the incident in Palm Beach. Nothing showed in his tanned, squarish face but he stepped to the door and glanced shoreward, thinking now about Dalton and wondering if he should go to the movie house. The decision was made for him a few minutes later when he heard the rapid tap of footsteps across the planking. In another second or two Lenore's face and figure took shape in the darkness and he stepped aside to let her in.

"Hello," she said.

"Where's Dalton?" Randall said.

"He brought me to the head of the dock and then he

remembered some things he wanted to get at the drug-store. Is there any liquor, Knox? Or must I settle for a beer?"

Randall said there was liquor and made highballs for all. As he served them Fournier appeared. "Excuse me," he said in his polite way. "I will take a little walk before bed." No, he said, smiling, he would not have a drink. He turned quickly and ducked through the door-way, but not before Randall got a glimpse of the bluish bruise on the hinge of his jaw.

The drink lasted for twenty minutes and then Julia rose and said good-night. Lenore said she wondered where Oliver was and a few minutes later he appeared along with John Barnard, who announced that he had run into some friends at the next yacht basin and had been talking over old times. As usual, Dalton had noth-ing to offer. Lenore stepped out on the dock and he fol-lowed her. Barnard went below, and Fournier re-ap-peared shortly and said his good-nights.

Randall and Nora remained in the deckhouse after Dalton and Lenore had gone to their cabins. The si-lence grew between them and now the girl's face was wooden and he could see the uncertainty growing in her gray eyes. He sensed the cause of her concern because he, too, was thinking about what Julia had said concern-ing the car from Florida and Alan Harding's interest in its occupants.

He asked her if she would like another drink. She shook her head and he went to mix one for himself. It was now nearly eleven o'clock and worry was growing in him by the minute, though he tried to keep it from his voice when he talked. Finally she stood up and ex-pressed the thought they both held.

"I'm worried, Knox."

"He's all right." Randall kept his voice confident. "He's out some place having a few beers."

He lit cigarettes and took some more of his drink. He let another ten minutes tick by and then he said:

"Maybe I'd better go have a look."

"Where would you look?"

He laughed to show the question was elementary. "The town isn't that big," he said. "I'll get a flashlight."

She was still standing when he came back. "I'll go with you," she said.

He said he didn't think she'd better. He said he might have to drag Alan out of some gin-mill and it would be easier if she weren't around.

She stepped to one side as he spoke and he saw that she was no longer looking at him. Turning, he followed her gaze with his own; then he saw the flashlights coming along the dock from the direction of the front office.

"Here he is now," she said.

Randall did not answer. He was wondering why there should be two flashlights. He watched them draw nearer while one bright beam swept the length of the boat. Then he could see that the two men were dressed in blue. He could see the brass buttons, the policeman's cap.

"Hello," one of them said, and hunkered down on the dock so he could glance inside.

"Hello," Randall said. "Come aboard."

He stepped close, seeing now the shield with the word: *Chief*. Its owner was young and sturdy looking. His eyes were busy but otherwise the broad face was expressionless.

"Missing anybody aboard?"

"Hardly that," Randall said. "There's one fellow who hasn't come back but—"

"Smallish, wiry, sandy-haired? Name of Harding?"

"Yes," Randall said and from behind him Nora's voice came quick and anxious: "Why?"

"There's been a little trouble. I'm afraid I'll have to ask you to come along."

"I'm going too," Nora said.

"Sorry, ma'am. I don't think you'd better."

"I'm going," Nora said, her young face pale and set. "He's my brother."

The chief gestured helplessly and straightened up. Somewhere in Randall's chest a nerve tightened and the back of his throat was dry. He fumbled for Nora's coat before he picked it up and held it for her. He wanted to speak to her, to tell her to stay behind but he found no words.

He took her arm and helped her out on the dock. He held on to the arm as they started along the length of rough boards which stretched darkly towards the street.

It was lighter here, but colder. He could feel the night breeze spiraling up his calves, but the cold around his heart came not from the wind but from his thoughts as they went on past the shops, following the two policemen, past the restaurant advertising shore dinners, the emptiness growing inside him as he walked.

They passed the restaurant where they had dined, and now he could see the lights of cars fifty yards ahead. Under his grasp Nora's arm was stiff, like his back where the tension had begun to work along the muscles. He saw now that one of the cars was an ambulance, and five or six men stood waiting, one of them in uniform. They stepped back as the quartet approached.

There was a narrow space on the right, hardly more than a foot in width, which separated a shed from a warehouse and stretched emptily towards the water. In front of this was a blanket-covered stretcher.

The chief stopped, eyes probing at Randall through the darkness. He cleared his throat, as though not knowing what to say.

Then Nora spoke, her voice tight and barely audible. "What is it, Knox?"

He moved ahead, knelt beside the stretcher. He pulled the blanket aside and now that he was sure he felt no shock or surprise because it seemed that he had known what to expect from the first.

In the shadows the thin, freckled face that had so often reminded him of a terrier was composed, revealing nothing in its last sleep. He did not look again but as he put the blanket back Nora spoke again in that thin small voice.

"Is he dead?"

"Yes, ma'am," the chief said. "Someone shot him. He was in there." He indicated the space between the buildings. "Might have been there 'till morning if we hadn't been lucky."

Randall turned to Nora and she came into his arms, her face buried in her hands. He felt her tremble against him, not crying, but breathing in convulsive gasps that shook her slender body. Then the chief was speaking in his soft southern accents, saying he was sorry but he guessed he'd have to question them.

Randall waited while the stretcher was moved into the ambulance. When it drove off he turned Nora gently, still holding her arm, and without a word she lowered her hands and walked submissively away at his side, head bent but making no sound.

14

THE chief of police—his name was MacQuade—roused the others aboard the *Julia* and told them what had happened. He asked them if anyone had any idea who had killed Harding—or why; when no information was forthcoming he said he would have to question them, individually and collectively, and since there was no room to do this properly on the boat they would have to accompany him to the police station.

They rode in two cars, no one saying a word or making any protest. It was, in those first few minutes, as if everyone was too shocked by the unexpected violence of what happened to think about such things as rights and privileges. They went up the steps of the station house, Randall on one side of Nora and Lenore on the other, following the chief past the desk and down a long corridor to a room in the rear. There was an oblong table here, and chairs for everyone, and when they were settled MacQuade nodded to Randall and said, in his soft southern drawl:

"Guess you might as well be first, Captain."

Randall rose reluctantly. He looked down at Nora and Lenore intercepted his glance. She nodded and said: "She'll be all right," softly.

He followed MacQuade through a doorway into a smaller adjoining room which, from the looks of it, was the chief's office. Another man in plain clothes, apparently a deputy, sat in a corner with a notebook and pencil, and presently Randall was telling what he knew

about the events of the evening, giving what information
he could, and repeating what Julia had told him about
Harding and his interest in the car with the Florida license.

"Why would Harding be interested in that?" Mac-
Quade asked when he had thought the matter over.

For some reason Randall was reluctant to bring
Lenore's problems into the discussion. He said such a
car had crowded their taxi to the curb in Palm Beach
but was frightened off. He did not know what the men in
it wanted. He did not know why the car—if it was the
same car—had followed them to North Carolina unless
the men were interested in someone aboard.

MacQuade nodded. "After we found Mr. Harding
one of my men remembered seeing that car. We notice
things in a small town like this," he said, "and when
he'd had a look at Harding he remembered seeing
Harding watching the car."

"Is that all?"

" 'Fraid so. When my man came back around an hour
later the car was gone. So was Harding. The first time
Harding had a woman with him—that dark-haired,
good-looking one—and when Harding stopped by the
car she went on into the movie house."

"Do you know how long he'd been dead when you
found him?"

"Not exactly. The way we found him, one of the fel-
lows that works in the restaurant was passing that way
and he stepped in that space there to get out of the wind
so he could light his pipe. Stumbled over Harding and
came running. That was about ten thirty, Captain. Now
what can you tell me about the hour and a half before
that? Where were you and who did you see?"

Randall told him and MacQuade said: "Was there

bad feeling between Harding and any of your other passengers? Anything you noticed?"

Randall lied then. He did not know why, except that he did not want to cause unnecessary trouble for Dalton or Fournier. Later, if it seemed advisable, he could mention these things and say they had slipped his mind.

"Not that I know of. We all got along pretty well."

It took MacQuade three-quarters of an hour to finish his individual questioning, and by then he was joined by a tall, gaunt-looking man of forty or so, who in turn was accompanied by a fellow in the uniform of the State Police. The three had a conference in the chief's office, and when they came out the tall one was introduced as Mr. Gates, the solicitor, a title designated by the state and unfamiliar to Randall until he realized that it meant the same thing as district attorney did in New York. It was Gates who then took over the group questioning.

"We don't seem to be getting anywhere," he said after he made some preliminary remarks. He had a drawl something like MacQuade's but there was a nasal quality to the words and somewhat less consideration. "I wouldn't want to say that any of you here are guilty of this crime, you understand, but I ought to tell you that unless we clear things up you folks may have to stay here awhile."

"For how long?"

The voice was Julia's. She was sitting erect, hands folded in her lap; her chin was up and her tapered eyes were cold and imperious.

Gates pushed out his lower lip. "Why, I don't rightly know, ma'am. Couple of days; maybe a week. You can be subpoenaed. Every last one of you."

"I suppose it's all right to make a telephone call."

Gates blinked and exchanged glances with Chief MacQuade. It was obvious that he was not used to such tactics and he did not yet know what to make of Julia.

"Yes, ma'am," he said finally. "Who'd you want to call?"

"A lawyer."

Gates blinked again. "And where's he?"

"In Miami . . . It won't cost the state of North Carolina anything," Julia went on, still haughty. "I can reverse the charges."

"You figure you're going to need a lawyer that bad, ma'am?"

"Does it matter to you?"

Gates colored and he tightened his mouth before he spoke. "Just step into the captain's office," he said. "Tell the operator who you want. She'll call us back."

Julia walked close to Randall on her way to the office. As she passed she winked and he knew then that her imperiousness was mostly for effect. He admired her spunk in trying to take the offensive away from Gates long enough to let him know that he could not push them around, but presently he was bogged down again in thoughts that gave him no peace.

For in his mind he was back in Miami, finding now no excuse for his panicky flight from Noland's house. Had he called the police then there would have been no trip, but neither would there have been another murder. That Harding had strayed beyond his depth in some misguided scheme of his own there seemed no doubt. It was as Nora told him when they rode from the boat in the police car.

Even then she had not cried but he could still hear in

fancy the choked voice that whispered: "I've been afraid something would happen sometime. Not this, not anything like this—but something."

Since then Randall had remembered the things she had told him about her brother. He reviewed the things that had happened, finding no answer for this tragedy in any of those who were aboard but coming back always to the car with the Florida license. Not because of Mondello and his blue-coated gunman; Mondello's interest had centered in Lenore and her potential testimony. That Harding could somehow have been involved in this seemed highly unlikely; what Randall could not forget was that, because of him, Noland was alive and free.

Harding worked for Noland. There was no telling what he knew or where he had been that Saturday night before they left. Harding felt the world owed him a living, he did what he could to collect that living, and he was not greatly bothered by such things as scruples. He had been ashore every night and it would have been easy for him to make a long distance call as it now was for Julia. A car with a Florida license did not mean it must belong to Mondello. If Mondello could follow a boat up the Inland Waterway, so could Noland, once the purpose of such a trip became important. . . .

His thoughts were severed by Gates' voice. He saw that Julia had returned. He reached down to take Nora's hand and it was cold and passive in his own.

"Chief MacQuade has been checking up on time and alibis," Gates said.

"Why don't you find that car with the Florida license?" Randall cut in.

"Maybe we will." Gates eyed him distastefully and went back to his project. "During the time we think Mr.

Harding was shot several of you were off the boat and
none of you admits to seeing anyone else you knew."

"I told you I was with friends," Barnard protested.

"Maybe not every minute of that time."

"But this is ridiculous." Barnard's gray hair was
tousled and his eyes snapped indignantly. "No one on
that boat had any motive for wanting to kill Alan Harding."

"Do you agree to that, Mr. Fournier?"

Randall sat up, wondering who had told MacQuade
about the argument. Fournier was fitting a cigarette into
a holder and now his fingers were still.

"I beg your pardon."

Gates repeated the question and Fournier completed
the operation with the cigarette. He looked about the
room, his eyes obscured behind his glasses, his shrug
saying he still did not understand the question.

"I'm afraid I do not follow," he said.

Gates put his elbows on the table and leaned on them.
"I'll put it this way, mister. The chief noticed that bruise
on your face. There was one something like it on Mr.
Harding's face and one of his knuckles was skinned,
like he'd been in an argument. What I'm saying is this:
If you killed Harding, now is the time to say so."

Fournier's forehead was moist, and beneath his thin-
ning black hair the scalp was shiny. He was not looking around now; he was looking at Gates, his face oddly
pale.

"I'll tell you why," Gates said. "If you had a fight with
Harding and killed him because of it you could probably get off with manslaughter; you might even convince
a jury it was self-defense, dependin' on the provocation and circumstances. Even with manslaughter—
and good behavior—you'd be a free man in a few years.

Of course I can't promise you anything now, but you make it easy on me, sir, and I'll do my best for you. I've been in this business awhile and I'm pretty sure it'll be just like I say."

He paused to bring out a cigar, rolling it between thumb and finger thoughtfully.

"On the other hand," he said slowly, "if you make it hard for me, if you make us go out and build a case— and keep these good people around while we're doing it—why then that fight won't be of much help because it'll look like you were trying to get away with something. That's why I say if you killed him—and we're sure going to find out if you did or not—you'd better say so now, sir, when it'll do you some good."

He bit at the cigar and flicked the tip from his tongue to the floor. He glanced at MacQuade, eyes narrowing and his disappointment showing through. Fournier said nothing. His face was impassive. Next to him his wife looked pale and frightened. She reached out to touch his arm and he put his hand over hers. Finally he sighed.

"I cannot help you," he said in his accented voice.

Gates lit the cigar and watched the smoke rise towards the ceiling. He cocked his head slightly, looking at nothing in particular, and he seemed to be in no hurry. He took the cigar from his mouth and examined the ash idly.

"You went to the drugstore, Mr. Dalton," he said, still watching the cigar. "What did you buy there?"

Dalton sat with folded arms. His broad face was expressionless and his jaw was like a rock.

"Nothing," he said. "It was closed."

Gates nodded and Randall, watching his reactions, decided the solicitor, if that was what you called him,

was pretty good. Whatever he thought did not show
through the brown mask of his assumed indifference,
and his tone of voice seldom changed.

"Five minutes from your boat to the drugstore and
five minutes back," he said. "What about those other
fifteen minutes? Maybe you took a walk."

"I did."

"Where?"

"Up and down the street." Dalton wet his lips and
now his eyes flicked nervously about the room. "Down
by the station."

"And down on the street where Harding was shot."

"No."

Gates glanced at MacQuade, one brow lifting. The
chief stepped to the hall door, called for someone, and
stepped back, holding the door. In a few moments a
squat, red-faced man in a wrinkled suit stepped in, his
hat in his hands.

"Could this be the man you saw, Jim?" Gates asked,
indicating Dalton.

"Could be."

"Were'd you see him?"

"Like I told you," Jim said, "I was drivin' along in
that little ol' car of mine and as I swung the corner I saw
someone in the headlights. I see it was a stranger and I
slowed down. Then I notice it ain't one man but two,
one helpin' the other like he was drunk."

"You didn't pass them?"

"Nope. Just slowed down at the corner before I made
my turn."

"Where were they when you saw them?"

"Front of Hodge's warehouse."

Gates nodded. MacQuade touched Jim's arm and

the witness withdrew. Gates looked back at Dalton.

"Did you kill him, Mr. Dalton? Or just move him where you thought no one would find him until your boat was gone in the morning?"

"Neither," Dalton said, and he said it stubbornly, his natural taciturnity giving him a temporary advantage.

Gates blew smoke at the overhead light. He took his time glancing at MacQuade's notes, and if he felt any disappointment he gave no indication of it.

"Guess the next thing we'd better do," he said to Mac-Quade, "is give that boat a good going over." He glanced at the state policeman, adding that he wanted a thorough job done.

Randall let go of Nora's hand and leaned forward, his rugged face grim and one brow bent. Something stirred in his consciousness and he said, more as a bluff than anything else: "Have you got a warrant?"

"We can get one right quick," Gates drawled. "And while we're getting it you folks can make yourself comfortable. Might as well get this part over tonight."

A flurry of movement swept the room with the announcement. Chairs scraped and someone coughed. Someone else cleared his throat and then a voice stilled the movement in the room, its words tight and incisive.

"That will not be necessary."

Randall recognized the accented tones at once but it was another moment or two before he could accept their significance. Fournier sat erect in his chair, eyes level behind the glasses, his face white and set.

Gates studied him. "What won't be necessary, Mr. Fournier?"

"The warrant you speak of—or the search."

Gates smiled for the first time since he entered the

room, but disbelief still lingered in the corners of his
eyes. "You mean you want to make a confession?"

"If I may be permitted to speak to my wife first—
alone."

For once Gates moved with alacrity. He was on his
feet instantly and now Fournier said:

"I have your promise to do what you can about this—
what you call manslaughter?"

"You have, sir. . . . This way. . . . Use the chief's
office."

Fournier moved stiffly across the room, not hurrying
but proudly erect, like his wife who looked neither to the
right nor left as the tears streamed down her cheeks.

When the door closed an uncomfortable silence descended on the room. Even Gates seemed less jubilant
and Randall was unable at first to assimilate what he
had heard, much less understand it. He heard Gates say
something about them waiting until Fournier had made
a statement, and gradually the confusion dissipated in
his brain. He still could not begin to understand the
enigma which was the Fourniers, but that the man had
been sufficiently aroused to strike Harding was in itself
testimony that could not be ignored. Thinking back it
seemed to him that if there was one overall quality
which had characterized the couple's behavior that
quality was fear. He did not know why he thought so,
and made no attempt to analyze further; he only knew
that if this was so it might explain why a man who had
to live with fear could rise up and destroy one who
threatened to bring reality to that fear. Yet even as he
thought all this, he was not satisfied, and he was glad
when the Fourniers came back.

It did not take long to learn what had happened.
Fournier stood at one side of the table, still erect as he

faced Gates across the polished surface. He said Gates had been right about the fight. He had exchanged blows with Harding before dinner.

"Why?"

"A personal matter." Fournier's tone was challenging. "I do not care to discuss it."

Gates knew when he was well off. He let it go. "All right. Go on."

"Later when I went for a walk I met Mr. Harding again. The quarrel was resumed."

"You had a gun."

"I often carry a gun. Not because of Mr. Harding. I met him quite by chance." He hesitated, remembered to stick his chin out. "As I say, the argument continued. I tried to push away and he struck at me. I lost my head. I shot him."

He went on hurriedly to explain how he had run away when Harding fell, how he had thrown the gun into the water before he returned to the boat.

Then he had finished and the room was still again. Gates thanked him. He said he would have the statement typed up and Fournier could sign it. As for the others they could sign individual statements later; if all went well they could continue on their way the following day.

15

KNOX RANDALL had a hard time getting to sleep that night. He lay a long time staring up through the darkness, his mind active and the pressure of his thoughts re-

lentless. Behind it all was his own feeling of guilt, not so
much in the death of Harding, since even now it seemed
to him that the little man had somehow overstepped and
brought about his downfall, but in allowing the murder
of Mr. X to go unreported.

He could find no connection between the murders
and knew that if Fournier had told the truth there was
none. It seemed to him that the motive was the key to
that confession, as it was the key to the fight the two had
had before dinner. Wihout that motive there was no understanding the murder and he gave up finally to find
that his thoughts of Nora were even more discouraging.

There would be no more Nora getting up in the morning to give a hand with lines and fenders before scurry-
ing back to bed for another hour's sleep. There would be
no more talks on the bridge, no dinners for two. Nora
would be leaving the *Julia*. Nora had a trip of her own to
make. Back to Connecticut. Alone while the body of her
brother rode in its casket in the baggage car. Randall
wanted to go with her and he tried to think of some way
it could be managed; he was still trying to find an answer when sleep finally overtook him.

It was eight o'clock when he opened his eyes the next
morning, and it was a few seconds before he remembered that on this day there was no need for early rising.
The sky was clear when he came topside a few minutes
later but it made no difference to him now. He wasn't
going anywhere today; neither was the *Julia*.

Coming into the deckhouse, he heard a noise in the
galley and went below to find Lenore working on the
juice extractor. She wore her familiar green housecoat—
and as was her custom, little else—and her hair was
twisted and pinned on top of her head. She had a

burner going on the stove and water was heating for
coffee.

"You're wonderful," he said, trying to break the black
mood that had come over him.

"I know," she said. "How do you light that damn hot
water heater?"

He lit it for her and she said: "Nora's awake. I'm making her stay in bed. I'm going to take her a tray." She
turned, her green eyes exploring his own. "You kids are
kind of in love, aren't you?"

"I am," Randall said.

"She'll be all right," Lenore promised. "She's got a lot
of what it takes. I talked with her a few minutes. She
cried some but—"

Randall cut in to say he was glad. He wished she had
cried the night before instead of trying to bottle up her
emotions that had become too much to handle.

Lenore said, "It's not so much the loss of her brother—
I don't think there was much left between them anyway
—it's just the shock. A thing like that is an awful shock,
and she's worrying about what she's going to do—you
know, about the undertaker, and getting the body back
home."

"You tell her to forget it," Randall said. "Keep her
mind occupied and let her do what she wants to. I'll
speak to Barnard. Between us we can handle everything."

He talked to John Barnard after breakfast. They dele-
gated to each other the things that had to be done, and
in bringing them out into the open that way they discovered that the problems were relatively simple. Barnard had buried his wife two years before and had sufficient knowledge of such things to take upon himself

the arrangements with the undertaker.

"I'll handle everything," he said. "You take care of the transportation. Find out about trains and connections. After that we can talk to Nora. . . .

When Randall returned to the boat shortly after noon he found that Nora had gone ashore.

"She went with Mrs. Fournier," said Julia, who was in the galley making sandwiches for lunch.

"Where?"

"To the jail—to see Mr. Fournier. Celine—I found out that's what her name was—is taking it pretty hard and Nora wanted to go with her." She smiled and touched his arm to make him look at her. "It'll do her good, Knox. She's wonderful. I don't wonder you're in love with her." She hesitated and said: "I'm going to have Eaton Gifford talk to Mr. Fournier."

"Gifford?" Randall stared at her, remembering now the long distance call Julia had made the night before. "Is he coming here?"

"He offered to and I said yes. He has some matters he wants to discuss with me, some papers to sign, and I told him if he wanted to come he could make the rest of the trip with us. You don't mind do you? . . . Now don't tell me it's my boat and I'm the boss," she said, her tone lightly reprimanding.

Randall grinned, liking this woman better now and no longer uncomfortable in her presence. "Sure," he said.

"Also," Julia added. "I want him to talk to Mr. Fournier and to that Mr. Gates. I want them both to know that we can have a lawyer on hand if we need one. Eaton will collect handsomely from settling the estate; let him earn his fee."

She pursed her small mouth and busied herself with

the sandwiches. "I don't know why Mr. Fournier killed Alan Harding, but if he did, he had a good reason. Alan Harding worked for my husband long enough for me to know that he was a little chiseler. Because he'd been brought up to have nice manners and plenty of charm when he wanted to use it, he thought he could do as he pleased. I don't want that district attorney or whatever you call him to pull any fast ones on Mr. Fournier after we've gone. If I have to I'll send Eaton back here for the trial."

Randall applauded her stand silently. He said it was a good idea and he knew Fournier would appreciate it. . . .

When Randall saw Mrs. Fournier and Nora coming along the dock a few minutes later, he went to meet them, his heart contracting when he saw the little woman's pale, drawn face, yet proud of Nora, who looked so slim and straight and unafraid as she walked along and held the older woman's arm. She saw at once that he wanted to talk to her, and after they had helped Mrs. Fournier on deck, Nora stepped back and smiled at him.

It was something short of radiant, that smile, but Randall gave her an A for effort and he wasted no time inquiring about her health. He made no expression of sorrow or sympathy, believing a simple, matter-of-fact manner to be more effective and kind. He said that he and John Barnard had made all the necessary arrangements, and that if any other details came up they would handle them as well.

She looked at him an instant, her smile small and grateful; then her eyes filled and she glanced quickly away. She wore a simple dark dress with a lightweight tweed topcoat. Her blonde hair glistened in the sunlight and in profile he could see her long lashes quickly blink the tears away.

He swallowed and hurried on, telling her that he had made reservations which she could pick up that afternoon. There was a morning train which would take her to Goldsboro, and from there she could change and go on to Washington and New York. Then he came to the part that distressed him most.

"If only you didn't have to make the trip alone," he said. "That's the part that kills me. I want to go with you," he said, "and I don't know—"

She turned to interrupt him.

"It's all right, Knox. I won't be alone."

He waited, unable quite to comprehend her words.

"Mrs. Fournier is going with me."

And still he waited, gratitude and incredulity battling it out in his mind until her eyes reassured him.

"Why"—he believed her now and the world seemed suddenly brighter—"that's wonderful."

"She didn't want to leave. She cried and protested at first, but her husband said she had to. He insisted. He said she could come back later but that she could not stay here now." Nora started to lift one hand, let it fall. "When she told me, I asked her why she didn't come with me. I guess we're both grateful," she said. "Now we can help each other."

Randall pressed her arm, his mind busy with new enthusiasm. He said they could go up after lunch and get reservations for Mrs. Fournier.

"She wants to talk to you," Nora said. "I don't know what about, but I said you'd be glad to."

"In the station," Randall said. "When we get the tickets. There was no one there this morning and there probably won't be this afternoon. It will be quiet there."

And so it was that at three o'clock they sat in one corner of the "White" side of the station where no one could hear them, and listened to Celine Fournier's story. Sitting between them, looking very small and timid in her black dress and shoes, she leaned back so that she could look from one to the other.

"This I should not be doing," she said in her soft, strange accent. "I made no promise but it was understood that I should tell no one. If my judgment is wrong it will mean much trouble." She paused, her dark eyes enormous as they looked first at Randall and then at Nora.

"But I have watched you both," she said. "You are the nice ones on that boat. Louis and I have discussed it before. Of this one"—her finger touched Nora's skirt— "I am sure . . . She trusts you," she said to Randall, "and now I trust you."

Randall was touched by the simple compliment. He felt he should say something, either to reassure her or to suggest that perhaps she should reconsider, but he could not find the proper words and presently she continued.

"You have wondered why we should make such a trip, two people like us who know so little about such things. I can tell that from the first, though you are too polite to say so. Now I tell you why. We are in your country"—she groped for a word and found it—"illegally."

She hesitated uncertainly, her glance watchful as it moved from one to the other. When no one spoke she said: "We got from Central Europe to Spain; from there to Cuba. There we stay until Louis says we must try to enter this country. He thinks there are some in Cuba who will do him harm and he arranges this trip.

It is to be on a boat like yours, but smaller and dirtier, with four others, strangers, yet like ourselves wanting to leave Cuba."

She went on to describe the trip with quiet sincerity and Randall's mind, seeking momentary refuge from this new revelation, found little in the pattern to surprise him. He remembered how simple his own original problem had seemed. He needed six or seven people with a hundred and fifty dollars, and he had signed up his passengers, believing them congenial and caring nothing at all about their private affairs. And not one was what he seemed. Even Lenore, whom he knew so well, had not told the whole truth.

Julia Noland was running away from a husband, now officially dead—except to Randall. Nora had given evasive replies so that she could come along to chaperon her brother. Dalton carried thirty thousand dollars in cash, for a reason that only he knew; Barnard had once owned the *Julia* and had been partners with Noland. Harding had been honest in part, and he was dead. Now the Fourniers—

"We landed safely," he heard the woman say. "We were to travel in two cars to Miami, Louis and I in one with two of the crew, the other four in the second car." She sighed heavily, her eyes remote. "That car was discovered. Louis felt sure that someone would tell the truth and then the police would be looking for us. He said we must not go to a railroad station or any place like that where people gather. We found a small hotel and then, the next morning, he saw your piece in the newspaper and said this was the best way for us to get to New York where we have friends."

She paused to examine them closely. "Do you believe this much?"

Randall glanced at Nora and saw the answer in her eyes. "Yes," they said. "We believe you."

"Then"—she took a small breath and fixed her gaze on Nora—"you must believe that my husband did not kill your brother."

Randall felt some compulsion to show surprise and yet there was very little of that feeling in his mind after the first instant. He knew somehow, that Celine Fournier was telling the truth, and the only surprise he felt came from the fact that she was telling this story at all. Somewhere, deep within him, there had lingered a small, ineradicable notion that Fournier's confession was not all it seemed; because of this doubt—and he had no alternative theory of any substance to replace it—he accepted Celine Fournier's statement now.

With Nora it was different. Under lifted brows her eyes were wide open and her jaw sagged. "But—he confessed! I mean, why should he—" The sentence dangled there ineffectually until Mrs. Fournier continued.

"He said it was best this way. A search of the boat last night would show that our passports were not in order. We have no visa for this country. When this was discovered he said we would be deported. This way I can go to New York and no one will know but our friends that I do not belong here."

"But to go to prison for something he didn't do," Nora whispered, aghast at the thought.

"Mr. Gates has told him it will only be for a few years and Louis says we have been in prison before—both of us—and he says if this should happen to him again he can wait because it will be more pleasant than other places we have been. Also this way I will be free."

"But Mrs. Fournier," Randall said. "Will you be free? Gates may not know yet that you are in the country illegally but he's bound to find out about you and your husband."

"Yes. But you see it is for me that Louis is doing this. Once I am in New York no one will know where to look for me. When Louis is certain, he can then tell the truth if he likes. He can deny the killing, knowing that even if he is deported I will be here, safe with our friends." She sighed again, her eyes miserable. "Me, I would rather go back to Europe and be with him."

"But you wouldn't have to go back to Europe." Randall saw that she did not understand him and he said: "If your passports were good enough to get you to Cuba legally, this country could only send you back to where you came from—to Cuba. You could wait there until you could get in under the quota."

"You are sure?"

Randall realized he was not sure. He remembered reading some such ruling in the newspaper but he had no real knowledge of the matter. When he hesitated, Celine Fournier said:

"I do not know about the law, or our passports. I only know that Louis made me promise, and in my country it is the husband who makes such decisions. The wife obeys; it is now a habit too strong to break."

She sat up and tried to smile. "There," she said. "I have told you. It was something I had to do. You have been kind to me, and I could not have you thinking bad things about my husband."

They helped her up and went back to the boat, and later, when he was alone with Nora, she put into words the thing that was uppermost in their thoughts.

"If Mr. Fournier didn't kill Alan, who did?"

Randall had thought of nothing else. He could begin to understand Fournier's sacrifice, now that he understood the background and came to realize that for some people there were some things worse than prison. He had his own vague hunch about the murder too, though he had very little to substantiate that hunch. To put the hunch into words, to say that he felt that Noland was in some way responsible for the murder of Nora's brother, was something he could not do because Noland was supposed to be dead. Some day he would tell Nora the whole story; right now all he could say was that he did not know.

16

EATON GIFFORD arrived late that afternoon, resplendent as always in his expensive sport clothes but a little out of sorts because of the exhaustive demands of his journey. He had, it seemed, taken a plane from Miami to Raleigh, another plane from there to New Bern, where he had hired a car. What he wanted most was a drink, and when this was supplied they told him about Alan Harding and Mr. Fournier. He went away as soon as Julia told him what she wanted him to do, and when he came back an hour and a half later his toothy smile was working and he was quite obviously pleased with the progress he had made.

He called them all into the deckhouse and saw that the women were seated. He stood before them, tall and impressive-looking, his wavy blond hair smoothly in place. When he smiled the suggested weakness around the mouth did not show, and now that he had the center of the stage he was enjoying himself hugely.

"It will be all right, Mrs. Fournier," he said with a
gesture. "I talked to your husband and to Gates. Gates
is smart enough to know just how much of a case he's
got. I'm glad you called me, Julia," he added, directing
his smile on his employer; "glad I could help."

"You are sure Mr. Gates will keep his word?" Mrs.
Fournier asked.

"I know he will," Gifford said, "and I'll tell you why.
Your husband has steadfastly refused to give any motive for the crime, and Gates has not been able to recover the gun. About the only thing he's really got is
that confession."

He opened his palm, struck it with the index finger of
his other hand. "Gates will ask for the minimum sentence. If he doesn't your husband repudiates that confession, and then Gates has to come up with some real
evidence and fight all the way. I'm not sure he can even
get a conviction the way things stand. Confessions have
been successfully repudiated before. As a matter of fact
I strongly advised your husband to fight." He shook his
head, smile momentarily fading. "I couldn't convince
him. He was pretty stubborn about it . . . But he was
really grateful for my help," he said, recovering his assurance. He smiled again at Julia. "He said to thank you
for your help and interest in him."

Lenore cleared her throat. She eyed the lawyer with a
sufficient lack of enthusiasm to indicate that she, for one,
was not impressed with Gifford's charm.

"It calls for a drink," she said. "All around. Except
you, Oliver," she said to Dalton. "You can have a
coke." . . .

The *Julia* made a late start the following morning because Randall insisted, over Nora's protest, that he see

her and Mrs. Fournier off at the station. Everyone was
there when the two-coach train pulled out, there had
been no hitch of any kind in the Fourniers' plans, and
when Randall went back to the boat he had Nora's New
York and Connecticut addresses in his pocket.

Bellhaven was the announced destination for the day,
and by now the Neuse River and the tail of Pamlico
Sound, which Randall could not help feeling served as
a contributory cause in the murder of Harding, sparkled
harmlessly under the mid-day sun.

Randall, however, had no illusions about the days
ahead. This, he knew, would be the last leisurely jump.
Already the impatience was upon him and from now on
he would drive himself and the *Julia*. He was a day late
but he had promised to telephone Nora in New York on
Sunday night and he intended to be there if he possibly
could.

The others offered no objection. On the first day they
rearranged quarters and laid out a tentative working
schedule. The two women decided to move to the
master's stateroom previously occupied by the Fourniers; Dalton and Barnard moved forward, and Gifford
took the room they had vacated. It was now Barnard
who shared the captain's duties with Randall, and apparently he liked the new responsibility. He was capable, experienced, and quite competent to handle the
wheel and controls, so that between them they drove
the *Julia* steadily northward.

The culinary and catering duties were divided in a
similar manner. Lenore had offered to do it all if someone would wash the dishes, but Julia said she hadn't had
all that food-demonstrating experience for nothing, and
as a result they took turns at breakfast and lunch, with
Dalton willingly—according to Lenore—washing the

dishes. The only reluctant member was Gifford. His
clothes were a little too smart for any honest duties, but
after a little needling by Julia he agreed to set the table
for each meal and clear away afterwards. He seldom
came to the bridge, and though it was now too cool for
any real sunbathing, he baked in the cockpit with Julia
whenever the opportunity offered.

In the evenings the two couples found things to do,
but for Barnard and Randall it was an hour of gin-
rummy after dinner and then to bed in preparation for
the next day's run, a strenuous schedule but one which
Randall found to his liking. During those hours on the
bridge his mind was busy with many things, and
although there was now a new loneliness to depress him,
by night he was too tired to think and sleep came easily.

And his luck held; so did the weather. Six o'clock the
following morning saw them leave Bellhaven behind.
The breaks were with them in the Dismal Swamp Canal,
for the locks at South Mills and Deep Creek were unoccupied and they lost little time. They made Norfolk that
night and the next day, though the run was hard and
wet up the Chesapeake so that the others were forced to
stay in the deckhouse for the most part, they made
Annapolis as scheduled

Saturday night found them in Cape May and Randall
and Barnard sat up to get the latest weather report. The
night was clear, with but a faint southwest breeze, and
if the weather held and the forecast was good, Randall
wanted to take the outside route to Sandy Hook.

"Sure," Barnard said when the weather report reassured them. "It'll save time and miles. Of course if we
get out there and it kicks up there aren't too many places
where we can get back inside. . . ."

The next morning Randall was up at five, and when

he saw the weather was still fine he made his decision.
As it turned out it was a good one, for the ocean was
glassy and there was only a slight ground swell to roll
them gently and remind them that they were at sea.

Atlantic City looked big and impressive and very
close with its long line of beach-front hotels. Lenore
came up to watch it from the bridge, and when she was
tired of looking she sat down and said she wanted to
have a little talk.

"I've been wondering about you," Randall said.
"What're you going to do about Mondello?"

"Nothing," Lenore said. "I'm going to a hotel—he'll
never try anything in the daylight—and stay there
tonight and call the district attorney's office in the morning. But that isn't what I want to talk about." She turned
and hooked her elbows on the chart stand, her gaze
fixed off the port quarter.

"I think I've got me a man," she said quietly.

"Dalton?"

"He wants to marry me."

Randall nodded. Thinking back he found nothing
unexpected in this announcement. Dalton had been a
faithful companion, almost doglike in his loyalty, and
now that he was sure, Randall felt a secret pleasure in
the news.

"Are you going to?"

"I'm thinking about it."

He said that was fine. He offered his congratulations;
yet as he watched her he knew she had not heard him.
She was occupied with other thoughts and there was
an absent quality in her voice.

"It's funny," she said. "You'd never think a girl like
me would look twice at a man like Oliver. A month ago I
would have thought he was a clod." Her laugh was

abrupt and mirthless. "That's what comes from running around with the sharpshooters and smart-money boys, with their padded shoulders and varnished hair. I guess I've never really known any other kind—except you."

Randall waited, knowing there was more. He studied her face from the corner of his eye. She wore very little makeup now; there was no eye-shadow and her mobile mouth was only faintly painted. The hint of worldliness, the slight veneer of hardness that she had worn for so long was almost gone. She looked younger, and there was a new brightness in her green eyes that he had never seen before.

"He made me think," she said in the same absent tones. "The answers I got weren't very encouraging. I told you I was twenty-six. I'll be twenty-nine my next birthday, and I got to wondering how much time I had left to get that husband I was always going to have— and what I was going to do with it." She sighed and said: "I've been propositioned ever since I was a kid. I've been proposed to as often as the next girl, but never by anyone who really loved me, and mostly by some fellow who was not exactly sober at the time."

She looked at him then, her smile strangely wistful. "You know me. A good number on a party, a lot of fun if you don't get too fresh, a kid who can hold her liquor and handle herself pretty well without screaming for help."

"I know you," Randall said, his secret pleasure now a warm and comforting thing. He winked at her. "I think you're swell."

She colored and glanced away. "Oliver loves me and he'll always be kind because that's the way he is. He'll be faithful, and he'll be able to take care of me because he's a good mechanic; he even has his own garage."

Also, Randall thought, and was then instantly ashamed, he's got thirty thousand bucks in his bag. "A man like that might bore you," he said.

"If he does, I can stand it. I think I've got my values straightened out this time."

"It may not be as easy as you think."

"Why won't it be?"

Randall considered the question. It was not his intention to argue against her beliefs, but he liked this girl and he was interested in knowing what she thought. He went on, thinking aloud, rather than trying to prove anything.

"Oliver looks like a solid citizen," he said. "He doesn't look as if he was used to women, or knew much about them."

"He doesn't."

"There's a worldliness about you that he doesn't have, and may never get. You know what I mean—the way you dress and put your makeup on, the way you walk. You're aware of things, men especially. Men know it, and look at you twice. They make passes, at least mental ones. . . . I'm not trying to talk you out of anything," he added hurriedly when she seemed about to interrupt. "I'm just talking. I'm wondering if you'll get used to staying around the house all day long with no company, and whether you can teach Oliver to step out now and then so you both can have some fun."

"I'll teach him."

"You can teach him a lot of things."

"Don't be nasty," Lenore said.

"I'm not." Randall laughed because, though he knew how his remarks sounded, he was telling the truth.

"You've got to stop being on the defensive too," he said, and then another, more important thought occurred to him. "Does he know about Mondello?"

"All about him."

"And what does he say?"

"He says it doesn't matter. He says he can take care of me and he's proud because he thinks I'm doing the right thing. . . . He knows about you too," she said. "Because of those first couple of days when he didn't understand why I should be so friendly with you. I told him how it was."

"What's he running away from?"

He had her attention then.

"What makes you think he's running away from any-thing?"

Randall thought of some reasons; then came back to the real one and told her about Harding and the money he had found.

"I'm not the only one who has been talking," she said. "I know as much about Oliver as he knows about me and you're right about his running away. He's running away from his sisters."

Randall blinked. He started to laugh, thought better of it. Lenore took it all in.

"Sure it sounds funny," she said, "but not when you know the rest of it." She put her weight on one hip. "He's almost forty," she said. "One sister is eight years older than he is; the other ten. They brought him up when their father died. They went to Florida when he was eighteen and got a couple of acres. One of the sisters taught school and the other kept house."

She shrugged and said: "The poor guy. Those two are about the only women he ever knew. Whenever he'd get a date they'd pick on him. Call it jealousy, posses-

siveness or whatever you like, but every time he'd try to
have a little fun they'd move in on him. First he was too
young for girls, and when they couldn't use that argument the school teacher one said she was going to quit,
and they'd need the money he earned. She did quit for
a year but she went back and she's been teaching ever
since. But by that time they had him about whipped. He
got out of the habit of having any fun; he forgot how to
talk to girls; he didn't drink or smoke; for a few years he
just gave up."

"What happened to change his mind?"

"Nothing special. He didn't like any part of it but he
took it because they'd been kind to him and he couldn't
make himself run out on them until he could make some
sort of provision for them. He knew he couldn't bring a
wife home, even if he could find one, but he was still tied
down, his idea of a good time being to take the sisters to
a movie. . . . No wonder I thought he was a hick," she
said.

"So—"

"So he started to make some plans. He kept putting
money aside—he'd already bought out this little garage
and was enlarging it—and giving the sisters some story
about investing it. Finally, a couple of weeks ago, he
made this deal to lease the garage for five years at a hundred dollars a week. He didn't tell the sisters, but he did
some figuring and decided this was the time to make the
break. He came to Miami and talked things over with a
lawyer. The house is in the sisters' name and he arranged it so the hundred a week would be paid to them
for five years; by that time he figured that he'd be able
to go back to the garage and live like a man or else the
whole thing would be hopeless anyway."

Randall still did not understand it all and he said so.

"But why this boat? What's the matter with the trains? He hadn't done anything wrong. Men run away from women all the time."

"Hah!" Lenore said. "Not like his sisters. He couldn't just disappear; he's not that kind of guy. He had to leave a letter telling them what he was doing, and why, but he didn't expect that to stop them. According to him they'd call in the cops, and the F.B.I. and the immigration authorities, and give them a story—phony if necessary—that would turn him up one way or another, and he knew that if they ever caught him and started to bawl him out he'd never have the courage to try it again. . . . Take my word for it," she said, shaking her finger at him, "there are women like that, and with him not knowing too much about such things anyway, he'd never have a chance."

Randall thought it over, something plucking at his mind. "Is that why he moved Harding's body?"

She drew a small, persecuted breath. She pushed out her lower jaw a quarter of an inch but her voice stayed even.

"Yes," she said. "And don't think he hasn't been half sick about it ever since. He got panicky when he saw Alan dead, and all he could think of was the questioning that would be coming, and the publicity, and those sisters rushing triumphantly up here to grab him. He just couldn't think straight. He knew he'd only be delaying the investigation but—"

She did not finish the thought and Randall, remembering his own panic and addle-headed actions that night at Noland's house, could understand how Dalton could have been motivated into a similar mistake. Whether this was the whole truth was something else

again. This was the story Dalton had told Lenore—and
nothing more.

Lenore went on as he hesitated, a note of defiance in
her voice as she focused her attention on her original argument. "What's so hard to understand about that?"
She looked down at him, her glance severe. "You say
men run away from women. Sure. Julia ran away from
her husband, too. What's the matter with running away
from a couple of bossy, old-maid sisters?"

"Nothing," Randall said.

"He wants to go out west again, maybe to California.
He's got money enough to start a business somewhere
and—" She stopped abruptly; then she laughed, dis-
missing the more somber aspects of the situation. "I
talked myself into it," she said. "I came up here thinking I might say yes; now I know I will. When he goes
west I'll be with him—and I'd like to see Mondello stop
me."

According to Randall's figures the *Julia* averaged
about eleven knots all the way from Cape May to Lower
Bay, and as he boiled through the Narrows he figured
he had a couple of hours of fair tide left. It was just four
thirty when he slid past Battery Park and into the smoky
murkiness which hung low over the East River while
high above, the downtown towers of Manhattan glistened in the late afternoon sun.

Docks, warehouses and chimneys whipped by at an
astonishing rate, and for a little while they seemed to be
pacing the cars on East River Drive; then he was angling in at Twenty-third Street, a combination dock and
skyport for planes, where he could tie up temporarily
and debark his passengers.

There were some floats here, and a gas and oil barge, and, luckily, a shore-side idler to take a line. A Prudential Line freighter was tied up at the next slip on the uptown side, but here there was a wide, fenced-in parking space, and it was a simple matter to unload both passengers and luggage.

The others had been on deck for the last hour, in city clothes now, their bags packed and in order. They gave Randall the names of the hotels at which they expected to stay in case they left anything aboard, and he had spoken to Julia about waiting over for a couple of days before taking the boat on to Falmouth. He said he could tie up at one of the yacht clubs in Flushing Bay, and she told him that this would be quite all right.

There were no waiting taxis beyond the iron fence, so Gifford and Dalton walked through the gate and past the gas station to see what they could do. As was expected, Gifford came back with the first one, and when he rode off with Julia and Barnard, Randall stood on the dock with Lenore. She took his hand, her color high now and not from makeup; rather it came from a new and extraordinary shyness for one normally so confident and forthright. He spoke about it. He said she was as shy as a new bride.

"I know it," she said. "I never thought I could be but I am. Maybe I'm a new woman. How do you think I'll do at it?"

"You'll do all right," Randall said. "You always have."

Dalton appeared then and hurried across the parking place. Randall gave them a hand with the bags. He said he'd walk to the cab with them, just to make sure that everything was all right. Dalton said not to worry.

"I can take care of her," he said.

"I believe you." Randall gave them his telephone

number and told them to let him know what happened. Lenore said she would. She kissed him, blushing over the operation for the first time, and got into the cab.

Dalton offered a hard, hamlike hand that closed like a vise on Randall's fingers. He was not an articulate man but his association with Lenore had loosened his tongue somewhat and now he said that he'd had a fine time. He said it was the best two weeks of his life and he'd never forget them, which, for Dalton, was quite a speech.

Randall watched them until the cab merged with the swiftly moving traffic in the Drive; then he hurried back to the dock and cast off. He angled out into the stream, cut to the starboard around a tug and its tow, and straightened out for the Queensboro Bridge. He slid under its lofty arch, feeling the downdraft on his neck, past Welfare Island and through Hell Gate, continuing on until he was about opposite the Triborough Bridge, then turning sharply past Rikers Island and LaGuardia Airport into Flushing Bay.

A few minutes later he nosed into a yacht club slip, made sure he could stay there a few days, and tied up. The attendant telephoned for a taxi while Randall secured things, and forty minutes later he was unlocking the door of his third-floor apartment on Lexington Avenue.

Without bothering to take off his hat or coat, he went immediately to the telephone and called Nora's number, holding his breath for fear there would be no answer and then feeling his heart thump when he heard her familiar voice.

"How are you?" he said, beginning to breathe again but having trouble with a growing eagerness that tended to scramble his words.

Nora said she was fine, and when did he get in. He

told her; he explained where he had left the boat. "Is it all right to come up now?" he asked.

"Yes," Nora said. "I—I wish you would."

Something in her voice struck him as odd and he was instantly disturbed. "Is there anything wrong? Are you all right?"

"Yes," Nora said. "I'm all right, only"—she hesitated—"only it looks as if somebody has been searching the place."

He started to question her. It was natural that he should and under normal circumstances he would have done so. Now, however, his thoughts confused and uncertain by the things that had happened, his alarm was real and he realized it was silly to waste time talking over the telephone.

He said he was on his way, and hung up. He hurried out of the room and down the stairs.

17

THE address Nora had given Randall proved to be a remodeled brownstone in the east eighties, and when he had paid the driver he took the high, stone steps two at a time, finding the first-floor door open and hustling up the bare worn stairs to the floor above. Here a single door stood to one side of the landing and he knocked and took off his hat.

All the way up in the cab the impatience had been riding him. Yet now, when the door opened and he saw her smile, all that impatience slid from his mind. She looked so lovely with her blonde hair and all that radi-

ance shining through her sweetly moulded face that he
stepped forward and, not thinking much about it, took
her arms in his hands and kissed her quickly. It was a
light and friendly kiss, and not until it was done did it
occur to him that this was the first time he even attempted such a demonstration. It surprised him and he
watched her anxiously, seeing in her gray eyes a suggestion of the same sort of surprise, quickly followed by
a gleam of amusement.

She turned then, telling him to take off his coat and sit
down. She asked him to excuse her a moment as she left
the room, and by the time he had a cigarette going she
was back with a tray, depositing it on the coffee table before he could help her.

"I didn't think you'd get here so soon," she said.
"Where did you leave the boat?"

The tiredness went out of his tanned, squarish face
when he saw the tray, and his mouth curved in a smile.
There was a bottle of Scotch, a bowl of ice, glasses, and
soda; there was a plate of tiny crackers and a dish of a
cheese spread she had made.

"What a girl," he said appreciatively, aware that this
was an understatement if he'd ever made one. "I've been
dying for a drink."

She asked if he would mix them, and as he busied
himself while she fixed some crackers, he told her about
the boat and the day's trip. Not until they drank together
did he remember his earlier anxiety and the reason he
had hurried to get here. His glance sobered as he looked
about the living room, which to him seemed neat, orderly, and attractively feminine.

"Hey, what about this searching business?"

"I don't know." She leaned back on the studio couch,
a tiny frown worrying the bridge of her nose and her

eyes thoughtful. "I just know that somebody did. I straightened things—Oh, I don't mean the place was wrecked or anything—but I could tell all the drawers here and in the bedroom had been opened and the closets looked into."

"Anything missing?"

"Not that I know of. That's the funny part."

Randall's mind moved on, seeking some answer and finding very little to help him. He wondered if this incident had anything to do with Alan Harding's death. He decided it was highly unlikely and yet he could not ignore the possibility.

"When did you get back from Connecticut?" he asked.

"About an hour before you called."

He glanced at his watch, trying to remember when his passengers had left the boat. There was, he admitted, a slight possibility that someone aboard might have had time to get up here and go through the apartment before Nora came back; yet even as he considered the theory he knew it did not stand up. There might have been time, but to have searched the rooms presupposed a key to the apartment, or at least a selection of skeleton keys that would serve the purpose.

Accepting the premise, he believed that the searching had been done, not by someone on the boat, but by someone who had been in New York prior to its arrival; someone who was very interested in Nora, or her brother. When he got that far he could think of only one man: Noland.

"Why?" she asked, her glance still puzzled.

"I was just wondering. I don't think it could have been done by anyone on the boat."

"But why should anyone—"

"I don't know. I was just thinking aloud." He grinned to show her that it was unimportant. "This place could have been searched yesterday or a week ago for all we know." He put his glass down and reached for her hand. "You know what?" he said.

"What?"

"I'm going to buy you a dinner."

"You are? How nice."

He stood up, still holding her hand so that he could pull her up. She was wearing a black-and-white checked suit with a simple white blouse, and now she glanced down at herself.

"Will a suit do?"

"Nicely," Randall said and let her go into the bedroom to fix her hair. . . .

They ate at a little place that Randall knew would be open on Sunday evenings. The headwaiter gave them a corner booth and Randall told her about the last few days of the trip. He related in part the talk he'd had with Lenore and spoke of her plans to marry Dalton. Nora was amused by this story and the background which had forced the man to run away from his sisters, but she said nothing at all of her trip with Mrs. Fournier and he asked no questions lest such thoughts depress her and destroy the friendly casualness of the moment.

They got back to her apartment around ten o'clock, and when they went up the steps she said she wanted to stop and get her accumulated mail from the landlord. He had been out when she first came that afternoon, but now he greeted her enthusiastically, wanting to know how she had been and if she enjoyed her trip as he handed over a twine-wrapped bundle of letters and cards and small packages.

She thanked him as Randall took the bundle, and then they went up the stairs to her door. He reached for her key, turned it, and pushed on the door, his intention being to step back and let her enter first.

At that particular moment he was not quite sure what made him change his mind, nor could he explain until later the instinctive impulse that made him hesitate that all important second or two. Actually it was a combination of his subconscious mind and his naturally keen gift of observation, though it is doubtful whether the reaction would have been as it was had it not been for a mind already disturbed and suspicious because of the events which had happened previously.

Already uneasy, there was an instant of warning, a faintly remembered gesture of Nora's as they left the apartment. With no time to be sure, it seemed to him that she had turned on a small lamp near the door as her final act before walking from the room. He had not bothered to glance upward to see if there was a light as they got out of the taxi, but the impression was so strong that now, when he opened the door into darkness, he clung to the knob and stopped.

There may have been some slight sound of movement in the room, a faint stirring of air in the shadows; whatever the reason he nudged Nora aside and stepped back to ask about the light. But this might not have saved him had there been a better marksman behind the gun.

The first shot exploded as he moved. He saw the small bright flash from the muzzle and heard, it seemed, the slap of a slug in the woodwork beside him. The second shot hammered almost at once, ripping through the door as he slammed it and jumped aside.

After that he was moving, Nora's arm in his, half

dragging, half supporting her as he raced down the stairs, hearing her small frightened cry but not stopping until he was in the lower hall. Then, as suddenly, he stopped.

He glanced back. He heard the landlord's door open and some startled words that demanded to know what was going on here. But now his mind was working and he said:

"Is there a back door?"

"Not to my place," Nora said.

"He won't come out this way," Randall said. "He won't dare now. . . . Stay with him!" he said, pushing Nora towards the landlord. Then he was moving through the foyer and down the steps to the street.

Without knowing anything about the layout of the apartment, he knew that there would be some windows overlooking a yard or court at the back. It would not be much of a drop from the second floor sills but it was unlikely that there would be many exits that a man could use to gain the street.

Standing now almost in the middle of the block, and seeing no method of egress from the backyard, he had two alternatives. Perhaps because Third Avenue seemed a step closer than Lexington, he swung that way, towards the elevated, and sprinted for the corner, brushing past a strolling couple and nearly falling over a man who was curbing his dog. Then he was at the corner, cutting to the right and seeing now a topcoated man emerge from some doorway and scurry into the street.

A taxi whipped past and then another, its top lights on to signify it was empty. Randall waved but it was already past, and now it was slowing, and the man he was watching trotted along side and opened the door.

Overhead a rumbling grew swiftly along the elevated

structure. A downtown train rocked past and there was
no other sound but this. Randall did not even try to yell.
He watched the man tumble into the cab before it
stopped and then, finding no other taxi in sight, he ran
on, watching the cab pick up speed. The roof light went
off as the driver flicked down the flag; then it rounded a
corner and was gone, like the elevated, leaving Randall
muttering to himself but in possession of one small clue
that might, with luck, have some significance.

He had presence of mind to read off the taxi's license
tag while it was still in sight, and now he took out a pencil and jotted the number down on the back of an envelope. He stepped back onto the sidewalk, continuing
along a block of small shops, all of them dark, until he
came to the doorway he had fixed in mind.

This, he saw at once, was not a proper doorway but a
wooden gate which now hung ajar and led down two
steps into a two-foot alleyway between a dry-cleaning
shop and a secondhand furniture store. Where, exactly,
it went, he did not care. For it was obvious now that if
the man he had seen was the one who had shot at him,
there was nothing to be gained by any backyard exploration; if this was not the man, it made no difference
anyway.

Nora and the landlord were waiting in the hall. When
Randall joined them they had a brief discussion as to
whether the police should be summoned, but in the end
Randall decided to go back upstairs and make sure that
the intruder had gone. The key was still in the lock and
he went in, finding the light he had remembered close
by and turning it on.

He walked on through the bedroom and into the hall
and kitchen. Here a window was open, and when he

glanced below he could trace the probable flight of the gunman over the enclosing fence and across the court beyond. He closed the window and came back, taking a moment to inspect the bullet holes in the door and frame, both of which were a foot or more over his head.

Nora and the landlord came up the stairs as he stood there. The landlord, still grumbling about wanting to call the police, made an inspection of the damage and kept right on grumbling, a dark-skinned man with a dour expression and not much hair.

"I still think we should call the police."

"Okay," said Randall who was getting a little tired of the landlord. "Nothing's missing and it was probably only a prowler, but go ahead and call them."

Faced with the necessity of meeting the issue squarely the landlord lost some of his scruples. Finally he shrugged. "It ain't my apartment that got searched— if that's what it was," he said. "If you don't want to call the cops, don't call them."

Nora smiled faintly at this sudden reversal, but when they were alone in the apartment there was no smile and her eyes were grave.

"Why, Knox?" she said. "Why?" She slipped off her coat and tossed it on a chair. "Do you think he was waiting for me?"

Randall shook his head, his frown lopsided because of that old scar on one brow. He said he did not think so. He asked her to look again and see if anything was missing.

She went to the secretary, opened it, and then glanced through the drawer; she inspected the occasional tables. She went into the bedroom and when she came back he saw the mask of doubt and uncertainty on her young face and knew she had no answer.

She paced back and forth, her movement quick and restless. Finally she stopped, skirt swirling, and slumped on the couch beside him.

"You're sure you have no idea who it was?"

Randall said no, his dark gaze fixed on the bundle of mail on the coffee table. He said he did not get within fifty yards of the man who had run out on Third Avenue.

"But what could he possibly want?"

Randall was still concentrating on the bundle and now the germ of an idea had taken root in his mind. As it began to sprout he sat up abruptly and tugged at the twine until it came loose and the mail spread out across the coffee table.

"Let's have a look," he said. "Go through it, will you?"

She did not argue, and together they sorted out the pieces, making a pile of the first-class mail, another of the advertisements; a third stack was made up of four parcel-post packages and it was these which Randall examined first. Three of them Nora identified as purchases she had made in Florida and had mailed north, the fourth was flat and oblong, its wrapping obviously the work of an amateur.

Nora picked it up; then she saw the handwriting and caught her breath. "Alan!" she said, half aloud.

For a second or two she just sat there, her face slack, making no move. Randall took the package from her, looking for a date and a postmark. He saw that Alan Harding had addressed the package to himself in care of his sister, and when he saw the date and realized its significance, a new excitement struck at him.

"He mailed it the day he was killed!"

He asked her if she remembered that Alan had gone to the post office that afternoon they came into Neuse

City. She shook her head. When he tried to hand her the
package she increased the violence of that shaking and
the ends of her hair flew back and forth.

"You open it," she said weakly.

Randall snapped the string and spread the brown
paper with tingling fingers. What he found inside was a
film pack for Harding's camera, and an album, the sort
that has a section for each photograph, all overlapping
so that when closed the object looked something like a
leather-covered index.

He handed it to her without comment and she began
to look through the pictures, her eyes clouding as the remembrance of other days opened up new hurts. They
were the sort of pictures a young man would have:
friends of his, many of them girls, against the varying
backgrounds of parks and beaches and boats. Nora
spoke about one of these which showed Alan and two
other men on the bridge of a cruiser that seemed identi-
cal with the *Julia*. When Randall saw it he flipped it
over and found two or three other boat pictures—one of
these showed a life ring with the name *Julia* painted
on it—showing men and women in various poses. In only
one of these was Alan pictured, but Randall, remembering the things Julia had said about the friends her husband asked aboard, could see that she had been right,
for even in photographs they somehow looked cheap
and common. . . . He realized Nora had asked a question and he said:

"I'm sorry."

"I just wondered if Mr. Noland was in any of these,"
she said.

He said no, and she went on, flipping over other pictures, and now his thoughts centered on the undeveloped film pack he held in his hand. He turned it over

thoughtfully, dark eyes speculative. He ran his fingers through his hair, for there was a film of moisture on his forehead now, though the room was not excessively warm.

"If the landlord had been home when you came back this afternoon, you would have stopped for the mail."

"What?" Nora struggled to get her mind off the album. "Yes," she said, sounding as if she did not yet know what he meant.

"This place was searched before you came back," he said. "If you'd brought the mail up it would have been here when we went out to dinner."

"Oh," she said, and now he had her attention. "You think that's why he came back? To get something that—"

Randall interrupted her. "You had the landlord collect and save your mail. Our friend with the gun found that out the first time he searched the place. Somehow he knew you came back and figured you'd collect the mail. He waited until you went out with me—or maybe he just happened to pick that time—and tried again."

"But what could he want?"

Randall took her hand, not liking what he had to say but seeing no other way out.

"Look," he said gently. "Let's face it. Alan must have had something someone wanted. Maybe it was connected with (he almost said, 'The murder of Mr. X') Noland's death and maybe not, but whatever it was— information or something more tangible—he must have been trying to collect on it. Otherwise why should he have been killed?"

She was watching him now, her lashes high. "You mean he was blackmailing someone."

He nodded, aware that he was hurting her but finding no alternative.

"Yes," she said honestly. "It's a thing he could do.
There was some incorrigible quality in him that made
him do things like that. He was never mean or malicious
but"—she sighed emptily—"he had this idea that the
world owed him a living and—" She stopped dejectedly;
then, suddenly, her voice was quick again. "But that
would mean someone on the boat killed him."

"Not necessarily," Randall said, and knew it was time
for him to start at the beginning and tell the truth.

She heard him out as he told her the details of that
Saturday night he had called at Noland's house to find
that murder had been done. He tried to make his panic
and indecision sound plausible, and he rationalized his
actions as best he could. They did not sound good now,
these things that he had to say, they had never sounded
good when he repeated them silently to his conscience,
and when he had finished he pointed out the results of
his mistake. He said if he had reported that murder at
once there would have been no further trouble. There
would have been no trip, and without the trip, Alan
would still be alive in Florida.

He fell silent then, feeling the weight of his weariness
and depression settle over him until he became conscious of the pressure of her hand. She tugged at it to
make him look at her, and when he did he saw that her
eyes were shining and that there was no censure in their
depths.

"Maybe it was wrong, Knox, what you did in Florida.
But you mustn't blame yourself for what happened to
Alan. That part is not your fault."

He waited, not quite understanding, and she said:

"If what you think is right—about the blackmailing or some such thing—then it's Alan's fault, not yours. If he had been honest about things, it wouldn't have happened." She paused and now her frown came again. "You think Mr. Noland is alive, even though Mr. Gifford and the police identified the body?"

"Gifford did the identifying. He only saw part of a face. I thought it was Noland and I suppose he thought so too, especially with those glasses and ring."

"And you think Alan knew something?"

"He had to know something if my hunch is right. If he did, and tried to collect from Noland, there's no reason Noland couldn't have followed us up by car the same way Mondello did. I think he killed Alan and came on up here ahead of us."

You think he was the one who searched here?" She paused again when he nodded, and now her thoughts went back to her original premise. "It's not your fault, Knox. Only the beginning of it, and that had nothing to do with Alan."

Randall was grateful for her understanding. He said all that did not excuse him. He said he wanted to find out for sure who killed Alan; he wanted to find Noland.

Her faint smile was not encouraging. "But how can you?"

"At least I've got a chance," he said, and told her about getting the taxi's number. "Did you ever notice that the drivers keep a record sheet up front? I think it's a police regulation. They're supposed to write down their trips. I know the company and the cab number so maybe I can get the driver. If so he should know where he took our friend." He spread his hands and said: "If he let him out on a street corner somewhere that'll be the end of it. But I just might get lucky."

He stood up, pulling her with him. "I'll get this film pack developed and printed in the morning and then maybe we'll know what it was that Alan had. Pack yourself a nightgown and a toothbrush and we'll be getting on."

"Getting on?" she said. "Where, Knox?"

He grinned at her reaction.

"Why, to my place. You can't stay here tonight." He saw the conflict in her eyes and could tell that she did not know whether he was kidding or not. "Tomorrow you can get the landlord to change the lock on the door, but for now—" He stopped so he could take more pains with his words. "Look," he said. "Twice our friend has been here. He didn't break in. He came in with a key and we can assume that he still has it. You can stay with me, or I'll stay here with you."

She looked over at the door which she now realized was small protection under the circumstances. Then she glanced back at him and smiled.

"Are you sure it's proper?"

"In the strict interpretation of the word, no," he said, his dark gaze amused, "but for tonight I'd say it was both excusable and essential."

"All right," she said, accepting his conclusion without further hesitation. "I'll only be a minute."

Randall pocketed the film pack and the album. He went to the telephone and called the taxi company; he was still talking when Nora came back with a tiny, blue-leather case.

18

KNOX RANDALL had been up the preceding morning at five o'clock and the demands of the past twenty-four hours had proved more exhausting than he realized. As a result his body claimed the sleep denied it and he did not wake up until nine thirty the next morning.

It took him a few seconds to marshal his thoughts and remember why it was he was sleeping on the couch instead of in the bedroom; then, glancing quickly at his watch, he rolled over and got his feet on the floor, noticing as he did so that a piece of note paper fluttered from his chest. When he picked it up he was muttering to himself, not only because he had overslept, but because the presence of the note seemed to indicate that Nora had already left the apartment.

The message confirmed his fears: *Today is Monday, Sleepyhead*, it said, *and I'm a working girl. I would have made breakfast for you if there had been any food in the place but the cupboard was bare. I'll phone the landlord about changing the lock and if you call me here at the office ask for extension 285.*

The note helped dissipate his disappointment, but he walked restlessly through the rooms which now seemed strangely empty. He finally summoned energy to shave and then he took a shower, leaving the bathroom door open so he could hear the buzzer if someone rang it. He folded the sheet and blanket he had used and put them away; he straightened the couch. By the time he was

dressed he was hungry and he had to settle for a cigarette because he was afraid to leave the place and take
the chance of missing the taxi driver.

An hour went by and his restlessness mounted. He
went over the conversation he had had the night before
with the taxi company, which had been reluctant to
give out any information but agreed to pass along his
message to the proper driver, a message that in itself
was vague and unconvincing. Because he could not
think of a good, straightforward excuse at the time, he
had said that he wished to see the driver on a personal
matter of great importance and would be glad to pay for
the man's time if he would call at this address.

He lit another cigarette as his grouchiness increased,
and promptly snuffed it out. He was not a before-break-
fast smoker, and on an empty stomach the tobacco had
a revolting taste. Even the smell irritated him, and he
went to dump the ashtray in the wastebasket; that was
how he happened to remember the film pack and the
album which stuck from his coat pocket.

Without removing them from the pocket he went to
the telephone and called his office. When he got his boss
he announced his return, grateful that the statement
brought forth sufficient enthusiasm to indicate that his
job was still open. He told about the boat and his obligation to take it to the Cape, but he promised to be back
the following Monday; meanwhile he'd stop in later in
the day and say hello in person. He asked to be
switched to the photographic department and when he
hung up he not only had made arrangements to have
the film pack developed and printed, but had asked that
an office boy be sent to pick it up.

The buzzer answered his hopes a few minutes later
and when he opened the door a stocky young man

watched him from the hall, his cap tilted carelessly over one eye. "Mr. Randall?" he said.

"Yes," Randall said as the driver explained who he was. "Come in."

"The office said it was a personal matter."

"Yes. I want a little information." Randall brought out some bills and gave the man a five. "Will that cover your time?"

The fellow eyed the bill approvingly and reached for it. "Sure," he said. "What do you want to know?"

Randall told him about the incident of the previous night, mentioning the time and the location. The driver remembered the passenger but now his glance was wary.

"You a cop?"

Randall smiled reassuringly and said he wasn't. He said: "The guy owes me dough and I haven't been able to locate him. I just happened to spot him last night."

The driver folded the bill and when he started to speak Randall mentally crossed his fingers and offered up a prayer that the information would be of some value.

"I guess it's okay," the driver said. "I took the guy to the Clay Hotel," he added, and mentioned the address.

Randall let his breath out. He thanked the man and opened the door. For a moment he felt a quick warm glow of satisfaction; then he forgot all about his good luck as a new and important thought occurred to him. "The Clay Hotel," he said softly when he was alone, and then he knew why the name was familiar. His mind went back to the previous afternoon when Eaton Gifford had left the boat to ride in the taxi with Julia and John Barnard; he could hear in fancy Gifford saying: "If you want me for anything I'll be at the Clay Hotel."

Coincidence?

He did not know. He was still wondering when the boy from the office came to pick up the film pack.

The Clay Hotel proved to be a modest-sized building west of Fifth, one of those hostelries little known to the commercial traveler or tourist, but managing a certain air of distinction by virtue of its appointments and a well-trained personnel. Fortunately for Randall, the lobby was sizable and there was enough traffic to and from the elevators, enough activity around the desk, so that he could take a chair off in one corner without being particularly noticeable. In his gray flannel suit and covert-cloth coat he looked like the prosperous young business man he was, and from all appearance could have been either a guest, or someone waiting for a guest.

A newspaper helped screen him from the desk, and by holding it in a certain way he could see with one eye the alcove which housed the elevator, while at the same time presenting a picture of a man interested primarily in the paper. Now and then he would turn a page, but never for more than a second or two could he take his attention from the job at hand, with the result that his task became increasingly awkward and boring as time went on.

He had stopped for breakfast and he was not worried about lunch. He was willing to sit there all afternoon if necessary, but he wondered how long he could pretend to read the same paper. He did not dare be without it, for he had no idea whether his man was in or out, or from what direction he might first appear. While he waited an attendant came twice to empty the ashtray next to the chair, and to sweep around it with his small broom and long-handled dust pan. The third time, a

half hour later, he examined Randall with surreptitious
curiosity and Randall wondered how long it would be
before others of the staff began to question his continued
presence.

He could not quit. He could not get up to stretch or
walk around. The first hour stretched into two and the
clock over the desk pointed to one fifty before his stubborn persistence paid him a dividend.

It happened when four people stepped from the elevator nearest the street—two women and two men. It
was at once apparent that the two women and one of the
men were together, for they moved towards the entrance
foyer while the other man circled to the desk.

This was the man Randall was interested in. He had
known from the first that on the face of it, the odds were
against him. He had not been able to get a look at the
man who had run into the street the night before and
tumbled into the taxi; he would not be able to identify
him if he saw him again. Therefore he had but one hope
—that the man who had searched Nora's apartment
twice was a man he would recognize if he once saw him.

Now, as his heart thumped and he ducked behind the
barrier of his paper, he felt a quick triumphant pleasure
in the moment. He took another furtive glance as the
man walked away but that glance was not really necessary. He recognized the bony face and the weak,
pointed chin the instant he saw them. There were no
glasses now and a blue double-breasted overcoat and
gray Homburg had replaced the flashy tan suit, but
there was no doubt in Randall's mind. Looking a little
too sharp for the Clay, looking in fact, as if he should be
standing on some Seventh Avenue corner ogling the
girls, this was nevertheless the man who owned the
Julia; this was Perry Noland.

Randall sat quite still until the man had passed through the foyer, wondering why he felt no great surprise until he analyzed a little more and found the reason. In the back of his head there had been a suspicion of Noland for some time. Noland fitted into a theory of his, and while he could not be positive that Noland and the man who rode here in a taxi last night were one and the same, this supposition would do until a better one came along.

At the moment he had no further plans until the film pack was developed, and he walked to the house telephones beyond the desk and asked for Noland's room, aware that it was highly unlikely the man would use his own name but wanting to be sure.

"One moment, sir," the operator said. "What name was that again?" she asked some seconds later.

"Noland. Perry Noland."

There was a pause, then: "I'm sorry, sir. We have no one registered by that name."

"How about a Mr. Gifford? Eaton Gifford."

"Yes, sir," the operator said presently. "Room 810. Shall I ring it?"

Randall said: "No thanks, not now," and hung up. He did not bother to make additional inquiries at the desk. He had an idea that Noland was registered here but the alias he was using was something Randall would have to find out by other methods.

19

KNOX RANDALL had counted rather heavily on the pictures from Alan Harding's film pack. In his mind the explanation for the searching of Nora's apartment lay in the undeveloped films, and he felt sure that from one of these would come a worthwhile clue. He was not looking for further breaks—he knew he had already had several—but this time the solution seemed so obvious that he was quite unprepared for the printed results.

The twelve photographs that the agency photographer handed him at three o'clock that afternoon were all good, and all typical of what any amateur might be expected to take on a trip such as Harding had made. The only exception was the flashlight exposure he had made when Mondello and his henchman came aboard that Saturday night before they left Fort Lauderdale. The others were either informal snaps taken aboard, or waterfront scenes such as Harding and Dalton had taken in Charleston.

Now Randall put them in his pocket, swallowing his disappointment as he slouched in his chair. For a little while he considered the Mondello picture, examing various premises, but in the end he decided it had no special significance. That Mondello might have wanted the picture was understandable; that he would know Harding had mailed it to New York in care of his sister was outside the realm of probability.

He brooded awhile about this and other things. He wandered back to the photographic department, an idea growing out of the ashes of his disappointment, not

yet full-formed but sufficiently promising to merit further consideration.

"Have you got a man who can take candid pictures?"
he asked of the department head, a man named Leland.
"Like a man walking along the street?"

"Sure."

"Is there any way of taking a picture like that without
the subject knowing it?"

"Not if he suspects anything, and is smart. We can
use an angle-view finder so that the lens is pointed at
right angles to the man who is using the finder. That
sometimes does the trick."

"Have you got a man I could borrow? Someone
who could do that kind of a job."

Leland buzzed for his secretary. "Tell Al Brady to
step in a minute, please," he said, and presently a stocky,
pleasant-faced youth with a shock of black hair appeared in the doorway. "This is Mr. Randall, from the
copy department, Al. He's got a little job for you. . . .
Who'll I charge this to?" he said to Randall.

"Me," Randall said. "It's sort of a personal assignment."

"In that case—"

"No," Randall said. "I'll take care of it. Could I have
Al tomorrow morning?"

Leland nodded. He said why not take Al along to
Randall's office and explain what he wanted.

Randall told the photographer as best he could. He
gave Al his address and told him to be there around
nine the following morning. He said he did not want
his man to know he was being photographed and the
only way he could think of working the matter successfully was to hire a car and park outside the hotel so he
could point the subject out to Al when Noland came out.

After that Al could do the best he could.

When he was alone again he telephoned Nora and asked if they could have dinner again. He said they could pick up her bag at his place and go on to her apartment to see if the lock had been changed; otherwise she ought to stay again with him.

"I'll put food in this time," he said, "so you won't have any excuse about not getting breakfast."

Her laugh was wonderful to hear and when he hung up he daydreamed a few minutes before he could bring his mind back to the subject of Noland. There was, he decided, one more thing he could do this afternoon.

About a year before he had spent the best part of a day talking with a young detective in order to get research for a piece of copy. He knew the name was Laughlin and that, at the time, he had been temporarily attached to the Homicide Squad, but it took him a long time and several calls before he located his man at the East 67th Street station.

Laughlin remembered him at once and said he was still with Homicide, which had now broken up into two sections, one functioning from the east side, the other from the west.

"What's on your mind?" he said. "Who'd you knock off?"

"Nobody," Randall said. "Not yet, anyway. It's sort of a personal matter."

"Oh?" Laughlin said, sounding doubtful.

"But it's about a homicide. It didn't happen here and I know you haven't any interest in Florida cases—"

"Sometimes we do. What's it about?"

"A man named Perry Noland was killed about two weeks ago in Miami."

"Wait a minute until I take this down. . . . Okay.

Perry Noland. Miami. What was the date?"

Randall told him and gave what details he could. "Noland had had some trouble with some gamblers over at the Beach, one of them a guy named Mondello."

"I know him."

"Somebody tried to kill Noland about a week before that and the last I heard the police were working along those lines."

"And where do I come in?"

"I saw Noland in New York this morning."

What Randall got then was a lot of silence, and when Laughlin finally spoke his tone was sardonic. "Sure, I know," he said. "They brought the guy back to life and he ran out on the undertaker."

Randall remained unperturbed. "I saw Noland in New York. The fellow in Miami had his face half blown off with a sawed-off shotgun. He was identified as Noland by Noland's lawyer. I say he made a mistake and I thought maybe you could check with Miami and see what they'd found out in the past couple of weeks."

"Your idea is, that this guy you say is in New York probably knocked off the guy in Miami instead of it being a gangster job, fixing it so it would wind up as a case of mistaken identity."

"It was just a thought," Randall said. "If you want to have lunch tomorrow I could tell you the rest of it."

Laughlin said the lunch idea sounded fine and he'd see what he could do on the other thing. Where, he wanted to know, would Randall be that evening in case Laughlin wanted to get in touch with him.

Randall said he would probably be home by eleven and gave the detective the number.

For awhile then he considered the things he had told the detective, but before long he found himself recalling

what he had said about Mondello, and with this came a
new concern, heretofore neglected because of the things
that had happened the night before.

He had heard nothing from Lenore, and it shamed
him now that he could have forgotten the potential
danger in which she had placed herself. He reached for
the telephone at once and called the hotel she had
named when she left with Dalton, wanting to be reassured that she was all right. Instead the hotel operator
informed him that there was no one registered by that
name, nor was there any record of an Oliver Dalton.

Randall hung up, a frown biting at the angles of his
eyes. He did not think Lenore would have deliberately
lied to him about where she was to stay. She could, of
course, have changed her mind, but it seemed more
probable that she was scared by something that had
happened and had registered under an assumed name.
It was, he admitted, the smart thing to do. For Mondello
was at home here, he would have connections and be
able to get assistance if needed, and a patient man could
locate anyone, given time, so long as a person registered
under his right name.

And Dalton?

Randall did not know, and he was worried. When he
remembered that Laughlin had said he knew the gambler, he called the East 67th Street station again, only to
learn that the detective had already left.

Randall hung up, muttering. He tried to think of
someone he knew in the district attorney's office who
might tell him whether Mondello had been picked up.
Finally he summoned his secretary and had her bring
him the afternoon papers. He took his time going
through them, scanning the smaller items, looking for
some mention of Mondello or Lenore, looking for any-

thing that had to do with arrests, or crime, or witnesses.

As it turned out, all this was a waste of time. He knew no more when he finished than he had in the beginning, and it was not until he called for Nora that he could force his mind on to other things and stop speculating about Lenore and Dalton and the thirty thousand dollars he carried in cash. . . .

The restaurant Randall picked was on East Fifty-second Street, not far from Madison. He was well known here and after one drink at the bar he was shown to a table in the rear. Two or three times during the meal a friend of his would spot him and come over to say hello, and each time he introduced Nora proudly and noticed the approval with which she was appraised.

To his way of thinking she was the most attractive girl in the room and it was with some reluctance that he put aside his thoughts of her and answered her questions about the events of the day. He told her how he had seen Noland and what he intended to do about it in the morning, though in this instance Nora had trouble following his line of reasoning.

"What good will a picture do?" she asked. "Even if you get one?"

"I want to show a copy to Mrs. Noland, for one thing. I want to show another copy to a friend of mine named Laughlin on the off chance that Noland's face is in their rogues' gallery down at Centre Street."

He went on to tell her the disappointing news about the film pack her brother had mailed to New York, and she said:

"But what could the man have wanted last night?"

Randall said he didn't know. "But," he said, "at least we know that now there is a definite connection between Noland and your apartment."

"Suppose you're right," she said. "Suppose Noland did kill Mr. X. Suppose he followed the boat up because of something my brother did—or tried to do—and came on to New York. What will you do then?"

"Hah!" Randall laughed shortly and there was no indecision in his reply. "I'm no cop," he said. "I'll tell Laughlin so he can pick up Noland at the Clay Hotel and go to work on him."

They left the restaurant shortly before nine and when they had taxied uptown to her apartment he told the driver to wait a minute.

"I just want to be sure about that lock," he said to Nora.

It was just as well he kept the cab because the landlord had a tale to tell about the shortages of labor and material. He had, it seemed, been able to find a lock after much time and effort but he had been unable to find anyone to make the substitution. Tomorrow he could promise everything would be all right but tonight there was nothing he could do about the matter.

On the way downtown Randall stopped at a delicatessen. He told Nora he wasn't kidding about breakfast and she laughed and said it was all right with her. She picked out the things they needed, and when they got back to the apartment they sat around listening to the radio until nearly eleven. He got out his sheets and blanket and pillow. This time she insisted on making the couch for him, and when she had finished he said he thought he would sit up a while longer in case Laughlin should call.

He made a drink after she had refused one, and got what things he needed from the bedroom. He took her hands as she said good-night and the things he saw in her eyes told him it would be all right to kiss her. He

did, this time with more warmth than might be called
for in a friendly kiss, and now she helped him, and her
lips were warm and exciting before she stepped back
and slipped into the bedroom.

The kiss and his thoughts of her helped sustain him
when there was no telephone call from Laughlin, and
when he awoke at eight the next morning he could hear
Nora stirring in the kitchen. By the time he was out of
the bathroom the smell of coffee filled the hall and he
saw that she had already squeezed the oranges.

"Do you like one egg or two?" she asked when she had
answered his good-morning, and it was such a familiar
question that he thought of Lenore and laughed aloud
because somehow this was so much better. "One," he
said. And then, seeing the radiant softness of her face
and the way her blond hair caressed it as she leaned
over the stove, he said: "You're beautiful."

She did not say anything but he saw the color touch
her cheeks and was content while they ate on the card
table he set up in the living room. He refused point
blank to let her wash the dishes, so when she had
stacked them she hurried off to work, promising to meet
him again for dinner.

Al Brady arrived ten minutes later and they looked
up the nearest Drive-Yourself establishment so they
could rent a car. On the way to the Clay Hotel, Randall
again went over his idea, and when they arrived they
pulled into the parking space reserved for guests who
arrived in their own cars and wished them sent to the
garage. Two dollars and a little speech persuaded the
doorman to let them stay there awhile, and there they
sat with Brady on the sidewalk side and Randall behind
the wheel.

He had already told the photographer that they

might have to sit here for hours, but in his estimate he was overly pessimistic. As though to make up for his wait of the previous day, they had been there less than an hour when Randall sat up and jabbed Brady.

"That's him," he said. "In the blue coat and gray Homburg."

They had already decided to follow Noland if he turned the wrong way, and take their chances on getting a picture at the next corner; now, to Randall's delight, the man turned left, buttoning his coat and heading for Fifth Avenue.

Brady had his camera adjusted, and he had already decided that the sun was high enough to give him the light he wanted without using a flashbulb. Now he screwed his eye to the angle-view finder which enabled him to sit facing the windshield and still have his lens pointed out the lowered window.

Randall started the motor and the sound of it made Noland turn his head. As he did so Brady tripped the shutter and it was then that Noland, already offering practically a full-faced target, spotted Brady and turned to stare.

Randall let the clutch out and angled from the curb, glancing over his shoulder as he did so. It was only a second before he looked away and he was not sure whether Noland had recognized him or not, but there was an instant when their eyes met through the windows and Randall muttered under his breath, annoyed that he should let his curiosity get the best of him.

"What's he doing?" he asked as he shifted into high.

"Watching us. . . . Now he's walking on towards Fifth Avenue."

Randall told himself it did not matter whether No-

land had seen him or not. Aloud he asked if everything
was okay, and did Brady get the picture? When Brady
said sure he had it, Randall swung into Sixth Avenue
and headed back towards the office.

Brady showed him the negative at eleven o'clock and
said it would take another half hour to make proper
prints. Randall said he'd wait, and now that he was sure
he had a satisfactory negative he went into his office
and called Laughlin.

"I thought you were going to call me," he said when
the detective answered.

"I've been calling you," said Laughlin with some impatience. "Ever since half past nine. I wanted to ask if
you'd been to see an oculist lately."

"Why?"

"I think you're seeing things."

Randall knew what the detective meant but he
would not accept it. He felt the sharp pressure of a sudden incredulity and his voice was brusque.

"I saw Noland!"

"No you didn't! Noland is dead. He's been positively
identified."

"By whom?" Randall demanded. "That lawyer? He
could have made a mistake."

"He could have but he didn't. Neither did the Miami
boys. You know, cops are not quite as dumb as some
people like to think."

"Who cares about that. No one said they were dumb.
All I said was—"

"I know what you said," Laughlin cut in. "But get
this. Perry Noland did some war work for a time. He
was fingerprinted. That corpse with the shot-off face
was fingerprinted. Those prints say the dead guy was

Noland and what I want to know is *where is the lad you think is Noland?*"

It took Randall a few seconds to answer. He felt as if someone had slugged him and he heard Laughlin repeat the question before he could make his vocal cords work.

"He's at the Clay Hotel," he said weakly. "But he's not registered under the name of Noland."

"We'll go see."

"I've already seen, damn it. If you want to wait a half hour I'll bring you a photograph I took this morning when he came out of the hotel. Maybe with that you can identify him and find out who he really is. Or do you want to do it your way?"

"I'll wait for the picture," Laughlin said without further argument. "Make it as soon as you can."

Randall hung up and slumped back in his chair, his arms dangling over the sides. Much of his incredulity had gone and in its place there was nothing but a strange numbness which for a time had no further capacity for thought or speculation. He had to accept the fact that it was Perry Noland and not Mr. X who had been murdered; beyond that he was unable to go.

20

THERE was very little in Ray Laughlin's manner or appearance to suggest that he was a first-grade detective until you examined his eyes, which were smoky blue and seemed never to be still. There was a certain narrowed watchfulness to his glance, even in repose, but aside from that he was no different from any other young business man of average size and build. Neatly dressed but no fashion-plate, he was not much older than Randall, and spoke with clipped, city-bred accents, verging now and then into the profane. Sitting behind his desk in the little office on the second floor of the station house, he wore a plain dark suit, a clean white shirt, a tie of conservative pattern.

"So this is Mr. Noland?" he said, glancing up from the photograph Randall had given him.

"Not according to you."

"What made you think he was Noland in the first place?"

Randall told him about the interview in Noland's Miami home. He explained how Noland had come to the boat that Sunday morning, and he took out his wallet to show the credit card made out in Noland's name, and the other card with Noland's New York apartment address and telephone number.

"Why wouldn't I think he was Noland?" he demanded.

"No reason." Laughlin gestured with the photograph. "Who else saw him when he came to the boat?"

"A fellow by the name of Alan Harding, and he's dead." He went on to explain about the murder and how Louis Fournier had confessed. He did not betray the man's reason for the confession but he said he believed that confession to be a phony brought about by Fournier's fear of some other threat.

Laughlin's eyes grew narrower in their watchfulness. "Where's Mrs. Fournier?"

Randall said he did not know. He had asked Nora

about this, and she told him that she had said good-bye
to Mrs. Fournier in the Pennsylvania Station. Mrs.
Fournier had good reason to keep her whereabouts a
secret and Nora, understanding this, had not even asked
where the other woman was going. Randall told none of
this to Laughlin. He simply said he had no idea where
Mrs. Fournier was, and the detective had to accept the
statement, though it was clear he was not happy about
it.

"It's getting kind of complicated," he said. "What's
your idea?"

Mr. X killed Noland," Randall said. "Both were the
same size and build, had the same color hair and eyes.
They didn't have to look alike, with Noland's face shot
half off. When I talked to him he wore Noland's glasses
and signet ring." He went on with other details and then
said: "I think Harding guessed the truth—he saw Mr. X
at the boat and he knew he wasn't Noland—and tried to
cash in. I think X followed him up, killed him in Neuse
City and came on ahead of us to New York."

"That leaves you the only one who knows that the
man who hired you is not Noland."

"Until now, yes."

Laughlin nodded. He studied the ceiling thoughtfully, pursing his lips, then sat up and asked if Randall
had another copy of the photograph. Randall had two
more prints and he gave the detective one of them.

"I'll send one of these downtown," Laughlin said.
"Maybe we can find out if Mr. X has a record with us.
We'll take the other one over to the Clay Hotel and see
what we can find out about him before we pick him up."

He stood up and thanked Randall for his help. He
said to keep in touch with him because they were going
to need him later on.

The rain, which even the weather man had not predicted, came in the form of a shower around one o'clock as Knox Randall turned into the Gracy Hotel, one of those small, unprepossessing establishments that are concentrated in the West Forties and continue to do business because of their rates.

The lobby was reached by a tunnel-like foyer from the street, the elevators were a little creaky, the upper halls gloomy. Room 412 was one of the better rooms and faced the street, but even so John Barnard felt the necessity of an explanation when he shook hands with Randall and asked him to sit down. He'd stayed at the Gracy for thirty years, he said, and it had got to be a habit, and what with the shortages and one thing or another he was afraid to change.

"What'll you have to drink?" he asked. "It was nice of you to phone me."

Randall said he'd take a rain-check on the drink. He saw the disappointment in Barnard's lean, weathered face, and now he felt guilty because he could not offer much information in return for the questions he wanted to ask. Because he could think of no other way to proceed, he pulled out the picture of Mr. X and asked Barnard if he knew the man.

The older man passed a palm over his thick gray hair and tipped back in his chair. He shook his head, pushing out his lower lip. He glanced up.

"Never saw him before."

Randall reached into his topcoat pocket and brought out the flat photograph album Alan Harding had mailed to his sister. He felt sure now that herein lay the answer to the searching of Nora's apartment, and he was annoyed with himself for not considering the possibility sooner.

"Take a look through that," he said. "See if you can find a picture of Perry Noland."

Barnard's eyes watched him from beneath graying brows as he accepted the folder. He seemed about to speak, thought better of it. He walked over to the window where the light was better and began to flip the photographs. Presently he stopped and Randall, already on his feet, moved up to him.

"Here," Barnard said and indicated the photograph Randall had noticed before, the one which showed Alan Harding and two other men on the bridge of the *Julia*. "The man without the cap," he said.

Randall exhaled slowly and reached for the folder. In the face of what had seemed like uncontrovertible evidence, he had clung to the slim chance that a mistake had been made; now that there was no further doubt in his mind he felt a mounting resentment as he began to understand the horrible cleverness with which he had been made an innocent but key figure in this murder scheme. Other than in size and a somewhat similar angularity of features, the man in the photograph could never have been mistaken for Mr. X without the sort of mutilation which would lead the police to believe that Noland had been killed in anger and vindictiveness by some gangster or hoodlum he had double-crossed in a business deal. That sawed-off shotgun and the earlier attempt on Noland—perhaps legitimate—was part of the plan, and until now it had been successful.

He closed the folder, aware that Barnard was watching him and not knowing what to say.

"Does this have to do with that murder in Miami?" the other said finally.

"Looks like it."

"But you can't talk about it."

Randall shook his head and was embarrassed. He said it was a police case now but it began to look as if the man who had given him the job of bringing the *Julia* were someone other than Noland.

Barnard was a gentleman. He pressed the matter no more and when he spoke again his voice was pleasantly casual. He said he had been thinking about the *Julia*.

"I was wondering if you'd want a hand when you take her on up to Falmouth. I'd be glad to go along at my own expense," he said. "Just for the fun of it."

Randall said he wasn't sure he'd be taking the *Julia* any farther but if he did, Barnard could consider himself invited. He said he was on his way to speak to Mrs. Noland about the matter and he would let Barnard know.

Knox Randall got a little wet before he found a cab, and then he rode north to an imposing, dark-brick apartment house on Central Park West. The uniformed attendant in the foyer relayed his name to the switchboard operator and presently he said:

"Mrs. Noland would like you to go up. 6-B."

Julia Noland looked very nice indeed when she opened the door for Randall. Her smile was quick and her tapered eyes had approving lights in them as she shook hands. She wore a black dress which fitted snugly the full deep curves of her torso, and flared at the hips to fall loosely and disguise somewhat the rather heavy legs.

"Throw your coat anywhere," she said, and when Randall said it was wet she opened a closet door and said so was hers and to hang it up in there. "I started to do some shopping and got caught," she said.

He followed her into a dropped living room that overlooked the Park and boasted a wall-to-wall rug, an impressive but non-wood-burning fireplace, and a lot of mirrors which seemed to increase the room's already generous dimensions. She settled herself on a red-upholstered Duncan Phyfe-styled sofa and patted a down-filled cushion beside her.

"Sit here," she said. "I suppose you want to know what to do about the *Julia*. Have you been having fun?"

Randall's thoughts were too perturbed to indulge long in the amenities he would have normally observed. He sat down on the edge of the sofa as he took out the photograph of Mr. X, but his smile was only surface deep and did not alter the level intentness of his gaze. He said he hadn't come about the *Julia*. He said some funny things had happened the past couple of days and he was trying to find out why. Then, watching some of the animation go out of her face, he passed her the picture.

"Have you ever seen that man before?"

For a moment as she accepted the print she continued to watch Randall, her half-smile curious. Then she dropped her glance and the resulting reaction was instantaneous and startling. She caught her breath, staring wide-eyed now, the sultriness of her mouth dissolving into flaccid-lipped astonishment.

"Where did you get it?" she breathed.

"Do you know him?" Randall said, unwilling to give her time to compose herself and pressing for an answer.

"Yes. It's Joe."

Randall waited while her mouth disciplined itself. Until the spasmodic thrust of her breasts against the fabric was still. Finally she glanced up.

"Joe who?" he asked gently.

"Joe Klimm," she replied, her astonishment coming under control. "My—my first husband."

It was Randall's turn to be surprised.

"The forger?"

He watched her nod. He sought to bring some order to the rising confusion in his mind.

"When did you see him last?" he asked.

"In Miami. A few days before we left."

She had herself in hand now as she returned the photograph. Uncertainty still lurked in the corners of her elongated eyes but her voice was quiet and impressed when he explained that he had no right to question her like this but that he hoped she would help him.

"He came to see you?" he said. "What did he want?"

"Money." Julia leaned back, her sigh resigned. "He always wanted money, though I hadn't seen him in years."

"Did he threaten you?"

Her short laugh had grim overtones. "Naturally. Not physically, but just with the promise to go to my husband and tell him a few things about the past—the time I almost went to jail, things like that—unless I paid."

Her mouth curled disdainfully. "I told him to go ahead. I didn't think he had nerve enough to go to Perry. He might have written some letters, just for spite, but by then I didn't care. I had already made up my mind to leave and I told Joe so. I laughed at him. I said if he needed money why didn't he try Perry's lawyer."

"Did he go see Gifford?"

"Yes. I think Eaton gave him a hundred and told him if he bothered me again he'd have him arrested. . . . But where," she said, sitting up again, "did you get the picture?"

Randall ducked that one. He had already found out what he wanted to know and he did not want to get involved in a lengthy, detailed story.

"Where I got it," he said, "is no longer important. The important thing is this: Joe Klimm is in New York. I saw him this morning. Also," he said, "I've got a hunch he murdered your husband."

She leaned forward, tipping her head. She started to laugh and cut it short. She took a quick breath, exhaled slowly. Then she said, her voice quiet: "You *are* serious, aren't you?"

Randall put the photograph away and stood up. "If he didn't kill your husband, I'd like to know how he could pose as Perry Noland and give me Perry Noland's credit card."

She rose slowly, lips parted, her manner almost somnambulant as she moved across the room. She turned near the steps to the foyer and waited until he came close.

"You ask me to believe that Joe Klimm is the man who hired you to bring the boat north?" she said finally.

"I know he did. Also—and this is only a guess—I think your friend Gifford was in on the deal."

He went on up to get his coat and hat from the closet. "In any case, what I think doesn't count any more. The police know about Klimm and where he's staying, and when they pick him up we'll find out what's what."

She said nothing more and neither did he. As he turned to close the door her eyes were fixed upon him but he was not sure that she actually saw him. The things she had heard were apparently too much for her to assimilate in so short a time, and though she was still beautiful she was no longer working at it.

Randall ate a late lunch, consisting of a sandwich and a glass of beer, and then went to his apartment in case Laughlin should try to call him. He telephoned Nora and was advised that she had called her landlord and been assured that a new lock had been installed. She said she might have to work a little late and why, since she had to stop at his place to get her overnight case, didn't he wait there for her.

He argued that it was no trouble to come for her but she said it was simpler for her to get a cab, and so he was waiting with a drink in hand when she came at a few minutes after six.

He kissed her, and again she helped him, not lingering over it but letting him know how she felt. "Yes," she said, "I'd like a drink. With plenty of water; I'm thirsty."

They sat together on the couch while he told her about the picture he and Al Brady had taken that morning of Joe Klimm; he explained how wrong he had been in thinking that Klimm was Noland. He told her about his call on John Barnard, and when he returned her brother's album he showed her the photograph of Noland aboard the *Julia* which Barnard had pointed out to him.

Nora sat very still then, not questioning him about other details or asking what he thought. Instead her mind was busy with some ideas of her own and presently she brought them into the open.

"Then Alan knew," she said woodenly. "He saw you talking to Joe Klimm that Sunday morning when he came to give you the money and the credit card. He knew from what you said that you thought the man was Noland and he knew it wasn't. Klimm had never seen Alan before and so it meant nothing to him. And being

Alan, with that mental quirk which was always looking for something for nothing, he decided to let you think so until he found out more about it."

What else she had to say she had no chance to finish because just then the telephone rang. When Randall answered it, a familiar voice said:

"Hi, Bruiser."

The quick, friendly cadence of Lenore's voice was at once reassuring but after his first quick thrust of relief there came a mild sense of annoyance, brought about by the concern she had caused him the day before.

"Where've you been?" he grumbled, and then to Nora: "It's Lenore. . . . I tried to get you. They said you weren't registered at the hotel."

"Oliver thought we ought to register under other names. He said it didn't make sense to take any chances with Mondello, and besides he couldn't be sure his sisters didn't have the police looking for him."

"You could have let me know."

"I know. I'm sorry, Knox."

She sounded as if she meant it and now the brief interlude of his annoyance seeped rapidly away. "All right," he said. "So how do you stand? How did it go with the D.A.?"

"It went all right," Lenore said, and the quick exuberance of her tone verified the statement. "He didn't put the arm on me but I have to stay in town until the trial. They picked up Mondello this morning so it looks like I can stop worrying."

"What about that western trip? And the guy with the thirty thousand bucks? And the demon sisters he was so afraid of?"

"The western trip is postponed," Lenore said, "and the sisters are going to be informed *after* the wedding.

That's why I called you. Oliver doesn't want to wait. He's got the license, and the day after tomorrow we're going to get married." She hesitated, a suggestion of timidity in her tone as she continued. "He doesn't know anybody and—he wondered if you'd stand up with us."

For a moment then Randall forgot his troubles. He felt good all over. He said: "I'd be proud to. Where? And when?"

Lenore told him; then, hesitating, with the same suggestion of doubt in her voice, she said: "Have you seen Nora? . . . Do you think she'd come too?"

Randall said she was right here and he would ask her. Or would Lenore like to speak to her. Lenore said no. "You ask her," she said. "Tell her it won't take long and —well—"

Randall told her to wait and turned to Nora, explaining what Lenore wanted. Nora nodded quickly, her gray eyes suddenly misty. "Oh, yes," she said. "I'd love to. Here, let me talk to her."

She took the telephone and chattered on enthusiastically for a few seconds while Randall waited and beamed at her. She was flushed with pleasure and excitement when she hung up but again she had no time to speak her thoughts. Before she could sit down the telephone rang again, insistently, and when Randall answered it Laughlin's voice came to him, blunt and demanding.

"I'm down on First Avenue," he said, and gave the address. "I want you to get down here right away."

Randall hesitated, his mood destroyed. He sensed the urgency of the request and was upset by its timing. He glanced at Nora and was undecided.

"I can't just now," he said. "I've got a date and—"

"Do you want to come down in a cab?" Laughlin cut in. "Or do you want me to send a couple of guys to bring you down? I'm sorry about the date but it'll have to wait."

Randall started to argue, thought better of it. "I'll get a cab," he said.

Nora was on her feet when he hung up. "What is it, Knox?" she said, and he told her it was the detective he had talked to that morning. He said Laughlin sounded a little tough and he guessed he would have to postpone dinner.

When she saw how troubled and disturbed he was she nodded and reached for her coat. She did not ask questions. She said she would wait for him at her place.

"Come when you can," she said as they went down the stairs and out into the street.

"It shouldn't be too long," he said.

"It doesn't matter."

They crossed the pavement, jaywalking diagonally towards the corner, and a few seconds later he flagged a cab and put her in. In another minute he found a taxi for himself and gave the driver the address Laughlin had mentioned.

The rain had stopped by mid-afternoon and now as the taxi made its turn into the broad reaches of First Avenue the pavement was dry and the street lights were battling it out with the thickening darkness. Diagonally ahead and towards the river, two tall stacks of a power plant rose with sturdy grace against the sky, their tops obscured and shadowy, their spindly safety ladders no longer visible; opposite was a row of four-story tenements with small, ground-floor shops, and it was here that Randall saw the cluster of cars and the uniformed policemen who stood in the street and waved the traffic past. When the driver, who had slowed down, started to obey the signal Randall spoke to him. The cab stopped and the nearest policeman walked truculently towards them, eyeing Randall suspiciously as he opened the door and said:

"Laughlin sent for me."

The officer told him to wait and Randall paid the driver. He could see the three police cars and the ambulance. He noticed that the sidewalk was blocked off for a distance of a hundred feet or so, the onlookers who had gathered there being held at bay by other policemen or detoured out into the street and back to the walk again by a widely circuitous route. Headlights on the police cars and ambulance glared vacantly into space but between them a small sedan was parked at the curb. It was from the group around this car that Laughlin finally emerged.

"This way, Mr. Randall," he said. "Got something I want to show you. We think we've found your Mr. X."

Randall moved across the curb, an odd hollowness growing where his stomach had been and his nerve ends tightening. He already had an idea as to what had happened but it did not help him much when Laughlin stopped beside a blanket-covered form on the sidewalk.

Laughlin twitched the blanket aside. "Know him?" he asked.

Randall felt a little sick as he glanced at the bony face. Death and the glare of the headlights bleached the skin, and the pointed chin was etched sharply against the sidewalk. He swallowed against his sickness and thought of another blanket-covered body, and this one was worse because it did not lay at ease, but in cramped, bent angles where rigor had stiffened it.

"We got him from that sedan," Laughlin said, as

though sensing what was going through Randall's mind. "Been dead a while when we found him."

"Yes, I know him," Randall said finally. "His real name is Joe Klimm. I thought you were going to pick him up at the Clay Hotel."

"He didn't show up. . . . Klimm, hunh? A small time forger, maybe, who came up here from Florida ten days ago, registered at the Clay, and has been hanging around there ever since. I'm wondering how you knew his name, Mr. Randall. I think maybe it's time you started to lay it on the line."

21

A DOZEN little things, all of them converging on one idea hitherto unconsidered, went through Randall's mind as he walked with Laughlin to one of the police cars. At first, because his brain was not accustomed to such considerations, he rejected the thought, but the more he inspected the premise the more important it became.

He had known from the minute he saw Joe Klimm in New York, even when he still thought he was Noland, that the murder of Noland and the subsequent planning of the trip in which he, Randall, was an important cog, was the work of more than one man. Now, for the first time, he wondered where Julia Noland came into the picture.

He thought back to his last talk with her, trying to remember her reactions and what she had said. It seemed obvious now that she would get in touch with the lawyer, Gifford. Innocent or guilty, Randall's announcement was her first knowledge that he knew Klimm was in town; Randall had told her that the police were looking for Klimm and if Julia were guilty then Klimm became a threat to her safety. Klimm was a weak one; Klimm might talk. . . .

He watched Laughlin climb into the car with two plain-clothes men and a driver. He remembered that he had left Julia at two o'clock, or shortly thereafter. Now he said:

"Do they know what time he was killed?"

"He was shot twice," Laughlin said. "At close range. Somebody shoved a small calibre gun against his side under the arm and pulled the trigger twice, probably while he was parked here in the rain and no one was on the street. The medical examiner gave him a quick check at seven o'clock; he says the guy'd been dead between five and seven hours. Put it between twelve and two, but not later."

Randall leaned back, his idea about Julia collapsing. Then as his thoughts again centered around Gifford he asked where they were going.

"To have that little talk. At the precinct house."

"Okay, if you say so," Randall said. "But that way you're wasting time."

"What would you suggest?" Laughlin's tone was quietly ironic.

"The Clay Hotel."

"Yeah? Why?"

"Somebody killed Klimm. That means this was a two-man job from the beginning. The other guy is Noland's lawyer. His name is Eaton Gifford and he's staying at the Clay. Why not get him? That way we can both talk."

Laughlin recognized a good idea when he heard one.

He spoke to the driver who altered his course at the next corner. Six minutes later they were pulling up in front of the Clay Hotel.

Laughlin went to the desk and his two companions stayed with Randall. Presently another man, middle-aged and with a pass-key in his hand, apparently the house detective, joined the party and they all went to the eighth floor.

The house detective knocked. When there was no answer he unlocked the door and snapped on the lights in the empty room. "I'll be around if you want me," he said, and went out.

The room was a large one, with a dressing room off the bath, and when the two plain-clothes men had finished poking around the closets Laughlin nodded to Randall.

"Make yourself comfortable," he said. "Let's get started on that story and see how it adds up."

Randall knew he was in for it, and in all justice he knew he had it coming so he made the best of it. He opened his coat, tipped his hat back and tossed a leg over the arm of the club chair. He started at the beginning, with the advertisement he had seen in the paper, and went on from there.

Now and then there were interruptions as Laughlin asked a question to clarify some point. He muttered sourly when Randall told about finding the murdered Noland. He waxed somewhat sarcastic when Randall gave his reasons for running away without informing the police. Otherwise he listened attentively until Randall got to the part where Nora's apartment was searched and the two shots fired at them, apparently by Klimm.

"Oh, fine!" Laughlin's disgust was vocal and explosive. He shook his head and glanced at his companions; then all looked severely at Randall. "You couldn't have reported that break, huh? You wanted to do it all yourself."

Randall flushed and his dark eyes were morose. "What would you have done?"

"You did a good job chasing the guy," Laughlin said. "If you had called the police you could have given them the taxi number and they could have followed it up."

"To the Clay Hotel? Then what? Who would you ask for, John Doe?"

Laughlin did not reply to that one and his smoky-blue eyes gave no clue as to whether he evaded it because he had no good answer, or whether he was thinking of something else. Finally he asked if the bullets were still in the woodwork, and when Randall said he thought they were, Laughlin reached for the telephone. When he hung up a few minutes later he said, his voice more reasonable now:

"Klimm had a gun on him. I'd like to know if that was the one he used when you surprised him." He walked over to the windows, glanced out, came back. "Let's say Klimm and Gifford were in it together. Klimm impersonates Noland and sells you a bill of goods about the boat. Where's Noland all this time? It took a few days, didn't it, from the time you answered the ad until the medical examiner gave his opinion of the time of death?"

"I think he was a prisoner in his own house," Randall said. "The Miami police say there were marks on Noland's ankles and wrists, as if he'd been tied up. They figured this tied in with the theory of a gang killing— and I think a sawed-off shotgun was used to make the police think just that," he added.

"But young Harding sees Klimm at the boat and knows it isn't Noland like you say," Laughlin said, taking it from there. "He's a cutie and he smells something so he decides to keep quiet until he finds out the score. Then two days later when the Miami cops look you up on the boat he knows it's murder, and he also knows that somebody's gone to a lot of trouble to pass Klimm off to you as Noland. He wonders why. He's got a photo album with a picture of the real Noland and the minute he shows it to you the plan—and Harding may not be sure what it is yet—blows up. But how does Klimm know this? How does he know enough to follow the boat to North Carolina and rub out Harding?"

"Harding doesn't have to know who Klimm is," Randall said. "But he does know Gifford. He figures—and rightly—that whatever the murder plan, Gifford might be mixed up in it. He phones Gifford from some shore station, and makes his bluff and this threat to talk unless he gets paid. Gifford tells Klimm and Klimm catches up with Harding in North Carolina."

Laughlin had a few more questions but finally he fell silent and glanced at his watch. Randall began to think about Nora. After a few minutes he pushed out of the chair and straightened his hat.

"Any reason why I can't go ahead with my date?" he asked, as though this was the most natural request in the world. "You don't need me here until you get Gifford, do you?"

He thought Laughlin was going to say yes. He could see the answer in the detective's eyes as he opened his mouth; then something happened to the eyes and the word that finally came out of Laughlin's mouth was:

"No."

Randall tried to disguise his surprise. He said that was

fine. He said he appreciated Laughlin's cooperation as
the detective glanced at one of his men.

"Where'll you be?" he said.

Randall said he would either be at his place or at
Nora Harding's apartment, and after that he got out
fast.

Julia Noland wore the same smart-looking black dress
she had worn earlier in the afternoon, but her welcome
as she opened the door for Randall lacked some of its
earlier cordiality. Her smile seemed forced and her
black eyes were opaque and expressionless.

He said he wouldn't stay long. He said he had some
news he thought she'd want to hear, and as he reached
behind him to close the door he slid his thumb along the
edge and pressed the release button so that the door
could be opened without a key.

"It's about Joe Klimm," he said when he had tossed
his hat and coat on a chair.

Julia did not sit on the red sofa or pat a cushion for
him. She picked up her bag and took it with her to a
wing chair. She brought out cigarettes and a gold
lighter and waved him away when he tried to strike a
match. She blew smoke at him and put her head back,
her gaze steady, her low contralto voice revealing nothing.

"What about Joe?"

"The police found him. In a rented car down on First
Avenue; with two bullets in his chest."

She showed no surprise at the announcement. Her
manner was resigned, her voice toneless. She crossed
her knees and gestured emptily with the cigarette,
watching Randall as he walked idly about the room.

"After what you told me this morning," she said, "I

can't say that I'm surprised. Joe never could keep out of trouble; he was never very smart. Do the police have any idea who did it?"

"I'm not sure, but I know they're looking for Gifford."

He got a reaction then. She brought her head forward and for an instant something that might have been alarm flickered in her eyes.

"Eaton?" she said. "Nonsense."

"They don't think so. It's just a question of time before they pick him up and then they'll know for sure. They think Klimm and Gifford were in the thing together and that once Gifford found out the police were closing in on Klimm, Gifford had to kill to protect himself."

He lit a cigarette and said: "With a little more luck he might have gotten away with it. With a little more luck Klimm, who had a record, would have been identified as a small time operator who apparently had been killed by some associate, also small time. It happens every week in big cities. You've seen the pieces in the papers— a body in a parked car or open lot, with a few bullets in it. It always turns out to be some little man who got too smart for his own good."

"I understand that," Julia said. "But where does the luck come in?"

"I was here around two o'clock or a little before," Randall said. "I showed you a picture which you identified as Klimm, and you told me what happened with him in Florida. I told you I thought he had killed your husband—I did think that at the time—and I assume you telephoned Gifford after I left."

"I did."

"But by then Klimm was dead. The luck part comes in here: If Gifford had known that I had already taken a picture to the police and that they were looking for

Klimm, Gifford would not have killed him. Because the minute the body was found it would be identified, not as Klimm the small-time forger, but—because I'd told my story—as Klimm who might be implicated in a Florida murder. The police think that if Gifford had known at noon what he found out from you at two o'clock, he would have tried to get Klimm out of town so he could not be found at all."

Randall shrugged and picked up an ashtray, keeping his voice casual but feeling anything but casual inside. "It doesn't make any difference now one way or the other—except to Klimm—because I told the police that when they found Gifford he would probably talk plenty."

"I'm sorry." Julia shrugged again and there was an ill-concealed annoyance in her tone. "I'm afraid I'm being frightfully obtuse. I don't seem to follow you. What makes you think he is implicated in the first place? Why should he talk?"

"Because," Randall said flatly, "I don't think he has any guts." He glanced again at the four cigarette butts in the ashtray, two of which were stained with lipstick while the other two were unmarked. "Why don't you ask him in?" he said. "Then we can find out for sure."

He started for the closed door at one side of the room, apparently giving on an inner hallway. He got halfway there, the ashtray still in his hand, when the door opened and Eaton Gifford came in.

For once the lawyer wasn't smiling. He was resplendent in an oxford-gray suit and his wavy hair was slick and shiny. His light brown eyes, looking darker in the shadows, were narrowed purposefully, and although he had tightened his mouth the inherent weakness still showed through.

It made Randall feel a little better. For if it hadn't
been for this weakness the .32 automatic Gifford carried would have seemed far more menacing.

22

KNOX RANDALL backed slowly to the sofa as Gifford
advanced. He put the ashtray aside and sat down. He
did not feel very brave but somehow the gun still did not
worry him much and he finally said so.

"What're you going to do with the gun?"

"That depends." Gifford's voice was harsh but it
lacked authority. "Depends on you."

Randall watched Julia snuff out her cigarette. "How
much money have you got in the place?" he asked
abruptly.

"Money?" Her brows came up.

"What is this?" Gifford said. "Another shakedown?"

Randall shook his head, calculating lights in his dark
eyes, his mouth grim. "I was just wondering what your
chances are. You haven't got much time. Maybe an
hour, maybe a day. But Julia"—he glanced again at her
—"might get out of town. With luck and some money
she might keep going. For awhile."

"Why should she go anywhere?" Gifford demanded.
"S—she hasn't done anything. Neither have I. If you're
trying to infer that we killed her husband you're crazy.
Mondello killed Noland, Mondello or some other Beach
gambler who had a grudge against him."

"That's what you wanted it to look like. But if you
thought so you wouldn't be waving that gun." Randall

paused and watched the lawyer lower the automatic until it hung straight down at his side. He looked back at Julia.

"In some ways," he said, "I guess I'm a sucker when it comes to women. Most men are at one time or another. I must have been brought up to think of women in a certain way; an old fashioned way maybe, that said you should treat them with respect and consideration and always give them the benefit of the doubt. I realized that they could kill, with proper provocation—and sometimes without it—but not viciously and without compunction."

He grunted softly. "I should have known from reading the papers that I was a little naïve. I should have realized that when women put their minds to a job, any job, they can be pretty good at it, and in the case of murder, just as cruel and savage as a man. Maybe it's because I never happened to know such a woman that made me develop a blind spot; maybe, just as Harding had a small mental quirk that made him act in devious ways, I had a similar weakness that refused to let me suspect a woman. First I thought it was Klimm—or Noland as I knew him—and then Gifford. Tonight I found out that neither could have killed Harding. I should have known before that neither of them had the courage for murder. They could plan, but they were not killers. That's your province, Julia."

"Really?" She opened her bag for cigarettes and this time she fitted one into a holder. "You interest me."

"I thought I would."

Gifford moved over to sit on the edge of a refectory table. His eyes were no longer narrowed; they bulged a little and traces of alarm were working in their depths.

Randall glanced from one to the other, making up his

mind. He had a theory about Laughlin. He did not know how good it was but he knew he needed time. He wanted also to get things straight while he could.

"Do you want me to start at the beginning?" he said.

Julia nodded. "If you like."

"Then let's start with the motive. I understand that's always important. You don't mind if I guess a little here and there?" He reached behind him for a cushion, put it across his knees and leaned his forearms on it.

"You told me once that you could tell by the way men looked at you that you had something they wanted. You had more than that; you knew you had something that could make men do the things you wanted them to do. Maybe it started with Klimm when you were eighteen, maybe before that. You had run away, and he took you a little farther away when he married you. He was a forger on the side and he went to prison, but Julia didn't."

"I told you," Julia said, "that I didn't know the checks I passed were bad."

"I know what you told me. Let's say you are right. Let's say it was a near thing for you, enough so that you decided to be more careful the next time. . . . I don't know what happened to you in that period between Klimm and Noland, and I'm not sure it matters, but in Noland you had what you wanted—enough money, a certain low level prestige, security. For a couple of years, according to you, everything was all right. Then something happened. What was it? Do you want to tell me, or shall I guess?"

"Guess." The word was flat, uninterested.

"I don't think I can, but I can guess at what happened as a result. I think your husband froze up on you. Do you know what I mean?" He paused, trying to find some answer in her bleak, elongated eyes. "You're the posses-sive sort, Julia. Selfish, domineering, grasping because of the things you lacked when you were young. And for once you found a man who had become impervious to your sexual allure and could not be softened by your talents. Because in Noland you had a man who was as ruthless as you were and even more calculating. Every-thing in his background, all his business dealings, prove that. When he made up his mind he was plenty tough, wasn't he?"

He said: "Maybe he caught you cheating on him, maybe he got fed up with your possessiveness, maybe he just got fed up. Somehow I think it was something more than that because he could have let you go and he didn't. He wanted to pay you back for something you had done and he was vindictive enough to know how. Did he cut down on your allowance, restrict your free-dom? You said he made you take those boat trips and all the time ignored you. You had a man who could give you the things you wanted, and you had lost the one hold you had on him, the physical one, and you didn't dare run away because you would be poor again."

He poked at the pillow and brought out another cig-arette. He glanced at Gifford as he lit it and Gifford sat on the edge of the table, mute and immobile, a paleness showing through his tan.

"You must have wanted to kill him often," Randall said, turning back to Julia, "but you were afraid, if not of him, then of the consequences when suspicion fell on you. Then, somewhere along the line, Gifford came into the picture."

He paused and let his thoughts flow as he looked from one to the other. Gifford, he knew, had the type of flashy good looks that would appeal to many women, the surface charm and manners that would flatter those who were susceptible. That Julia should turn to him was understandable; that Gifford should in turn be taken with her obvious charms was equally understandable.

"Have you finished guessing?" Julia looked bored, all but her eyes and the tight line of her mouth.

"Almost," Randall said. "There's a little more on this motive business and I'll give you the benefit of the doubt. Let's say you didn't work on Gifford because you could use him, let's say you were in love with him, in your fashion. Let's say it was mutual. However it was, I think your husband found out about you—probably shortly before I entered the picture. If that is true you both must have been a little scared because you knew Noland was a man who knew how to strike back."

Randall waved one hand negligently. "I could be wrong. Maybe you loved Gifford and made up your mind to kill your husband to be free, as other women have done before; maybe you wanted the money he had while you were still mentioned in the will; maybe it was a combination of the two. Whatever the reason you made up your mind to act, and then you got a break. Joe Klimm showed up. Joe wanted money. . . . I don't know whose idea it was but it doesn't matter now. It was a good idea, if Joe would play along. Joe had fallen for you once, and you were even better now with your perfume and soft hands, and eyes that promised things he wanted, and a face and body to excite and tempt him. Also there was money to be had."

"Listen!" Gifford started to rise, his tone a mixture of anger and bluster. "You can't talk that way—"

"Be quiet." Julia waved him back. "Let him finish."

"You had a plan," Randall said. "But you needed a fall guy. Me. I guess Noland had talked of sending the boat north and someone came up with an idea that would give you both an air-tight alibi for the murder you planned, because by then you realized that Joe was the same size and build as your husband. He did not look like him but he had the same color hair and eyes and a reasonable similarity in the bone structure of the face."

"Why should that make any difference?" Julia asked lazily.

"I'll come to that." Randall kept his voice matter-of-fact. He felt almost matter-of-fact inside. The gun that dangled loosely from Gifford's hand did not bother him and his own concentration was such that he was absorbed in this effort of making his theory stand up. "Let's take one thing at a time," he said.

"Take me—and that ad you put in the paper, Gifford. By that time you and Klimm must have grabbed Noland and tied him up. You kept him right in the house, didn't you? . . . Anyway," he said when there was no answer, "you needed a man to take the boat north, a man who was unacquainted with Lauderdale and Miami, who would be unfamiliar with waterfront gossip, and above all a man who knew nothing about Noland. You interviewed the applicants and I filled the bill. You made an appointment for me at Noland's house and Klimm, as Noland, did all right. He had the credit card from Noland's wallet and there was no reason for me to suspect anything wrong."

He said: "I liked the idea of taking some paying passengers; it was a swell idea. It worked. I agreed to take Julia and later when she told me she was running away from her husband I believed her. It sounded reasonable, her shipping aboard her husband's boat, because it seemed like the last place he would think of looking

for her. She knows how to make a man believe about
what she wants him to believe—for awhile anyway—
and besides, I wanted to take her. I liked her; she had a
certain fascination that was a little beyond my experience."

"Thanks," said Julia.

Randall's grin was fixed and mirthless. He continued
to Gifford. "I didn't know until tonight why she really
came aboard and spent Saturday night there. She had
to have an alibi, and so did you. I gave you both one.
What you didn't know was that I knew Noland had
been murdered Saturday night—before Julia came
aboard."

Gifford stiffened and his cheeks blanched. Julia uttered a small, unidentifiable sound that was half gasp,
half exclamation. Her face went slack all over and it
was a moment before she could rearrange. When she
spoke her voice was all right.

"Oh?" she said. "Tell us about it."

Randall did, his tone flat and incisive. He went over
each detail of his discovery and went into his reasons for
running away.

"That could have been a bad break for you," he said.
"If I hadn't been a complete idiot that would have been
the payoff right then. Neither of you had alibis and you
would have been picked up that night." He grunted
sourly. "But I did you a favor. I played on your side.
You didn't know I had seen the body, and after I ran
out I couldn't talk. You would have been in the clear
from then on if it hadn't been for Harding," he said.

"You had your timing perfect. Klimm came to the
boat on Sunday morning to set the alibi—which is why
he made it a point not to give me the credit card before
—and by then you had been aboard twelve hours," he

said to Julia. "And Gifford was already on his way to
Havana with a friend. You planned it so the murder
would not be discovered until the following noon because with Noland dead that long the medical examiner
could not be accurate in his estimation of the time of
death. I swore that Noland had been at the boat between nine thirty and ten; the doctor said he had been
dead more than twenty-four hours, and the only obvious
solution was that he had been killed after he left the
boat—between ten and twelve o'clock, or was it one?"

He cocked an eye at Julia. "You want to know about
the mutilation and why it was important? Well, I was a
little off on that. I thought the same way as the police,
that you used a sawed-off shotgun because it would look
like a revenge killing, done by professionals. That was
only part of it. The real reason you had to shoot your
husband in the face was because you knew I might be
brought back to identify the body. Once the police
started investigating, Gifford would have to tell them
about the boat—and me. He had to have me for an alibi
the same way you did. He knew you were aboard,
though he pretended he didn't, and he told the Miami
police about the trip and they caught up with us at Eau
Gallie. If they had not accepted my statement—corrob-
orated by Harding—I would have had to return to
Miami. I would have been shown the body, and I would
have said the dead man was Noland because his face
was so mutilated I couldn't think anything else under
the circumstances."

He put the cushion on the sofa arm and leaned on it,
his voice disdainful. "It was a wonderful idea. I don't
know whose it was, or if it was a collaboration, but it was
a honey. You had all the breaks too; all but one." He
was watching Julia now and he said:

"You didn't know Harding was aboard until we pulled out that Sunday morning, and he didn't know about you. He knew something was up when I identified a man as your husband that Harding knew was not your husband. He kept still because that twist in his mind told him to. Until he found out about the murder. He knew enough then to make some hints to you. Noland was dead; a phony Noland had shown up at the boat. That was enough for Harding. He smelled easy money and he knew he could collect. The minute he told the truth you and Gifford were done and your plan fell apart. He had that album which showed a picture of the real Noland. Barnard could identify it; anyone who knew Noland could identify it."

He said: "You had killed once and now you had to kill again because you were afraid. You could never trust Harding for long, even if you paid him something, and I can understand that. You didn't bother to tell Gifford. You didn't need any help either, did you? I don't know why you picked Neuse City but I guess it was because Harding was ready to force a showdown and you didn't have enough cash. I do know that he must have been a little leery of you because it was that afternoon that he mailed that album to his sister. I guess he must have told you, figuring probably that it would give a little protection. But that album wasn't the important thing then. You were afraid to wait any longer—or was it because of the fight Harding had just had with Fournier?

"You didn't expect any confession. That was just another lucky break for you. You thought you were safe enough, and you were ready to sit it out and let the police there try to prove something. You telephoned Gifford, and somewhere along the line you telephoned to

Klimm who had come on to New York. You told him
about the album and where it was, and he had a key
made and took a look. Only the album hadn't arrived.
The landlord had Nora's mail and Klimm didn't know
it. Later, when he tried again and we surprised him, he
shot twice so he could get away."

He sighed and arched his back. He did not know why
but a strange tension had begun to build inside him and
he tried to ease the muscles in his neck and shoulders.

"The album was hardly worth murder," he said. "It
was a good thing to have but perhaps not too important. If you had thought so you would not have sent
Klimm back. Klimm was no killer. He shot high—deliberately."

"He should have killed you," Julia said, some new
quality in her voice that Randall had not heard before.
The cadence was still low but there was a flat, hard
coldness underneath the words that jarred him. For the
first time his assurance faltered and he felt a queer uneasiness rising in him as she said: "It would have been
better if he had."

"He would have been alive now," Randall said, "if
that's what you mean. Maybe he wouldn't have escaped
the chair for long, but he would be around now."

"You're awfully sure it was me, aren't you?" Julia said
in those same disturbing tones.

"With Harding, it had to be you. I didn't think so until tonight. I didn't want to think so. I knew it could not
be Gifford because he was in Miami, but I thought
Klimm had followed us up in a car. There was a car in
Neuse City but it must have been Mondello again. It
wasn't Klimm."

He digressed to tell of his conversation with Laughlin
as they stood on First Avenue. "Laughlin learned that

Klimm had been registered at the Clay Hotel for the past ten days," he said. "He had been hanging around there ever since. Which means that Klimm could not have been in Neuse City the night Harding was murdered. You killed Harding. I think you did the same thing to your husband; you're the only one of the three who had enough of that cold, unemotional cruelty to stand there and shoot him while he was tied to the chair. He was tied, wasn't he? By Gifford or Klimm?"

Julia had heard enough. She had no further argument and apparently her mind was made up. Her mouth hardened and her eyes were half-closed.

"He wasn't tied then," she said. "Eaton and Joe carried him into the room and got out. He was drugged," she said, as if this explained everything. "He never felt a thing."

A cold breeze, more fancied than real, swirled about Randall's ankles and he shivered at the supreme callousness of her remark.

"And today," he said, "it had to be Klimm—or me. And Klimm was easier. You had handled Klimm before. You could think of some reason why he should hire a car and ride with you awhile, why he should park in the rain with you over there on First Avenue. The reason wouldn't have to be too good, because Klimm was scared. Klimm saw the man with the camera this morning and he saw me in the car."

He shook his head as though to clear it of thoughts he was reluctant to admit. "I was wrong about that too. I forgot that you had a wet coat when I came this afternoon; I never dreamed you had been out with Klimm. I wasn't smart enough to realize that if Klimm saw me he would get in touch with you. And when you heard about that you knew what you had to do to Klimm.

What you didn't know, until I called and showed you
the picture, was that the police already were looking for
Klimm. By then it was too late. Klimm was dead and
you must have known that when they found his body
they would soon know that he was the man who pretended to be Noland. But even then, while I was talking to you, you played it straight. You admitted he was
your former husband because it was the smart thing to
do."

He left the cushion on the sofa arm and stood up. "I
guess that's all," he said. "I wanted to get it straight, so
that when the police catch up with you I can tell them
what happened." He picked up his hat and coat. As he
turned towards the foyer, Julia spoke.

"Where do you think you're going?"

He looked at her and the things he saw in her tight,
hard face started the tension working on him again. She
still sat in the chair, her gaze fixed and uncompromis-
ing.

"Out," he said levelly. "Downstairs. Out."

"Oh, no you're not."

He gave her back her stare but there were butterflies
in his stomach. He turned slowly and put on his hat.

"Stop him, Eaton!"

Gifford slid his thigh from the corner of the table and
straightened, his face pasty and new alarm in his eyes.
He started to lift the gun but his heart wasn't in it.

Randall watched him a moment, gambling on his
earlier estimation of the man's courage. He remembered
his first impression in the lawyer's office. He had decided then that Gifford had no stomach for a fight, had
never been a front line guy. He was even surer of it now
as he took another step. Then he stopped, stiffening at
the uncontrolled fury of the woman's voice.

"Then I will," she said. "Turn around!"

Randall turned. He saw the gun she had taken from her bag, a small, short-barreled revolver; he watched her put the bag aside and move slowly towards him.

He retreated automatically, not knowing he had done so until he felt the arm of the sofa touch his thigh. He saw the quick scorn in her glance as it flicked past Gifford, and then he was looking straight into those tapered eyes.

"You weren't too far wrong about Eaton," she said, biting off her words. "Now what about me? Do you think I'm afraid to use this?"

By some odd mental process which allowed his thoughts to digress momentarily, it now occurred to Randall that in a way he had been right about Julia too. Stripping her of her facial prettiness and the alluring promise of her soft, rounded body, he had thought of her as possessive, determined, unafraid of anything life could offer. That he had for so long overlooked such potentialities came, he knew, from his unwillingness to associate her with murder and violence.

Now, without even thinking back to what had happened before, he knew the answer. It was in the twist of her mouth, in the implacable intentness of her hot bright gaze. There was no sign of pity or compassion in the things he saw, and it took a conscious and determined effort on his part to try to shrug, to pretend it didn't matter as he leaned back against the arm of the sofa and waited for what came next.

23

THEY stood like that for perhaps five seconds, all three of them silent and immobile. The sound of someone's breathing was for Randall the only audible thing in the room and he was surprised to discover that it was his own. He swallowed to clear the back of his throat and tried to discipline his voice lest it waver and betray the fact that fear was working on him.

"So?" he said finally.

The one word seemed to break the spell, as though there was in it the assurance that he would do as he was told. Julia's fingers loosened slightly on the gun. She lost none of her wariness, but with the need for immediate action over, she was more confident and at ease, her voice again controlled.

"Turn on the radio, Eaton."

Gifford's face was still pasty and his reaction was slow.

"What?" he said vacantly.

"The radio. Turn it on! Then go in the bedroom and get that bag I packed. The small one."

Gifford backed a step uncertainly, his glance moving doubtfully from Randall to the woman; then he turned and hurried to the radio which stood near the hall door. He put his gun away as he fiddled with the control knobs, and when the sound of music swelled in the room he disappeared along the hall.

When he came back he carried a black overnight case

which he placed on the refectory table at Julia's command.

"Open it!" she said, never taking her eyes from Randall. "The money you brought me from Florida is in there somewhere. Bring it here. How much is left?"

Gifford had a thick sheaf of bills which he counted with trembling fingers as he crossed the room. "About eighteen thousand," he said.

"Stuff it in my handbag."

Randall roused himself. He had been fascinated by the woman's orders and the gun in her hand; now he began to think.

"Eighteen thousand," he said, trying to sound sardonic. "And if it hadn't been for Harding you'd have had it all. How much would that be, Gifford?"

Gifford looked at him. He might have answered, so complete was his disintegration, had not Julia interrupted him.

"It's better than nothing," she said. "Get your hat and coat, Eaton. Get my fur coat and the black cloth one from the foyer closet."

Again Gifford obeyed, and Randall said: "Have you got a plan, Julia?"

"Yes, I have."

Gifford piled the coats beside the overnight case and came forward. His once good-looking face was wet with perspiration and he sounded out of breath when he spoke.

"What is it?" he said. "Where are we going?"

Randall looked at Julia and she stared back at him. The hard bright glint was still in her narrowed eyes and her voice was low and decisive. She was taking pains with her words now, and she meant just what she said.

"When we take care of him"—she gave the gun a little jab at Randall—"we're getting out of here."

It was a hard thing for Randall to understand. Thinking back over the things she had said and the things she had done he knew she would have no compunctions about pulling that trigger when the time came, and still he could not believe it. A man, yes; but a woman—

That was what stopped him—that she was a woman. It was here, he knew, that he had made his mistake. Women did such things, but never the sort of women he had known. His intelligence told him that this thing was happening and his emotions still revolted until he understood that it could never be a question of a man or a woman. Julia was simply a person whose moral values and decency had disintegrated beyond recall. From now on her own life was forfeit. She had nothing more to lose, and very little to gain except time, but even now Randall could understand that to a condemned man, time had great value.

She had killed once, deliberately, as part of a clever and well-thought-out plan. Whether for love, or greed, or some personal vindictiveness brought on by a neurotic urging, she had carried out that plan with purpose and cruelty. Alan Harding threatened her safety, as had Klimm. Both were dead . . . He heard someone speak and he had to glance round to find out it was Gifford.

The lawyer was shaking his head. "No," he said. "Not again, Julia! I won't allow it."

"You don't have to. I'm the one who had to do it three times before."

"But how—"

"That foyer closet has a lock." Julia's eyes never

moved from Randall, nor did the gun waver, yet when she spoke to Gifford her tone was businesslike and forceful. "I'll leave word at the desk that I'll be away for a day or two. I'll tell them not to touch the apartment until I get back."

"But you don't have to kill. Good God, Julia! Not again." Gifford wiped the perspiration from his face with his bare hand. "We can lock him in the closet just as well. He can't get out before morning, if then. It's big enough. If we do that—" He stopped to glance at his watch. "It's still early. We can get a plane, we can go—"

"You're not going anywhere," Randall said with a confidence he certainly did not feel. He stopped looking at Julia and tried to ignore the gun. He went on hurriedly, making the most of an idea that had been in the back of his mind ever since he came, knowing he had to keep talking and hoping that the thought he now tried to put across would really come to pass. He knew he could no longer count on any help, but he spoke as convincingly as he could.

"You don't think I'd walk in here, knowing you killed the others, knowing you probably still had the gun around that you used on Joe Klimm unless I thought I could get away with it?"

Gifford gave him a nervous glance and Randall said: "I left a detective from the Homicide Squad and two plain-clothes men in your room at the Clay Hotel." He thought back, remembering how Laughlin had been about to refuse him permission to leave, how he apparently changed his mind. He remembered the knowing glance Laughlin had exchanged with one of his companions. He told all this now, hoping that he was right and that it was not a case of the wish being father to the thought.

"I told them about you," he said to Julia, though he
did not look at her. "Laughlin must have had an idea I'd
come here or he wouldn't have let me go. . . . As a
matter of fact," he said, stretching the truth a little, "I
know a taxi followed me here and I'll lay you even
money Laughlin or some of his men are downstairs now,
if they're not waiting in the hall. You'll never get past
the lobby, either of you."

He had their attention while he spoke. He got
another second of silence; then Julia said:

"Stand up!"

He had to look at her then and by some odd mental
aberration his thoughts slid off on a tangent. He thought
how much better he would feel if Gifford held the gun
instead of Julia. He felt the perspiration on his own
forehead now, and the cold trickle of it along his sides.
He straightened, waiting, knowing there was not much
time left.

"Now go up those steps and into the foyer. I'll be
right behind you and if you—"

"Nuts!" Randall said, a sudden anger rising unex-
pectedly within him. "Do you think I'm going to walk
into that closet and make it easier for you?"

"No, Julia!" Gifford's voice was shrill and he moved
closer to her.

"Keep thinking, Gifford," Randall said to him. "Think
hard. Suppose you *could* get away with Julia, which
you can't. How do you think it would work out for you?
You liked her, didn't you? You figured it would be fun,
and so it would—for awhile; for so long as you did the
things she wanted you to. You know what I mean—give
her the attention she wants, make love when she says so,
buy her the things she wants and wait on her when she
tells you to. . . . But what happens when you get tired

of that, or when she gets tired of you?" he said impatiently.

"What happens when the quarrels start and the money runs out, or when some other chump comes along. Maybe then you'll begin to realize that she has already killed two husbands and that it could happen to you. Oh, not with a gun necessarily; maybe it will be a funny taste in your coffee or your orange juice, and always knowing you can never be sure until maybe it's too late. You're not a complete fool are you? You know something about the law. You're already an accessory to murder—that's what they call it, isn't it?—even though you haven't killed anyone. You'll have to pay somehow, but you can also talk and lighten the penalty."

He took a quick breath and now it was an effort not to look at Julia, not to be able to tell what was coming.

"They'll get her all right but it's not always easy, is it, to convict a woman of first degree murder? Wouldn't you rather make a deal with the district attorney and take a few years rather than—"

"Shut up!"

Julia's voice shook with fury. Randall had to look at her. The tapered eyes were cold and merciless now and so was her voice.

"Will you walk up those stairs, or won't you?"

"No," Randall said.

"All right."

Randall saw the hand tighten on the gun, a once small soft hand that was now white and rigid. He saw, from the corner of his eye that Gifford had started to move.

What happened then was all over in two seconds and though Randall did what he could, it was Gifford who

really saved him. The lawyer, even now, had no stomach for murder. He was closer to the woman than Randall and he reached out towards the gun, not a decisive
movement nor even a daring one, but rather it was a
preventive gesture, hesitant but nonetheless a threat.

Julia moved when she saw Gifford's intent, so did
Randall. He saw Julia step back, teeth bared in her frustration, and in that instant she swung the gun at Gifford.

Randall did not know, then or later, whether the
woman intended to shoot. It was an instinctive, almost
involuntary reaction, brought on by the abnormalcy of
the situation and the warped, hate-ridden mind. What
he did understand was that this would be his one
chance and he was moving even as the gun swung away
from him.

Still standing with his back to the arm of the sofa, he
had reached behind him and now, as Gifford faltered,
he had the corner of the cushion he had left there in his
hand. With that same continuous motion he spun sideways and scaled that cushion at Julia.

To Randall it seemed that in the next instant time
stopped so that what happened was in slow motion. To
him the cushion spun lazily through the air and he
could not understand why the woman did not turn back
to him and fire, why he should be standing there doing
nothing.

Actually the cushion struck Julia's forearm a split-
instant after it left his hand. The arm jerked sideways.
As it did so the gun roared and was simultaneously
struck from her grasp.

Over by the foyer he thought he saw a flurry of movement. He thought he heard someone call out and had
no idea why he should think so since neither Julia nor

Gifford had made a sound. It made no difference then, for he was moving now, seeing Julia wheel and pounce cat-like upon the gun.

Gifford, staggered for an instant, kept on, his face twisted and looking oddly surprised. He was on top of her as she turned and straightened. He grabbed for the gun, missed, and now there was no longer any indecision in his reaction. Still following up he made his one decisive gesture, his act man-like and instinctive as he hooked hard with his right hand.

The blow had a loud, unreal sound as fist met flesh. The gun fell from Julia's hand before she could find the trigger. She went over backwards, turning and crumpling as she dropped; she rolled over on the gun, and lay still.

Randall stopped a foot away from Gifford and the room was quiet. He stood on trembling knees as reaction hit him, watching the lawyer and not understanding the look of amazement that had begun to creep over the gray, shiny face. For now Gifford was looking down at the front of his coat, feeling of the lapel. There was nothing that Randall could see until the other slid his hand inside the coat. Only when the hand came out and he saw the blood on the shaking fingers did he realize what had happened to Julia's shot.

Yet even then Randall could not look away. Not until Gifford backed drunkenly to the table and reached out to brace himself, did he think to wonder about the voice he had heard. Then, as he glanced up, he saw Laughlin and another man moving down the steps and into the room.

They put their guns away as they advanced and Laughlin did not speak then but went directly to Julia. He told his companion to get the gun. He picked up the woman's limp form and carried it to the couch. Then he was ready for Randall.

"You had to do it your way, hunh?" he said curtly but not unkindly. "You had to get here first."

Randall began to breathe again. He did not want to argue with Laughlin or explain that he had to have it out with Julia first because of the guilt he felt about Harding's death. He knew now that his first hunch was right, that Laughlin had followed him, that there *had* been a taxi close behind him. He had, he realized, counted on Laughlin, as he had told Julia. It had been because of this that he had fixed the door on latch, should Laughlin want to come in without knocking. It had, he knew now, made no real difference, that fixing of the door, but it had seemed like a good idea at the time.

"What took you so long?" he said, resentment showing in his voice.

"It wasn't so long." Laughlin glanced at his companion. "Max tailed you and called me back. If you had behaved yourself after you got here, we'd have had plenty of time."

Randall sighed, no longer caring. "Well," he said, "at least I left the door unlocked for you."

The next two hours were busy ones for Knox Randall. They took him first to the precinct station, along with Julia, and here he again told his story, this time officially noted, to Laughlin, the precinct captain, an assistant district attorney from the Homicide Bureau, and assorted officials. Simultaneously another question-and-answer session was going on at the hospital where Eaton Gifford's condition was said to be serious but not critical.

For her part, Julia said exactly nothing. They talked

to her in Randall's presence; they took her into other rooms and talked to her again, collectively and separately, and brought her back. There was a lump on one side of her pretty face now, but hate and defiance still smoldered in her black eyes and in spite of all arguments, she remained mute.

They told her she would never go back to Florida or to North Carolina, that she would be tried and convicted for the murder of Joe Klimm, so why didn't she get it off her chest. They said the slug from her gun had passed through Gifford's chest and lodged under the skin of his back where it had been easily removed. They explained that a quick ballistic check indicated that this bullet and the two removed from Joe Klimm's body had come from the same gun.

Such evidence was convincing but not overwhelming, and Laughlin felt a lot better when he learned that Gifford had decided to talk. The lawyer was still a young man; he had no further illusions about Julia; he wisely agreed that a few years of being a model prisoner appealed to him more than any trial on first degree murder charges, and the things he had to say not only tightened the case against Julia but would presently help to get the release of Louis Fournier in Neuse City, since he had not yet come to trial. All in all it had been a successful evening for Laughlin and he said so when he parked the police car in front of Nora's apartment at eleven thirty and leaned back to light a cigarette.

He talked awhile but presently he decided that Randall wasn't paying much attention, and he said: "Still worrying about that dame?"

Randall roused himself, aware that part of his mind had been busy with some such thought. "Not worrying," he said. "It's just that—"

"Sure, I know. It's kind of a shock, hunh? I guess you never got around to figuring that there are dames like that in the world, just like there are the good ones. . . . Didn't you ever take any psychology courses in college? Then you ought to know more about human behavior— though I guess you get a better perspective on such things in my business. . . . Women," he said resignedly. "Did you ever read about Ruth Snyder and her lover-boy? You aren't old enough to remember the trial, neither am I."

"I read about it," Randall said.

"A sash-weight, she used. Is that any worse than a shotgun? You know what she told them in court when they asked her why she had killed her husband? It was very simple the way she put it; she said: 'Because I wanted to get rid of him.'"

He reached across and opened the car door. He said that they would need Randall for the trial, that he'd see him around. Then the car was rolling down the street and Randall wheeled and started up the steps, his thoughts turning to Nora.

When she answered his knock the door opened on a chain fastener. "Hello," she said. "Do I know you?"

"Captain Randall of the good ship *Julia*."

"Come in, Captain."

Her smile was quick as she opened the door but her gray eyes were anxious beneath her trim brows. She wore a trailing hostess gown, fresher-looking, trimmer somehow, than Lenore's; her blonde hair was burnished brightly by the room's lights. She looked young and poised and radiant; she looked wonderful.

He had telephoned her before he left with Laughlin and now he could smell coffee perking in the kitchen. The sandwiches were made, she said, but the coffee

wasn't quite ready so why didn't he have a drink first.
For another moment as she spoke her glance remained
anxious as it surveyed the tired lines in Randall's face
where the stamp of fatigue had left its mark. Then, apparently satisfied with what she saw, she turned and
went along the hall.

He followed slowly and when he tried to help her
with the ice she shook her head. "You go sit down," she
said, busying herself with the glass and the Scotch.
"Rest up for all that talking you're going to have to do."

Standing close behind her an impulse came to him
which he could not resist. He lifted her hair where it
curled over her shoulders and kissed lightly the back of
her neck. For a second she stood quite still; then she
laughed and went on with her work.

"You mustn't bother the cook," she said, and turning,
handed him the glass. She pushed him gently about and
shoved him towards the door.

He realized how tired he was when he slumped
down on the couch. The weariness pressed in on him
and he was emotionally battered. He knew he would
have to tell her lots of things but when he saw her coming with the tray he knew he wouldn't mind. It might
not be as much fun as the other nights, because this
time he would have to go back to his apartment. But
even that he didn't mind too much. This thing that they
had was right and good, and he knew now that he could
wait until the time came when they could work things
out together.

Women
in Search
of Truth

Women in Search of Truth

Converts to Catholicism Tell Their Stories

Jennifer Ferrara
Patricia Sodano Ireland

Our Sunday Visitor Publishing Division
Our Sunday Visitor, Inc.
Huntington, Indiana 46750

Our Sunday Visitor Publishing Division
Our Sunday Visitor, Inc.
200 Noll Plaza
Huntington, IN 46750

ISBN: 978-1-59276-523-2 (Inventory No. T799)
LCCN: 2003113173

Cover design by Monica Haneline.
Cover image, "The Annunciation of the Lord," by Anthony La Femina, © 2000, courtesy of Reverend Monsignor Anthony A. La Femina, S.T.L., J.C.D. Digital file courtesy of New Hope Publications. Interior design by Sherri L. Hoffman.

PRINTED IN THE UNITED STATES OF AMERICA

Dedication and Acknowledgments

We dedicate this book to our children, who have taught us more than anyone else about the inexhaustible joy of being women and mothers, and to our husbands, who have patiently endured the many ups and downs of our faith journeys. Without the love and encouragement of our families, this book would not have been possible.

We wish to thank Dr. Jeffrey Finch and Father Joseph Wilson for putting us in touch with many of the contributors to this book, and for their support and advice along the way. We also thank Michael Dubruiel, acquisitions editor at Our Sunday Visitor, for approaching us with the idea for the book and for placing his trust in us. We are especially grateful to our contributors, women who have given generously of themselves so that others might be drawn closer to Christ and His Church. This motivation lies behind every one of the stories in this book, and it is our fervent prayer that they might all bear fruit.

Table of Contents

Building on the Rock of Truth

When a violent torrential storm hits, only those whose houses have been built on rock can escape unharmed. In the 1960s, both the Church and the world were hit by such a storm. Everything seemed to be put in question; everything was challenged. The winds of change promised "liberation"—liberation from social and sexual taboos, from enslavement for minorities and women, from the shackles of a medieval past. Down with the crushing notion of authority. Down with the burdensome laws of marriage. Down with the Church's uninformed conception of man's sexual drives. Down with the exploitation of women and their shameful subordination to the male sex.

Aided by the pervasive, worldwide expansion of the news media, this was the age when relativism and subjectivism triumphed. The "right of conscience" was loudly proclaimed and acclaimed, but it was a conscience that was malleable and always in accord with one's personal wishes. Subjectivism, which had been taught in schools and universities, achieved a total victory. Freedom called for a "freedom of choice," and, so it was thought, mature human beings no longer needed directives, help, or guidance.

Everything was challenged. During this turbulent time, priests left the priesthood, nuns left their convents, and Catholics flirted with agnosticism or even atheism. Protestants of all denominations, many of whom had already endorsed artificial birth control in 1930,[1] now started endorsing the ordination of women, abortion, and homosexuality. Few were those who kept what G. K. Chesterton called "a steely sanity." Marriages broke up; motherhood was considered to be an unfair burden.

Many women sought "self-fulfillment" in professional work, entering the fields of politics, business, medicine, law, and ministry. The world had finally opened up for what Simone de Beauvoir[2] called the "second sex." Betty Friedan, in her widely publicized book *The Feminine Mystique,* had succeeded in making women realize how oppressed, victimized, and abused they had been by their husbands, as well as by the authoritarian paternalism of the church. Increasing numbers of women were led to believe they had been treated like servants, good enough only to give birth to babies, to cook, clean, and be at the beck and call of the "stronger" sex.

During this time, the promises of liberation and freedom were alluring indeed, but as the years continued, it became apparent that this "broad" way led to metaphysical seasickness. Not only did true freedom remain unfulfilled, but it was accompanied now by confusion and despair. For many women, it became evident that freedom had turned to license and that sexual liberation was actually slavery to sin. After years of dizziness, the same old questions reappeared on the screen of one's conscience: "What is true?" "Why don't I find self-fulfillment?"

Women in Search of Truth relates the fascinating stories of women who, in various ways, were affected by the great storm of

---

[1] The Anglican Church approved the use of birth control at its 1930 Lambeth Conference. Subsequently, most Protestant denominations also accepted birth control as a moral means of family planning.

[2] Simone de Beauvoir was a French existentialist writer and social essayist. In *The Second Sex*, she explores the history of women's oppression, stating that women are not born, but are "made," thus declaring women's emancipation from men.

the 1960s. Many of them sought self-fulfillment by becoming ministers or professional women; others postponed motherhood, and in one case, had an abortion. All of them—through suffering and disappointments—experienced a growing restlessness: The Hound of Heaven[3] was gently pursuing them and calling them to journey home. This book poignantly relates the struggles, sufferings, and, at times, the dilemmas these women had to face—the anguish of "betraying" their past, husbands, family members, or friends. In all of these stories, however, grace triumphed.

Women in Search of Truth is a book of HOPE. It shows that however confused one's background has been, however mixed up one has become, however lonesome one can feel, however much one can be threatened by despair, God does not abandon those who seek Him in truth. *Prope est Dominus omnibus invocantibus eum, invocantibus eum in veritate*—"The LORD is near to all who call upon him, / to all who call upon him in truth" (Psalm 145:18).

For some, the journey home was facilitated by the example of faithful Catholics whose faith, rooted in charity, reflected the power of God's grace. They practiced what my husband called "the apostolate of being"—neither preaching nor pontificating, but lovingly and peacefully living an authentic Catholic life, radiating the mystery of their inner life. Weak as human beings are, God often allows that their modest efforts to follow Him bestow a radiance and peace to which others are drawn.

The value of these moving testimonies lies in the fact that, however different each woman's background might be or how varied the obstacles to faith, one dominant note prevails: God's grace and that, as St. Augustine expressed so powerfully in his

---

[3] See Francis Thompson's poem, the *Hound of Heaven*, at the end of this book.

Confessions, all souls are made for Him and "are restless until they rest in Him."

ALICE VON HILDEBRAND
FEAST OF THE PRESENTATION

Dr. Alice von Hildebrand received a master's degree and doctorate in philosophy from Fordham University in New York. She taught at the Hunter College of the City University in New York; the Catechetical Institute in Dunwoodie, New York; the Catechetical Institute in Arlington, Virginia; the Thomas More College in Rome, Italy; Franciscan University in Steubenville, Ohio; and Ave Maria College in Ypsilanti, Michigan. She lectures in Canada, South America, Western Europe, and the United States; has been featured in several television series on EWTN (Eternal Word Television Network); and is the author of several books, including The Privilege of Being a Woman, The Soul of a Lion, A Philosophy of Religion, By Love Refined, By Grief Refined, *and* Greek Culture: The Adventure of the Human Spirit. *With her husband, Dietrich von Hildebrand, she co-authored several books including* The Art of Living, Situation Ethics, *and* Graven Images.

Introduction

When I was seriously contemplating becoming Catholic, I shared my thoughts with a neighbor who is a cradle Catholic, thinking she might understand. Instead, a look of complete shock came over her face followed by, "You don't want to do that!" "Why not?" I sputtered. "Because after being a Lutheran minister, you would be taking a giant step backward," she replied. She continued, "Since I was raised in the Catholic Church, I don't feel as if I can leave, but I would never choose it."

My neighbor was not the only one to express surprise at my decision to become Roman Catholic. When I told my former Lutheran bishop, his first question was, "How can you join a denomination which does not ordain women?" I can hardly blame him for his amazement. Catholics and non-Catholics alike take it as a truth, universally acknowledged, that the Catholic Church is no place for self-respecting, intelligent women. For many people, it is simply a given that the Church is patriarchal, oppressive, repressive, and suffocatingly chauvinistic. As a result, they are sympathetic to the feminists who could care less about the Church but, nonetheless, relentlessly agitate for a complete restructuring of the Church, the centerpiece of which is women's ordination.

Though the radical feminists often yell the loudest, they do not speak for everyone. As *Women in Search of Truth* clearly demonstrates, intelligent, articulate women are indeed attracted to the Church. Each story in this collection offers a unique account of the author's reasons for becoming Catholic. The contributors to this book come from and reflect a wide variety of religious, ethnic, socioeconomic, and professional backgrounds. What is most fascinating to me, therefore, are the common themes that run through all of the stories. The authors describe feelings of being irresistibly drawn to the Church, in some cases, seemingly against their very wills. The Catholic Church has such an appeal because she is not just one institution among others, but a living entity whose very nature is feminine and maternal. The Church calls to us as a mother to her children and does not rest until we are safely within her care. All of the women in this book experienced a sense of restlessness and profound feelings of unfulfillment, until they finally came to rest in the bosom of their true Mother, the Church.

The word "fulfillment" has been greatly misused and overused, so I hesitated to use it in the subtitle. Certainly, the fulfillment the women in this book experienced upon entering the Church was not of the variety described by feminists. In *The Feminine Mystique*, Betty Friedan argues that women's personal fulfillment is, first and foremost, to be found in "masculine" forms of achievement. By contrast, the women in our book did not find fulfillment through various forms of personal achievement (though many have had successful careers) but in a final letting go of self in order that God's will might be done. It is in this sense that we dare to talk of fulfillment—the fulfillment that comes from the emptying of ourselves that we might become instruments of God's will. This capacity for receptivity is the true feminine mystique and is the mystique of the Catholic Church, the Bride of Christ and Mother of us all. This love which seeks to serve is the true nature of the Church, a truth to which all of the women in this book felt drawn and to which they attest.

Patricia and I are profoundly grateful for their willingness to share their stories and pray that, through them, others will be drawn to the Church or, if they are already in the Church, might develop a better appreciation for their Mother, who loves and cares for them through this life and into the next. We also give thanks to the Blessed Mother, womb and archetype of the Church, for being the ultimate role model for us and a constant source of inspiration.

JENNIFER FERRARA
FEAST OF OUR LADY OF LOURDES

1

Real Churches Don't Kill Babies

Jennifer Ferrara

"Real churches don't kill babies." My trek to Rome began in the spring of 1996, the day I read this line by former Lutheran Pastor Leonard Klein.[4] This was his critique of the decision of the Church Council of the Evangelical Lutheran Church in America (ELCA) to reject its own health care provider's carefully worked out restrictions on payment for abortions. Instead, the Church Council decided to cover the cost of any and all abortions procured by ELCA employees and their dependents. As I read Klein's editorial on the topic, I began to hyperventilate; I knew my life as a Lutheran pastor was never going to be the same.

Prior to this point, I had never seriously considered becoming Roman Catholic. The thought did briefly cross my mind when Richard John Neuhaus made the transition in 1990. He was a Lutheran pastor and the *de facto* leader of the "evangelical catholic" cause with which I identified myself. Evangelical catholics view Lutheranism as a reform movement within and for the one Church of Christ. They believe Martin Luther never intended to create a permanently separated communion of

---

[4] Leonard Klein, along with his wife and daughters, entered into full communion with the Roman Catholic Church in 2003.

Christians; therefore, Lutherans have a responsibility to work toward reconciliation with Rome. If such an understanding of Lutheranism ever had a chance of becoming the predominant view among Lutherans, Neuhaus's departure seemed to dash all such hopes. He forced me and others to confront the fact that Lutheranism's separated ecclesial existence is accepted by most Lutherans, not reluctantly for the sake of the Gospel, but whole-heartedly as the preferred state of affairs. In other words, Lutheranism has become, perhaps always has been, just another Protestant denomination among Protestant denominations.

When Neuhaus made the move, I was hurt. I had been an admirer of his since my seminary days. My father had attended seminary with Neuhaus in the 1950s and had occasionally men-tioned him while I was growing up. When I was in seminary, I started to read Neuhaus's writings out of curiosity. At the time, he was editor of *Forum Letter*, a newsletter that is associated with the journal *Lutheran Forum*. When I began seminary, I was a garden-variety feminist liberal. Thanks, in large measure, to some college and graduate level classes I took in the University of Virginia Religious Studies Department, I was not particularly orthodox in my beliefs. As I read Neuhaus month after month, I gradually came to see the error of my ways, was brought back into the fold of orthodox Christianity, and came to define myself as an evangelical catholic. When Neuhaus decided to become Catholic, I, along with many other evangelical catholics, felt he had betrayed our cause. In the end, I chose to ignore the impli-cations of his move. The idea of following him to Rome was incomprehensible. He was an unmarried male and intended to become a priest; I was a married, ordained female pastor and wanted to remain one. Though I knew nothing of Neuhaus's thoughts about women's ordination, I could not understand his decision to join a church that still excluded women from the priesthood, and that lessened the significance of his move in my mind. In the fall of 1990, I began to take graduate level courses at the Lutheran Theological Seminary in Philadelphia. Once again, I was happy to be a fourth-generation Lutheran pastor steeped in the traditions, theology, and ethos of Lutheranism. I was not contemplating conversion at all.

A storm shakes my inmost calm

Leonard Klein's editorial, which appeared in *Lutheran Forum*, shattered the relative calm of my life. He called the decision of the Church Council of the ELCA to fund abortions schismatic: "The ELCA's inability to honor an ancient moral consensus of the Church and the widest witness of the most vibrant Christian communities to the present, along with the collapse of morality into subjectivity, would appear to make it something other than the One, Holy, Catholic and Apostolic Church confessed in the creeds."

I knew the phrase "culture of death," but I had never read Pope John Paul II's encyclical *Evangelium Vitae*. I did and was awestruck. I couldn't help but compare it to ELCA documents, such as the Division for Church in Society's 1993 social statement on human sexuality. It states: "As Lutherans, we offer guidelines but we also affirm our Christian freedom to make responsible decisions specific to our life situations." It proceeds to explain that not everyone's life situation falls into the categories of marriage or celibacy, the other situations being cohabitation and homosexual relationships. From their enlightened perch, the authors of the document judge both Scripture (especially St. Paul's writings) and Church Tradition to be hopelessly out of touch with modern views of human sexuality and marriage. According to them, "mutual commitment" and "not the license or ceremony" is what counts. By contrast, in *Evangelium Vitae*, I encountered the constancy of the Church's moral teachings on sexual morality and human life stated in the loving and compelling way that is a hallmark of John Paul II. Like a person coming to terms with the terminal illness of a loved one, I saw that the leadership of my church had fallen captive to the culture of death.

We live in strange and deeply disconcerting times, when many in our churches have ceased to recognize the most basic of Christian beliefs in God as Creator and Redeemer. When we reject human life at any stage in its development, we reject the triune God and begin to live as if He did not exist. Pope John Paul II explains: "It is precisely in the 'flesh' of every person that Christ continues to reveal Himself and to enter into fellowship with us, so that rejection of human life, in whatever form that rejection takes, is really a rejection of Christ." As John Cardinal O'Connor said, "The culture of death is a culture without God." I was serving a church whose leadership seemed incapable of understanding that its position on the abortion issue amounted to a rejection of God.

As a pastor, I had come face-to-face with the terrible reality of abortion. Several of my parishioners opted to have abortions. Though I told these women abortion is murder, I sounded as if I were offering an opinion. I failed to explain that abortion is "really a rejection of Christ." I failed to tell them such action would put their very souls at stake. I failed to be the voice of a Church and Tradition that regard abortion as the murder of God's most innocent creatures. However, I also recognized that to take a firm stand on abortion was extremely difficult in a church that offers no authoritative stance on a single matter having to do with sexual ethics or the sanctity of human life. My friend and fellow pastor Patricia Ireland admitted to having similar experiences with parishioners who had had abortions. Together, we confessed our failure in an open letter published by

Lutheran Forum. In the letter, we pleaded with the bishops of the ELCA to take up their proper role as defenders of doctrine and morals and condemn the decision of the ELCA Church Council to fund any and all abortions. We also said if they failed to take such action, we would have to decide if we could continue to serve the ELCA. Needless to say, the bishops took no action. None even bothered to respond to our letter.

At times, I wondered if I was insane. Why did this abortion issue bother me so much more than my colleagues? There are many orthodox, pro-life Christians in the ELCA, and I have respect for the battle some of them wage against the leadership of their own church. However, everyone with whom I spoke, including some renowned Lutheran theologians, thought the ELCA's position on abortion was not reason enough to leave the denomination. I found it increasingly difficult to understand their thinking. Though they respected the Roman Catholic Church's pro-life stance, it did not outweigh what they perceived to be basic doctrinal problems with Roman Catholicism. When I pressed them to explain those problems, they pointed to the Church's exclusion of women from the priesthood, the Marian doctrines, and the doctrine of papal infallibility. I did not find those answers convincing. Even if those were problems with the Church, how could they be compared to murder? That is what I believed and continue to believe: The ELCA, as an institution, is an accomplice in the murder of unborn children. At least my friend Patricia agreed with me. When I asked her if she thought the abortion issue was reason enough to leave the ELCA, her unwavering response was, "Of course it is." In the fall of 1996, she did just that and returned to the Church of her childhood.

What was I to do? Was the ELCA's decision to fund abortions sufficient reason to leave? Colleagues suggested I should stay and struggle against the forces of evil within the Lutheran

Church. I did not wish to judge their decisions, but I seriously doubted that I could do that. John Paul II says in *Evangelium Vitae*:

> Not only is the fact of the destruction of so many human lives still to be born or in their final stage extremely grave and disturbing, but no less grave and disturbing is the fact that conscience itself, darkened as it were by . . . widespread conditioning, is finding it increasingly difficult to distinguish between good and evil in what concerns the basic value of human life.

I worried about my own conscience. Would I begin to lose my ability to distinguish between good and evil if I stayed in a church that had lost such powers of discernment? Was I spiritually and emotionally strong enough to wage a lifelong battle against the leadership of my church? Would it be good for my soul to do so? Scripture says we must, at some point, separate ourselves from evildoers.[5] I was beginning to think I needed to do just that.

By this time, another friend whom I deeply respect, the patristics scholar Robert Wilken, had left the Lutheran ministry in order to become Roman Catholic. In a letter he wrote to me about his experiences as a new Catholic, he said the difficulty with the Reformation was that it conceived of the Church's continuity with the past and its unity in terms of an idea (justification by grace through faith). By contrast, Catholicism thinks first of the concrete life of the Church—the life of a community with tangible links stretching back over the centuries. This observation made a profound impression upon me. Leonard Klein had written of the ELCA's decision to fund abortions: "We need not

---

[5] See Psalms 26:5 and 119:115.

doubt that faithful congregations and synods are still church, but in a most critical sense the wider fellowship to which they belong no longer deserves the credence which one would expect to give to 'the Church.'" As I have said, I do not doubt there are orthodox people, congregations, and maybe even synods within the ELCA. However, in what sense are congregations and synods still Church if the wider fellowship to which they belong is not Church? According to the *Augsburg Confession*[6]: "It is sufficient for the true unity of the Christian church that the Gospel is preached in conformity with a pure understanding of it and that the sacraments be administered in accordance with the divine Word." I was finding this definition of church increasingly unsatisfactory. Surely, something else was required to ensure true unity and to provide tangible links to Christians across time and place. I had an image in my mind of Lutheran congregations floating around, untethered, in deep, dark space.

I was now questioning not only the actions of the ELCA but also the foundations of Lutheranism's separate existence as a church. Was it possible that Lutheranism was misconceived from its inception? Was the ELCA's funding of abortions a symptom of a more serious disease? A fellow pastor convert, Jeffrey Finch, puts it this way: "The reformation had introduced two cancerous doctrines (*sola fide* and *sola scriptura*), which eventually metastasized and destroyed the very foundation of the faith as a whole, especially its accession to private judgment over the teaching authority of the Church." Shared societal standards had masked the problem for five hundred years, but those original critics of Luther's theology who had warned of its tendencies toward antinomianism (lawlessness) had turned out to be right. I was becoming increasingly convinced Christians cannot do

---

[6] Written by Philip Melanchthon, a follower of Martin Luther, the *Augsburg Confession* is considered the most important of the Lutheran Confessions.

without a Magisterium that interprets Scripture in light of the great Tradition of the Church.

Several Lutherans recommended the conservative Lutheran Church Missouri Synod (the Protestant denomination of my youth) as an alternative. The LCMS is ardently pro-life, and for that, I give it credit; however, the LCMS is also a perfect example of why Scripture alone cannot act as a final authority. When I was growing up, my father taught at Concordia Seminary in St. Louis. In 1974, the majority of faculty members and students walked out to protest the firings of several of the seminary's professors. In dispute was the nature of the authority of Scripture. The leadership of the Missouri Synod responded by firing all the professors who had walked out. My father was among those who had to leave; my family was given three weeks to move out of our faculty housing. The faculty and students formed a new seminary called Seminex (Seminary-in-Exile). Many congregations and pastors left the Missouri Synod to form a new church body, the Association of Evangelical Lutheran Churches. I was in ninth grade at the time and had preoccupations besides the theological split within the Lutheran Church Missouri Synod; however, the experience scarred my father emotionally and left a deep impression upon me. As I thought about becoming Roman Catholic, I reflected upon the implications of the split. History demonstrates that an insistence upon Scripture alone, no matter how much authority we grant it, inevitably leads to schism. If the teachings of Scripture are as self-evident as Luther argued, why do we have so many different Protestant groups all claiming their interpretation of Scripture is the right one? I could not believe the purest form of the Church was to be found in a remnant of a remnant of a remnant . . .

As I mulled over these questions, I continued to read— papal encyclicals, Vatican II documents, the *Catechism of the*

Catholic Church, theologians such as John Henry Newman, Louis Bouyer, Hans Urs von Balthasar, and Joseph Cardinal Ratzinger. I was struck again and again by the contrast between official Catholic Church documents and the statements emanating from the offices of the ELCA leadership. I wondered what would happen if we had to rely upon the leadership of the ELCA to preserve Christianity for future generations. The leaders of the ELCA had demonstrated a singular lack of courage in dealing with the defining issues of our time. Friends suggested I was seeking a parental-type authority in order to alleviate my own anxieties about the moral disintegration of Western culture. I could not completely discount this notion, though I wasn't exactly sure what was wrong with it. Perhaps my anxieties were pointing me toward the truth. The leadership of the Magisterium in these times of cultural turmoil suggested it was exactly what it claimed to be.

Protestants and the papacy

I was becoming increasingly unlike most Protestants who consider personal or ecclesial reconciliation with Rome an impossibility as long as the authority of the Magisterium, and especially of the Pope, remains intact. Even those who are not theologically trained believe papal tyranny made necessary the Reformation and think the papacy, as an institution, can never be trusted. When former Lutheran colleagues say Rome has problems, too, they usually have in mind past and current perceived papal abuses. Better to live free, even if that freedom involves the risk of antinomianism. According to Lutheran theology, freedom from the law is at the heart of the Gospel, which is the promise of justification by grace through faith (apart from works of the law). In other words, Lutherans are allergic to anything that could possibly be construed as a law one must follow in order to be saved. They believe popes throughout history have been responsible for promulgating many such laws and that the institution of the papacy itself stands between and impedes the relationship between the believer and God. So goes the Lutheran way of thinking. These are extremely hard notions to dispel. Lutherans do not take kindly to being told there are things other than the Gospel message they are required to believe.

By contrast, for Catholics, servitude to the moral and ecclesial law leads to freedom, that is, freedom from sin—ergo, freedom to be fully human. We do not need to be free from the law in order to truly love and serve others, as Luther claimed. Through the sacraments of the Church, God grants us the grace to fulfill the law. By entering into communion with Christ's body, the Church, we embark on a pilgrimage of holiness. Though we shall always fall short of perfect fulfillment of the law, we are able with God's help to make progress. Our hearts expand more and more to the grace of God, and we become more loving, more like Christ, which is the goal of our earthly existence.[7] The moral and ecclesial laws are the guideposts for this journey toward holiness. The Magisterium, with the Pope at its head, provides us with the means of grace and the moral guidance to grow in love for God and others. Father Neuhaus has written:

> For the ecclesial Christian, Christ the head and his body the Church are inseparable; faith in Christ and faith in the Church is one act of faith; the imperative of fidelity is to be in closest communion with the Church most fully and rightly ordered through time.

By the fall of 1996, I had come to believe the Magisterium of the Roman Catholic Church best orders the Church catholic

---

[7] See 1 John 3:2.

(universal) through time. Once I had accepted the authority of the Magisterium, I passed through a door into a land from which there was no turning back.

A blessing in disguise

However, I was not ready to take my insights to their logical conclusion of joining the Catholic Church. At the time, my personal life and professional life were in a state of limbo. I was not serving a parish because I had three small children and had decided to take a leave from parish work to care for them. I had left somewhat reluctantly, but the time off turned out to be a blessing because I could not have carried on with the kind of doubts I was experiencing. I was finding it increasingly difficult to attend Lutheran worship but could not yet bring myself to attend Mass. Though I had given my mind over to the Church, I had not as yet given my heart to her. It was perhaps the most spiritually arid time of my adult life. I was afraid to pray about my struggles because I did not want to receive an answer. When surveying the simple facts, the decision should have been a fairly easy one. In fact, some former colleagues have suggested, with a certain amount of bitterness, that my conversion was, as one colleague put it, a "cake walk." They say that because I can afford not to work and because I am married to a Roman Catholic.

They are mostly right. I am indeed fortunate to be married to a lifelong Catholic. When I look over the course of my life, it now appears I have been on a path toward Rome the whole time. However, when I married a Catholic, I did not secretly yearn to be Roman Catholic. Steve, my husband, comes from a devout Italian Roman Catholic family who strenuously objected to their oldest son marrying a Lutheran minister. Steve's parents were extremely worried he would leave the Church. His mother became emotionally distraught whenever she thought about it. At the time, I thought they were hope-lessly intolerant, but now that I have children of my own, I understand. By contrast, my family had no objections to the marriage. I am half German, half Italian. My mother grew up in the Catholic Church. She joined the Lutheran Church in order to marry my father. My father never spoke disparagingly or even disrespectfully of the Catholic Church. Perhaps because he taught religion and literature courses and focused on Catholic authors, he held Catholicism in high esteem. He did his Ph.D. dissertation on the Catholic writer Flannery O'Con-nor and encouraged me to read her. I, therefore, had a vague awareness, even as a child and later as a young adult, that the Catholic Church, though foreign, was somehow special.

However, I had chosen to become a Lutheran minister, so my relationship with my in-laws was a battle with winners and losers, and I had apparently won. Though Steve remained a Catholic in name, in reality my ministry took him away from the Catholic Church. While I was in the parish, he attended my serv-ices and was active within the congregation. After we had chil-dren, I baptized them, and we always went to a Lutheran church. On a very personal level, I did not want to relinquish that for which I had fought so hard, namely my identity as a Lutheran minister.

Steve, who knew all this about me, did not try to persuade me either way. He understood that if I made a precipitous deci-sion, I might regret it down the line. However, he did begin to talk about the need to be united in our faith for the sake of the children. Though he was trying to be helpful, this added to the pressure I already felt to make a decision. Our twin sons were approaching first communion age. They were fond of their Lutheran church and Sunday school but had no real attachment to Lutheranism. It would have been a good time to make the transition. Yet, I could not bring myself to do it. We continued to worship at our Lutheran parish, and I became more and more disconnected from what was taking place on Sunday morning.

Shadow worship?

Louis Bouyer, in *Spirit and Forms of Protestantism*, suggests Lutheran worship is a shadow or imitation of Roman Catholic worship—beautiful perhaps but without substance. This metaphor colored my perceptions as I went through the motions of attending Lutheran services, and especially as I received communion. As a Lutheran, I believed in the bodily presence of Christ in the eucharistic elements; however, I also believed they remain bread and wine. Growing up, I was taught Christ is in, with, and under the elements. As a child, I did not know what that meant, and I still don't as an adult. (By contrast, my own children understand they are receiving Jesus when they receive the Eucharist and that the Host is really Christ's Body and Blood.)

In seminary, I learned Lutherans do not agree on whether Christ remains present in the elements after the congregation finishes receiving communion. Luther seemed to believe in a spatial, irreversible change; whereas, Philip Melanchthon[8] suggested Christ's presence is a temporal, that is, temporary event. Or so I was taught. In any case, the vast majority of Lutherans do not reserve the host, suggesting whatever takes place ceases to be after the communion is over. As a pastor, I did not reserve the host or finish the wine and was not bothered in the least. Now I found myself deeply troubled by what I was observing. Many Lutherans today are fond of using baked bread for communion. What this means is crumbs of all sizes invariably end up on the

---

[8] See footnote 2.

floor. These crumbs became the focus of my communion experience. I knew the sexton would simply vacuum them up later in the day. I thought, if Lutherans treat the elements with such obvious irreverence, they cannot possibly believe they signify much of anything. If they believed the bread was Christ's Body, they would not send it out with the trash. I began to doubt that anything was occurring during Lutheran communion services beyond a remembrance of Christ's death and resurrection.

As a Lutheran, I often pointed out the similarities in the Lutheran and Catholic understandings of the Eucharist. I even felt free to receive Holy Communion at Catholic Mass because I believed in the Real Presence of Christ. I now saw our agreement was illusory. The words we use to describe the Eucharist are similar, but the theological connotations are entirely different. According to Lutheran theology, the Holy Spirit, operating through the spoken words of institution, brings about whatever change takes place in the elements. In the end, it does not matter who speaks the words. Some Lutherans argue only ordained pastors should speak the words of institution for the sake of good order, if nothing else. However, I am personally familiar with circumstances in which bishops have given laypeople permission to preside at communion services. The very fact there is disagreement over this issue demonstrates how ambiguous is the Lutheran theology of the Eucharist. For Roman Catholics, the identity of the speaker of the words of institution is the key to the sacrament's efficacy. The priest represents Christ at the sacrifice of the Eucharist, and only a man who has received the Sacrament of Holy Orders[9] may preside. He is the conduit through which the Holy Spirit operates.

---

[9] This *sacrament*, whereby a man is ordained to the priesthood, leaves an indelible mark on his soul. He is a priest forever.

Questioning the validity of my ordination

As my contemplation of the Eucharist deepened, I began to question the validity of my own ordination. What do I mean by that? I know this is a highly charged subject for many mainline Protestants and Catholics, so I want to be clear. I do not mean I did no good as a Lutheran pastor. I do not mean I did not serve a valid function within the Lutheran Church. In fact, that is exactly what I did: I served a function. I preached, and I taught. I conducted marriages and funerals, and I visited the sick. I made a difference in some people's lives. I found it all profoundly rewarding; however, I had not received the special charism which would allow the Holy Spirit to work through me to change bread and wine into the Body and Blood of Christ. What is more, I could not have, not only because I had not received the Sacrament of Holy Orders but because I, as a woman, could not represent Jesus Christ at the Eucharist. Therefore, I could not say my service in the Lutheran Church was some sort of imperfect version of the priesthood.

The women's ordination issue is a wrinkle many converts do not have to deal with directly. I had to because the first question almost everyone asked when I expressed an interest in converting was, "How can you become a member of a church body which does not ordain women?" Catholics asked it with the same frequency as Lutherans. Catholics who believe women should be ordained view me as a traitor to the cause. Better to stay in the Lutheran Church and operate as a role model who might just help persuade the hierarchy to relent on two millennia of Tradition. In the opinion of these Catholics, I was taking a giant step backward. When my friend Patricia Ireland and I first started talking about converting, I immediately said I did not want to become "a poster child" for those who oppose women's ordination. That I could completely change my mind on the subject had not yet occurred to me. I knew some people who had converted to

Catholicism and took their belief in women's ordination with them into the Church. I also knew I could never do that; I did not want to be a dissenting Roman Catholic.

I must confess I was never entirely comfortable in my role as a female pastor. Even more telling, I never felt completely at ease at services conducted by female pastors. Somehow, I figured it was different when I did them. In my experience, most ordained female pastors are theological liberals, and I reasoned that was the source of my discomfort; however, I also knew some highly competent, orthodox female ministers. I was associated with a loosely organized group of female clergy who believed the Lutheran Church had never adequately addressed the issue of women's ordination from a scriptural or confessional standpoint. I felt so strongly about this that I made an effort to present scriptural and confessional arguments for women's ordination in an article published by *Lutheran Forum* in 1993. For several years, I accepted my own reasoning on the subject. In a nutshell, I believed women in the past were not ordained for cultural and social reasons and that this was, in fact, proper. Men's dominion over women was accepted as a matter of natural law. To ordain women and put them in a position of authority over men would have given scandal to the Gospel. Now that women's equality with men was accepted as a matter of law throughout much of the world, it was scandalous not to ordain women and constituted a modern-day impediment to people's conversion and continued belief in Christianity. That women could serve as competently as men in the role of pastor was beyond dispute, I thought. It was time to allow them to do so.

I begin thinking with the Church
As I seriously contemplated becoming Roman Catholic, I began, on the advice of Robert Wilken "to try to think with the

Church." Out of deference and obedience to the Magisterium, I finally concluded the Church knows better than I on this issue. I do not intend to trivialize the issue when I say this or imply there is no room for the workings of individual conscience in the Catholic Church. However, for Catholics, to have faith is to be obedient to the faith, that is, to a body of teachings and doctrines that define one's faith. I cannot pick and choose areas where I recognize the authority of the Church—to be able to do so would make the Roman Catholic Church no different from mainline Protestant communities which elevate individual conscience over even commonsense understandings of God's law. In other words, I cannot decide I like the Church's position on abortion but reject it in the case of women's ordination.

Over time, I have come to see the all-male priesthood as essential to the faith of the Church, not only to her eucharistic theology, but to the Catholic understanding of creation and the inherent differences between men and women and their respective roles in life. In other words, what is at stake in ordaining women is not the Gospel, as I had previously believed, but a truly Christian scriptural and doctrinal anthropology. I certainly continue to believe women and men are of equal dignity and worth and that women can do many of the jobs traditionally filled by men. However, I also believe God-ordained differences between men and women make the ordination of women as Catholic priests an impossibility. At the heart of the diversity between men and women lie the differences between motherhood and fatherhood. To state what has ceased to be obvious in a society governed in large measure by the principle of androgyny, women cannot be fathers. This means they cannot be priests because priests are not simply father figures—they are our spiritual fathers. Consecrated women are our spiritual mothers. We do not elevate the status of women by convincing them that what they need to be is men.

Those who insist otherwise reject all that is noble and holy about being wives and mothers (biological and spiritual) and, thereby, deny the importance of the feminine (Mother Church) in the whole economy of salvation. Christ, the embodiment of the Father's love, pours Himself out into the bridal Church. The male priest is an icon of Christ and acts "in persona Christi" at the altar and in the confessional. The woman Mary, representing all women, is an icon of the Church. These symbols, which tell us much about what it means to be male and female, are not interchangeable. Female priests would destroy not only this symbolism but the entire Catholic understanding of how God works through His creation to bring about our salvation.

I did not fully see this by the summer of 1997, but the women's ordination issue no longer posed a barrier to my conversion. I had arrived at the doorstep of *Lumen Gentium* (no. 14): "Whosoever, therefore, knowing that the Catholic Church was made necessary by God through Jesus Christ, would refuse to enter or to remain in her could not be saved." Even if I was willing to take a chance with my own soul, I had my children to consider, and that concentrates the mind. After years of relative silence on the issue, my husband was now openly stating his preference to return to the Church. My intense search for the truth served to confirm in his own mind that he needed to go home to Rome. That was now weighing heavily on my conscience as well. I had led a Roman Catholic away from the Church and possibly into apostasy. He would never have strayed if it were not for me. I was having all of these thoughts because I was really no longer an outsider but had entered the embrace of the Church.

Dealing with Mary

I found my thoughts turning increasingly toward Mary, the Mother of God. No convert can avoid the issue of Mary. After the Pope, she represents in most Protestants' minds the great divide between them and Catholics. In the parish, when I would tell my parishioners my husband was Catholic, the most common response was: "They believe in Mary, don't they?" The role of Mary is a stumbling block for the most sophisticated Protestant theologians, as well. Protestants believe Roman Catholics allow Mary to usurp the role of Christ as sole mediator between God and us. Moreover, they think the importance Catholics ascribe to Mary is simply unscriptural. One of the great contributions of Luther to the Church, they argue, was to take Mary down a notch or two and present a "biblical" view of her.

When I was Lutheran, I was drawn to Mary, but I never allowed myself to act on my feelings, with one exception. Once, I prayed directly to her and asked for her intercession during a particularly difficult time in my life. My prayer was answered. I never told anyone about this experience but kept the secret deep within my heart. Another strange episode in my life involved the stained-glass windows of the first church to which I was called as a pastor. The church building, which dates from the early 1800s, has beautiful windows. I decided to put together a brochure with pictures of the windows and explanations of the symbols found on them. The only problem was I did not understand the window with the thing that looked like an "M" with Easter lilies protruding from it. I showed a picture of it to several colleagues, and one finally identified it as the symbol for Mary with the Easter lilies representing her virginity and Christ's resurrection. How could this be? My colleague and I concluded the maker of the windows must have been Catholic. I have found no other Lutheran church with such a symbol in my area. I now believe Mary was pursuing me even then. To be able to openly believe in her intercession has come as a great relief. The claims the Church makes about her conception and assumption seem natural outgrowths of her role as *Theotokos* ("God-bearer").

As a Lutheran, I took it for granted that Luther had corrected hundreds of years of misunderstanding about the proper role of Mary and the saints. In yet another epiphany, I have come to see it as one of the great tragedies of the Reformation. The longer I am Catholic, the sadder I become for my Protestant friends who seem to harbor a bitterness toward the saints, especially Mary. They, of course, believe that devotion to Mary detracts from one's faith in Christ. Nothing could be farther from the truth. She alone bore God in her womb; she alone formed Christ's Body from her own; she alone bore the grief of a mother at the foot of the cross. How can one spend too much time contemplating her? In my experience, true contemplation of her sacrifice, her service, her suffering, inevitably leads to a deeper faith in her Son for whom she lived.

The famous convert G. K. Chesterton once said the Church is ever so much larger from the inside than from the outside. One of the effects of the Reformation was to shrink the Church. In the Catholic Church, I have discovered a fascinating and wonderful world populated by many different characters and encompassing a seemingly endless variety of traditions, all held together by the invisible threads of a shared ecclesial communion spun like a web out of Rome. A friend of mine, Father Joseph Wilson, compares the Catholic Church to a vast Gothic cathedral, with many side chapels and intimate ways to experience God, but all opening onto the one altar. As a Catholic, I never cease to be amazed by the astonishing diversity of private devotions: devotions surrounding saints, religious orders and movements with distinctive patterns of discipleship, and rich schools of spirituality with writings inexhaustible in their depth. As Father Wilson says, "Real love finds a multitude of ways in which to express itself." Lutheranism is one-dimensional, by comparison, and despite the fact some Lutherans now ordain women, starkly masculine. One result of the loss of the saints is a lack of women for Protestants to turn to for guidance. To be able to pray to women and reflect upon their lives has added a new and unexpected dimension to my spiritual life. Much to my surprise, I have felt a greater sense of affirmation as a woman in the Catholic Church than I ever had, even as a pastor, in the Lutheran Church.

Leaving the ELCA

By the fall of 1998, I had entered a spiritual no-man's-land. I was still a rostered pastor, but I was no longer Lutheran in mind or spirit. I had begun to attend Mass with my family. I had hoped this would lead to a sort of spiritual awakening, because I had felt dead inside for so long. It only made things worse. I found it much easier to be an intellectual Catholic than a practicing one. The longing which I felt to receive Holy Communion while studying Roman Catholicism disappeared when I began to attend Mass. Instead, I was an observer and a reluctant one at that. I was angry, and I took it out on Steve, using phrases such as "you Catholics…" and "your church…." Catholic worship simply did not meet with my expectations. I was disappointed by the seeming lack of reverence for tradition, and I could not help but wonder if those leading and participating in worship really believed what they said they believed. I had actually hoped to participate in the ancient traditions and mysteries of the Church. Instead, I experienced modern music and liturgies that tend to secularize and trivialize the sacred order. The result is a mind-numbing uniformity in worship that is simply astonishing, given the vastness of the Church's treasure of liturgical music and practices. At the same time, I missed the traditional Lutheran liturgy and music. I missed the sense of community that is a characteristic of most Protestant parishes. I missed hearing good preaching. Since I did not receive the Eucharist, the truth is I often felt I got nothing out of Mass. Though I knew the purpose of Mass was not for me "to get something out of it," I still felt let down.

Around this time, I received notice from my Lutheran bishop that I needed to come speak to him about my future plans. I knew this was coming, but now I had to face it squarely. If I told him about my plans to convert, there was no turning back. Yet, I knew I must do just that—anything else would be dishonest. So, much to his great shock, I informed him of my intention to become Catholic. I took the opportunity to confront him on the abortion issue and the attempt by some in the ELCA leadership, including the former presiding bishop,[10] to advance the cause of homosexuals who wished to marry and be ordained. By this time, the ELCA had entered into altar and pulpit fellowship with the United Church of Christ, a denomination which ordains practicing homosexuals. I told my former bishop that I thought he should take a stand on these issues. He, in turn, was very "pastoral." He told me he would miss me but took joy in the fact that I had found a new church home where I would feel more comfortable. Whatever his true feelings may have been, he seemed unmoved by my assertions. He told me I had a right to my opinions, but the abortion issue, in particular, was not an issue about which the laity cared, as if that were the point. At least I left knowing I had made the right decision.

I just couldn't figure out why I didn't feel any better. Though I had announced to my bishop that I was becoming Roman Catholic, I took no real steps to do so. I did not look into RCIA

---

[10] In the Evangelical Lutheran Church in America, the presiding bishop oversees the entire church body, which is separated into synods, each with its own local bishop.

classes; I did not speak to any priests. I was in conversation with some former Protestant pastors who had converted. They all seemed to know I needed time to work this out on my own. My conscience had driven me to this point, but my heart still lagged behind. C. S. Lewis once wrote of his conversion to Christianity: "The hardness of God is kinder than the softness of men, and His compulsion is our liberation." I hung onto these words because at the time I was experiencing the hardness of God.

I find Christ in the Eucharist

After several months of existing in this limbo, Patricia Ireland insisted I go on a retreat with her for pro-life professional women at the Sisters of Life Convent in New York. As a pastor, I had been on more retreats than I could count and was not a big fan of them. I often found them to be hokey and a little more touchy-feely than I care to be. I told her I was not interested; she continued to push. So I found myself on a wintry weekend in March traveling to New York, proclaiming most of the way I was sure I would hate this.

Several things happened to me that weekend. I heard a theology of sanctification based upon the writings of St. Teresa of Ávila that helped explain the spiritual desert in which I found myself. Saints often experience feelings of abandonment by God. They have given these times names such as dark night of the soul, night of the spirit, or night of the senses. I certainly do not mean to compare my life to that of the saints, but learning about their experiences of spiritual dryness helped me to better understand what I had been through. The spiritually arid times in our lives are often steps toward a deeper union with God. At the Sisters of Life Convent, I was given a taste of a spirituality about which I had previously known nothing. As a Lutheran, I felt I understood the essence of the Christian life as set out in the law/Gospel dialect of Luther's theology. I had always thought of myself as being *simul iustus et peccator* ("at the same time both saint and sinner"). The idea that one can make actual progress toward becoming a better person (more Christ-like) is looked upon with great suspicion by many Lutherans. The view of the Christian life as a pilgrimage in holiness was a revolutionary one to me.

What's more, no one had ever told me about the lives of the saints, the writings of the spiritual giants, the incorruptibles, the truth about those who had received the stigmata, the apparitions of Mary—I could go on and on. The point is, as a Lutheran, I knew nothing about these great gifts and, therefore, could not draw on them for strength in my own spiritual life. Lutherans tend to emphasize faith as trust in that which is unseen. There is something to be said for that understanding, but not when it blinds us to the direct evidence for the faith which exists everywhere around us. Catholics live in a world infused with the supernatural, a universe where there are good and evil powers which can directly affect our lives.

For Catholics, the supernatural breaks into the natural every time the Mass is said. At the Sisters of Life Convent, I participated, for the first time, in an adoration of the Eucharist and genuinely longed to receive the true Body and Blood of Christ with my heart, as well as my mind. When I was Lutheran, I did not have a deeply personal relationship with Christ, which was a problem because the most faithful Protestants I knew had that one-on-one relationship with our Lord and Savior. I was drawn to Catholicism, in part, because I thought it would offer in the sacraments and sacramentals more props for my faith. On the retreat, I realized I was completely mistaken about this. Those "props" are not some sort of substitute for my relationship with Christ and are not, as many Protestants maintain, barriers to a close relationship but are, rather, the means by which one is brought into an intimate relationship with him. There can be nothing more intimate than to receive into one's own body, Christ's Body and Blood. Catholics believe Jesus not only laid down His life for us once and for all on the cross but makes present that Sacrifice at every Holy Mass. Every time we receive the Sacrament of the Holy Eucharist, we offer our own lives of sacrificial love in union with His Sacrifice. The longer I am Catholic, the closer I draw to Jesus.

I also experienced the mystery, splendor, and otherworldliness of the Church in worship and in prayer at the convent. The sisters are a group of women unlike any I had ever met before. Though I had met individuals in my life whom I regarded as holy, I had never been in an environment such as this one. Holy people and places are not central to the Lutheran experience. While at the convent, I had an opportunity to step out of the madness of our world for a few precious days. Though the dwelling and chapel of the convent are as plain and unimpressive as can be, it is a holy place where those who enter its confines experience the love of Christ through the ministrations of the sisters.

After my experience at the Sisters of Life Convent, I moved rapidly toward becoming Roman Catholic. I finally spoke with a local priest and told him of my difficulties in finding a parish where I could comfortably worship. After being initially surprised by my desire to convert, he recommended an inner city Italian parish named Holy Rosary. I immediately went to find it. I walked into an unabashedly traditional sanctuary filled with statues and paintings of Jesus, Mary, and Joseph. It was aglow with flickering votive candles positioned under statues of Mary holding pink Rosary beads and of Joseph holding a plump baby Jesus. It was Lent, and the organist was practicing the hymn "O Sacred Head, Surrounded." The following Sunday, I attended my first Mass at Holy Rosary. There, I discovered a seemingly end-less variety of Catholic devotions. At Holy Rosary, I felt as if I had entered a world with endless layers of meaning, with the mystery of Christ in the Eucharist at its center.

On Corpus Christi Sunday of 1998, I was received into full communion with the Catholic Church by Father C. John McClosky in a small chapel of the Aquinas Institute at Princeton University. This seemed fitting, given the fact that I had begun my studies for the Lutheran ministry in Princeton. Since then, I have never once looked back. Whatever suffering I may have endured in the transition, I now count as joy, and I look forward to the time when by God's grace, I may be perfect and lacking in nothing.[11]

Jennifer Ferrara grew up on the campus of a Lutheran seminary where her father taught homiletics and literature courses. After attending Princeton Theological Seminary and the Lutheran Theo-logical Seminary in Philadelphia, she was ordained to the Ministry of Word and Sacrament in the Lutheran Church in America. She was a pastor for eleven years before converting to Catholicism in June 1998. She resides in Pennsylvania with her husband, Steve; twin sons, Anthony and Joseph; and daughter, Katherine. She is a full-time mother and part-time writer and speaker.

---

[11] See James 1:2-4.

2

From Promise to Fulfillment

Rosalind Moss

Christmas 1978

"Ros, I'm going to midnight Mass; you're welcome to come."

I'm welcome to come? To a Catholic church? For Mass? Oy! What's a Jewish Evangelical to do?

There was only one thing I could do: I would accompany my brother. But I would be risking the effects of venturing into the heart of "Satan's system." Still, it would be a risk worth taking if, through it, I could persuade David of the error and the danger of that Church and rescue him from the unthinkable fate of becoming Catholic.

Off we went. It was a cold but beautiful and still Christmas Eve in upstate New York. Snowflakes dropped like lace petals. As we approached the small church, I had to fight the sense of beauty and warmth that shone from the stained-glass windows. I wasn't about to let myself be taken in by what I knew was false. It would be just like Satan to make error enticing.

As we climbed the front steps and entered the church, I think I held my breath. People coming in around us dipped their fingers in a small basin of water and crossed themselves.

Paganism, I thought. What has *that* to do with knowing Christ as your personal Lord and Savior? Most of the people genuflected before entering a pew. Another pagan ritual, I supposed. How could my brother be drawn to this? What was his problem? What was missing from his Evangelical faith? How could he have found the truth of Christianity, that Jesus Christ is indeed the Jewish Messiah, God come to earth, and still be looking farther—looking into the Catholic Church of all places?

I loved being Jewish
My thoughts went back to our childhood, to our Jewish home in Brooklyn. I was the middle child of three. My brother David was two years older, and my sister Susan was not quite three years younger. From my earliest years, I can recall being filled with a sense of grace (though I wouldn't have known that word for it). We had been taught there were basically two kinds of people in the world: Jews and non-Jews. And since the Jews were God's chosen people, I felt it a great gift to have been born of Jewish seed. I never thought of it as a matter of pride; I had nothing to do with my birth. In fact, I remember, in my child's mind, asking myself: If we had the *true* God, whom did the rest of the world have? Those who were not of the Hebrew race had no choice in their birth either, so surely they could not be blamed for not knowing the God of Abraham. Such a mystery I was content to leave with God, who knew what I did not.

I loved our traditions, like the smell of challah baking in the oven and the celebration of Chanukah to commemorate the victory of Judah Maccabee against Antiochus Epiphanes, King of Syria, and the miracle of the oil that burned for eight days in the temple. I enjoyed the festivities of Purim, which remember Esther's victory over the evil Haman in his attempt to destroy the Jewish people, and Sukkot, which is a taste of what it might have been like to live in booths in the wilderness during God's protection of the Israelites through their forty years of wandering. There was also Shavuot, which is the rejoicing over the giving of the Law at Mt. Sinai, and Rosh Hashanah, the Jewish New Year, with the blowing of a ram's horn. I recall one Rosh Hashanah when the entire neighborhood joined in the celebration—whether they wished to or not—as David blew the ram's horn outside our apartment building in Brooklyn. Ten days later came Yom Kippur, the Day of Atonement, the holiest day of all, which we spent fasting and praying in *schul* (Yiddish for "synagogue"), asking God to forgive our sins.

As the world celebrated Easter, my family sat down to the Passover table, which begins the feast year in the religious calendar. We were not orthodox Jews, so our observance was only a partial rendering of what might have been. Yet, we would make sure that every bit of leaven was out of the house for the eight days of Passover.

We loved Pesach (Passover). We loved the food we got to eat at that time each year: matzo made with chicken fat, matzo brei, special noodle kugel, gefilte fish, and horseradish on everything. And we loved the Seder (Passover Service). If our extended family gathered at only one time during the year, it was at Passover. Days of preparation climaxed around a long table filled with elements that told the story of our people's deliverance from slavery in Egypt: matzo, parsley, salt water, bitter herbs, charoset, a roasted lamb shank. My Uncle Murray would lead us through the Passover Haggadah, recounting the journey, in word and song, partaking of the symbolic foods along the way, singing the Hallel (Psalms 113-118), and drinking of the four cups of wine.

Two of the rituals became embedded in my memory. One was the first of four questions which began the Seder: "Why is this night different from all others?" As we sang of Moses leading the Israelites to freedom through the sea, I knew that we, thousands of years later, were a part of that story and that our freedom as a people came from that deliverance. This night, indeed, was different from all others. It served as a reminder and, in a sense, a participation in that drama of deliverance, and it gave us the opportunity to thank God, who did not and would not abandon His people.

The second ritual I would recall long after our family traditions had ceased, was the Seder's end. Regardless of what had transpired during the evening—or during the year, for that matter—we would leave the Passover table singing: "Next year in Jerusalem." One year, maybe next year, the Messiah would come. When he[12] did, we would gather together in Jerusalem from the four corners of the earth to be with him in his kingdom, the kingdom he would establish on earth. There would be peace, and all things would be made new.

I remember the year it was my turn to see if the Messiah had come and if (perhaps!) he were waiting outside our house at the door left ajar for him at every Passover. My legs were shaking as I set off, and I was filled with disappointment and relief (I'm not sure in what proportion) to find the hallway empty of the long-awaited guest.

"Next year in Jerusalem," we'd sing as we left the table. Next year, when he comes.

Something is missing
"Thou hast made us for thyself, O Lord. . . ."

If only I had known those blessed words of St. Augustine through the years of emptiness that followed. What was missing

---

[12] Pronouns referring to Jewish religion's understandings of the "Messiah" are not capitalized, to distinguish from the Second Person of the Trinity, Jesus Christ.

Rosalind Moss

from my Jewish upbringing? Many things, perhaps, but nothing that could answer the silent questions I lived with from the time I was a young child: "Why are we here? Why do we exist? What will our life on earth have been for?"

My brother, David, searched for "truth." For years, he searched. "What makes you think there's such a thing as truth?" I thought. "And what makes you think you can find it?" Suppose truth meant that God really existed. Then what? How would knowing that change your life?

I never searched. "I am" because of "what is," I figured. If "what is" means there's a God, therefore, I am. If "what is" means there's *no* God; therefore, I am. My knowledge or lack of it doesn't determine "what is," so why know? How can *knowing* make a difference in one's life?

David declared himself an atheist; I called myself an agnostic. You have to know a *lot*, I thought, to *know* there's no God. I jumped into business in New York City, had an active social life, and did my best to survive the consuming agony of my heart that there was no reason to exist. No amount of love, money, or success could dispel the sense of purposelessness I lived with.

The Messiah?

". . . and our hearts are restless until they find their rest in Thee."

An unexpected phone call from David in the summer of 1976 was about to change the course of my life. He phoned to tell me some news involving his wife of twelve years, Janet.

"Ros," he said, "Janet has come to believe in Christ. She's been going to the Baptist church near our house. I haven't come to any conclusions yet, but as long as Janet has a strong conviction, the children will follow her. If and when I come to answers, I'll deal with the situation then."

47

I hung up the phone in shock. How could my brother love his children and let them be raised to believe in a *man*? Prophet, teacher, whoever Christ was, we're Jews. And *if* there's a God, we have a direct connection; we don't need to go through anyone.

I visited them that summer. In one of our marathon conversations, David told me about an article he had read that said there was such a thing as Jewish people, in *this* day, who believe that Jesus Christ (a name forbidden to us) was, in fact, the Jewish Messiah for whom we had been waiting.

The Messiah? They believe the Messiah had came? Already? How would that be possible? If there was a Messiah, if the faith of my childhood was true, he was the only hope the world had. He was to set up his kingdom. How could the Messiah have come and no one have a clue? He didn't make an impact when he came? There's no kingdom? No peace? Nothing? And he left? What an insanity that would be. How could we even consider such a thing? Obviously, those "Jews" who believed this were troubled, and their beliefs had nothing to do with me or with truth.

Not long after that conversation, I moved to California, and within three months my path crossed that of these so-called Jewish believers. They were handing out tracts in Westwood Village near UCLA. The tract read: "If being born hasn't given you much satisfaction, try being born again." Oh, if ever a message penetrated my heart! But I dared not let it show, not with these people. Not only did they affirm their belief that Christ was the Messiah, but they believed that He was God come to earth. God! A man? The least educated Jew knew that a man can't be God, that one cannot even look on God and live.

But, what if? What if there's really a God, and you could know that? Could knowing make a difference in your life? And what if, as they claimed, you could know him? I entered a bit of a Twilight Zone. I wasn't interested in what people concocted to help them deal with the emptiness of life. I'd rather live in despair all my life than live a lie, but if by chance they were onto something, I had nothing to lose by checking it out

For months, they tried to convince me that *Christ died for our sins* and that faith in Him was the only way to know you would spend eternity with God. They might as well have been speaking a foreign language—until one night, one life-changing night.

Twelve of *them*—Jewish believers (Jewish Evangelical Christians, I later would discover)—and I, at dinner, were deep in conversation about this supposed salvation drama. "For the sake of discussion," I interrupted, "let's say Christ died for your sins, my sins, and the sins of the world. Whatever that language means, let's say it happened. My question is: "What for? Why did He do it? What was in His *mind* when He did that?'"

For the next two hours, those dear Christians took me through the sacrificial system of the Old Testament scriptures (Tanach), which I had never known through all my years in synagogue. They explained that God *Is*, that He is holy, and that He cannot come into the presence of sin. More, that the wages of sin is death—separation from God—now and through all eternity. They demonstrated through the Torah that God required the blood of a perfect offering to atone for the sins of man. They explained that as an individual brought his offering (a bull, goat, or lamb) to the altar, he would place his hand on the head of that animal. It was symbolic of the sins being transferred from the individual onto the offering. And that lamb who, through no fault of his own, now bore the sins of the individual, was slain and his blood shed on the altar as an offering to God, in payment of that person's sin.

"Why?" I thought. Why would God put an innocent animal to death for *my* sin? Put *me* to death. It made no sense to me, but

I began to see that sin was no light issue to God. They explained further that the blood of tens of thousands of lambs slain through fifteen hundred years of that sacrificial system could not take away sin, nor had these sacrifices the power to change the heart of the worshipper. Those sacrifices were a sign that pointed to the One who would one day come and take upon Himself—not the sin of *a* person for *a* time, but the sin of *all* men—past, present, and future—for *all* time.

I thought I had fairly well grasped their explanation up to this point, but I could never have anticipated what followed. "When Jesus came," they said, "John the Baptist looked at Him and said: *"Behold, the Lamb of God who takes away the sin of the world!"*"

At last, my life has purpose

Time stopped. I don't recall another word they said. I sat at that restaurant table shattered. The lamb? *The* Lamb? The Lamb to which every Old Testament lamb pointed, who died for the sins of the world . . . and mine? And the reason His Blood alone could atone was because It was the Blood of the sinless, spotless Son of God? But how can a man be God? He cannot. That night, however, I realized for the first time that, while a man cannot be God, God can become a man; He can do anything He wants to do. It wasn't for me to tell Him how to be God!

Not long after that most blessed night, I gave my life to that incomparable Lamb who changed my life overnight and gave me—at last—a purpose for every second I breathe. The world was new and I a new creation in Him. How I wished for a ladder to reach the moon and tell the world of such a Savior!

Some months later, I told the head of the advertising company for which I worked, that I was not going to continue on with them to open up a San Francisco branch office. Certainly, there was nothing wrong with Christians in business, but God had changed my heart. I wasn't sure where I belonged anymore.

"Why do you have to be a fanatic!" he responded. "Why can't you have this thing in balance: eight hours of work, eight hours of sleep, and eight hours of God!"

"I can't." I tried in vain to explain: "Think of one born blind, who suddenly, one day, can see. He can't even appreciate a tree yet, because he's too overwhelmed with the fact that he even *sees* that tree!" Settle down? Eight hours a day?

I went to work for a halfway house for troubled teens, jumped into Bible study at my nondenominational Evangelical church, and worked in every form of neighborhood outreach, including jails and juvenile halls. I jettisoned every thing and every relationship that would not honor the God who loved me and gave Himself for me.

A year later, my brother, who, a year earlier, thought my so-called Christianity was not much more than an emotional experience, called from New York to tell me he had given his life to Christ, believing Him to be the Messiah and God come to earth. Shortly after, my sister, who also had been searching, came to put her trust in Christ. What joy for the three of us to have come to believe! "Infinite, marvelous, matchless grace...."

Anything but Catholic!

> *"... our hearts are restless until they find their rest in Thee."*

"Ros," David began, in what was to be one of many long phone conversations, "something's wrong. I believe the Bible is the Word of God and, as such, infallible. But how is it that so many men, pastors who love God, who study the Word of God in humility and sincerity and with all the tools of biblical interpretation, come out with such different understandings of

Scripture—and in such crucial areas? If Christ established His Church on earth and left us His Word, wouldn't He have left us a way to know what He *meant* by what He said?"

"Yes, David, but we see through a glass dimly. One day we'll know as we are known. For now, we simply do the best we can."

David didn't buy it. He said that Christ had prayed that we would be *one* as He and the Father are one. How could He have established His Church on earth and left us to the confusion of thousands of denominations, with new ones budding almost daily?

Again, David searched. Within a year, he was seriously looking into the Catholic Church. Oh no, I thought, *anything* but Catholic! If David only knew what I knew. My first Bible study was taught by an ex-Catholic who had been taught by an ex-priest, so I had gotten the "truth" of Catholicism from the horse's mouth: It was a cult, a false religious system leading millions astray. Surely, David was not about to be taken in by such deception.

Before long, he was studying with a monk. That did it! I flew to New York and met with David and the monk. For hours we went back and forth on Reformation issues. I thought for sure I was in the presence of one of Satan's emissaries. Yet, when Christmas Eve came a few days later, I agreed to accompany David to midnight Mass. It would be the first time I'd ever gone to a Catholic Mass.

Christmas 1978

As Mass began, and the procession of people and priest moved slowly down the central aisle toward the front altar, the foreign character of this "cult" began to have a faint sense of familiarity. As I took in the surroundings—the reverence, the posture in prayer, the formality of the liturgy, the sacredness with which the Word of God was handled and read, the candles, the *appearance* of worship (How could this *truly* be worship? I was in a *Catholic church*!)—the sense of familiarity turned to a measure of horror.

The Mass ended. We filed out of the church with everyone else—past the water basins into which people again dipped their fingers, past the priest with whom I'd have no contact under any circumstances, down the steps, and toward the car in silence.

"Whad'ya think?" David asked, as we began the half-hour drive home. I couldn't even speak; I was in shock and sick inside, but could not put my finger on why. Not a word transpired between us the entire trip home. When we reached the door, David begged, "Say *something*, anything." I realized what was bothering me so deeply. "David—*that* is a *synagogue*, but with Christ!"

"That's right!"

"No!" I said, "That's wrong!" What was David's problem? Did he have a hang-up from our Jewish background: the liturgy, the aesthetics? Didn't he understand that Christ was the end to which it all pointed?

Two months later, David was Catholic. I grieved, but all wasn't necessarily lost. There was still a ray of hope. Perhaps as he plunged into the depths of that "system," he would see it for what it was. Surely, if he had *truly* given his life to Christ, he couldn't *remain* Catholic. But the passage of time only shattered my hope and deepened David's conviction that the Catholic Church is the Church Christ had established.

Catholic apologetics, what's that?

In the ten-year span that followed, I completed the Bible Institute program at my church, went through missions training, became part of the Bible Institute staff, and earned a master's degree at Talbot Theological Seminary on the Biola University campus in La Mirada, California. During my time at Talbot, I worked full-time as chaplain of a women's jail facility in Lancaster, California.

It was the summer of 1990. I would transition from the jail chaplaincy to the staff of an Evangelical church in California as Director of Women's Ministries. The pastor of this particular church within the "Friends" denomination was an ex-Catholic with Baptist training. He had reinstituted the "ordinances" of baptism and communion discarded by George Fox in the seventeenth century. With the month of June to myself, I spent two weeks with David and my sister, Susan, in New York. We barely came up for air the entire time, as we wrestled with every issue of faith.

At a seemingly inopportune moment—not that there ever would have been an opportune one—David handed me a magazine:

"Have you ever seen this?"

"*This Rock*? No."

"It's a Catholic apologetics publication. You might be interested."

A Catholic *apologetics* magazine? What kind of a phenomenon was that? Catholics have a defense for their faith? I had never met a Catholic who knew his faith. No Catholic ever told me the Gospel. But there was something more. I never knew Catholics *cared* that anyone else know it. I thought: "If you even *think* you have the truth, and the truth means your soul, and the souls of everyone alive on the face of the earth, how do you keep that to yourself?"

I had a measure of respect for any group of Catholics who would want the world to know what they believe. I took the magazine back with me to California, and in it came across a full-page advertisement: *Presbyterian Minister Becomes Catholic.*

His name was Scott Hahn. I had never heard of him. I had never heard of such a thing. I thought: I don't care what his title was, or what his function was; he could not have known Christ.

He could not have had a personal relationship with the Lord Jesus Christ and *then* become Catholic. Perhaps he wasn't a Christian when he was a Presbyterian and just became one when he entered the Catholic Church, not knowing any better that he shouldn't buy into all that stuff. However, because his background was close enough to mine, theologically, I ordered the set of four tapes offered in the ad.

A week from my starting date at the Friends church, while packing up my apartment in Lancaster, I listened to the tapes, which contained Scott Hahn's testimony and a two-part debate with a Presbyterian theologian on the Reformation issues of *sola fide* and *sola scriptura* ("faith alone" and "scripture alone"). Scott Hahn was the stronger of the two, I had to admit. It wasn't because he had the truth, I thought. It was because he was better able to articulate his position. I listened in growing frustration, thinking of all that the Presbyterian minister did *not* say but surely must know.

Toward the conclusion of the debate, each was given fifteen minutes to summarize his position. In Scott Hahn's concluding remarks, he said that if you look into the claims of the Catholic Church—two thousand years of Church history, the Church Fathers, and the rest—you will experience a "holy shock and a glorious amazement" to find that that Church, the very Church you might have been battling to save people from, is the very Church that Christ established on earth two thousand years ago.

Holy shock are the only words to describe what went through me at that instant. "Oh no." I thought (that sense of horror returned), "Don't tell me there's any truth to this thing." I stood paralyzed, and I knew, in that instant of time, that if I did not look into the claims of the Catholic Church, I'd be turning from God.

After two years with the Friends church, I moved to New York to immerse myself in study full-time. I began by reading every Protestant work *against* the Catholic Church that I could find, in the hope of being rescued from ever becoming Catholic. In short order, though, I was utterly alone. It was obvious that Protestant writers were not fighting the Catholic Church, but rather what they *thought* the Catholic Church taught.

I left no stone unturned: Scripture, Tradition, the papacy, apostolic succession, the communion of saints, purgatory, every issue concerning Mary, the sacramental nature of the Church, the Mass, and above all, the Eucharist. As I studied history, the Fathers, the councils, the understanding of the faith through the writings of popes, bishops, theologians, and saints, my world began to change. I began to discover a design for God's Church on earth more beautiful, more majestic, more *whole* than anything I could have fathomed. I discovered in time that the differences between Catholicism and Protestantism are not doctrinal only, but constitute a whole way of seeing.

The agony of my heart turned to longing for the intense beauty of what I had come to believe was true. A four-and-a-half-year journey and eighteen years of Evangelical Protestantism had come to an end.

I go all the way

At the Easter Vigil of 1995, I once again visited a Catholic church. As I walked up the front steps through the entrance, I again held my breath. This time, though, I dipped my finger in the water basin and crossed myself in thanksgiving and submission to the God who gave Himself for me. I walked down the central aisle, stopped before entering the pew, and went down on my knees before the tabernacle in which that God dwelt—the God of Abraham, who not only became Man but also became our Food.

The readings from Scripture that night were very familiar to me, but amazingly, so were the prayers offered in the Mass:

Blessed are You, Lord, God of all creation. Through Your goodness we have this bread to offer, which earth has given and human hands have made. It will become the Bread of Life.

Could it be? I thought back to *Shabbos*, to the Sabbath prayers of our Jewish home:

Baruch ata Adonai Elohenu Melech haOlam hamotzi lechem min ha'aretz. ("Blessed art Thou, O Lord, our God, King of the Universe, who brings forth bread from the earth.")

"I came," Jesus said, "not to abolish, but to fulfill." Here was the Living Bread to which every lamb and every grain of manna pointed. A mere symbol would not be the fulfillment of such Old Testament types. Christ alone was the One to which every sign pointed. The Eucharist was not symbolic, but Christ Himself.

I thought about my Jewish relatives still living in Brooklyn, and about one particular family who, to that day, would not allow me in their home because I'd become a Christian and thereby, to their way of thinking, had betrayed our people. My cousin had said to me one day: "I know a woman just like you. She was also a 'Jew for Jesus,' but she went *all* the way and became Catholic." How did my cousin know? How did he know that to become Catholic was to go "all the way," to be as fully Christian as a person can get?

As I was received into the Catholic Church that night, the true Jewish Messiah—Body and Blood, Soul and Divinity—was placed on my tongue. Oh, how could it be? What once seemed an insanity and utterly unthinkable had become to me the measure of the "breadth and length and height and depth" of His fathomless love and condescension "for us men and for our salvation." O glorious mystery of the unapproachable God who became our Food! I sobbed uncontrollably at having at last come home—all the way home.

I imagine that my parents were rejoicing in heaven that night, just as David, Susan, and I had rejoiced when they had been baptized some years earlier in a Baptist church in upstate New York (but that's another story!). Susan is now a local missions coordinator with the Missouri Synod Lutheran Church in Ann Arbor, Michigan. David is president of the Association of Hebrew Catholics in Mt. Upton, New York. I am a staff apologist with Catholic Answers, publisher of *This Rock*, the Catholic apologetics magazine that began my journey from my Evangelical Christian faith to its fullness in the whole Christ.

> O the depth of the riches and wisdom and knowledge of God! How unsearchable are his judgments and how inscrutable his ways! . . . / For from him and through him and to him are all things. To him be glory for ever. Amen.[13]

Baruch haba b'Shem Adonai! "Blessed is He who comes in the name of the Lord!"

Rosalind Moss is a staff apologist at Catholic Answers, a nonprofit organization dedicated to promoting the Catholic faith through all

---

[13] Romans 11:33, 36.

forms of media. She travels the world speaking and teaching at parishes, conferences, and women's retreats and is a frequent guest on both Catholic and non-Catholic radio and television broadcasts. In addition to a number of articles, Rosalind has written for Catholic publications, including This Rock *magazine, published by Catholic Answers. She is the editor of* Home at Last: 11 Who found their Way to the Catholic Church, *from which this story is taken. She also is a frequent radio guest on* Catholic Answers Live, *and together with Kristine Franklin, co-hosts EWTN's* Household of Faith *and* Now That We're Catholic!

Reprinted, with permission, from the book *Home At Last*, published by Catholic Answers, Inc. (2020 Gillespie Way, El Cajon, CA 92020; [619] 387-7200; www.catholic.com).

3

A Path Through the Wilderness: Finding a Way Home

Kristen McLaughlin

It was the singing that began it.

"For You are my God, You alone are my joy, defend me, O Lord. . . ."

The words came at me across a pond in southern New Hampshire. Loaded down with groceries, I was walking a half-mile path through the woods from our car to the wilderness cottage my husband and I rented when these voices reached my ears and pulled me to a standstill, listening:

> You give marvelous comrades to me, the faithful who dwell in Your land, those who choose alien gods have chosen an alien band, for You are my God, You alone are my joy, defend me, O Lord. . . .

Across the pond was an Adirondack lodge owned by our landlords, Nick and Jane Healy. Jane's sister, Pat, who lived two miles down the road, had mentioned that a group of Catholic priests and laypeople would be arriving for a retreat. It was their voices, then, that I was hearing. Mesmerized, I set down my groceries, feeling a sudden yearning toward these sounds, these words:

> You show me the path for my life, in Your presence the fullness of joy, to be at Your right hand forever, for me would be happiness always, for You are my God, You alone are my joy, defend me, O Lord. . . .

Finally there was only silence, only wind on the water and wind in the leaves. I picked up my groceries and headed once more toward our cottage, puzzled and bewildered not only at what I'd heard but at my own reactions to it.

That night I lay awake in bed next to my husband, wondering. Lately I'd begun not to ignore these inner stirrings, not to intellectualize them away. But the song I'd heard, that I'd been drawn to, spoke of a Christian God, and Christianity was something I'd turned my back on years ago. Now I was reading only Eastern mysticism, especially Buddhism.

Suddenly I remembered a long-forgotten comment of a physician friend. "All that Eastern philosophy is fascinating, of course," he'd said. "Historically interesting, intellectually chic. But I wonder—is it truth you're after?"

"Of course," I'd said, surprised at the question.

"Well," he said, "you won't find it there."

"Then—where?"

"Christianity," he'd said, in a nonchalant, matter-of-fact way. And that had been the end of it. I wasn't interested. He, thankfully, didn't proselytize.

But now here it was again—Christianity tugging at me, trying to get my attention. Or was it God?

Nostalgia and fear

In the days following the singing, a strange thing happened: I began losing interest in my books on Eastern spirituality. I also found myself unable to meditate as before. One day, feeling an inner nudging, I shifted into Christian prayer posture—kneeling, hands clasped together the way I'd learned as a child. As I did this, however, I experienced an odd mixture of nostalgia and fear.

Nostalgia, because I began remembering things from my Lutheran childhood: the gold-framed picture of Jesus next to my bed; the little glow-in-the-dark cross that hung on a purple cord from my lamp; the Lutheran hymnal my grandparents had given me when I began playing the piano; Miss Dokken and her flannel board Bible stories in Sunday school; listening to my record of Margaret O'Brien reading *Joseph and His Coat of Many Colors*; the white leather Bible my parents presented me when I was confirmed; the experience I'd had the first time I received communion, wondering if anyone could see the light I felt all around me.

Fear, because my husband, Buzz, and I lived in the world of the arts and academia—hardly hospitable ground for Christianity. He was a professor of theater at Drew University in New Jersey, and the two of us had spent the previous ten years writing screenplays. Since that whole venture had been hugely unsuccessful, he was just returning to playwriting and considering starting a professional theater company, while I was pondering a renewed career in journalism.

Furthermore, some years previously, an actress friend of ours, Ann, had gone through a conversion experience and "given her life to the Lord," which prompted Buzz to write a humorous song titled "I Just Lost Another Friend to Jesus." Ann kept sending us books and pamphlets about Christianity, along with a number of Bibles in modern translations, but the whole affair had a kind of embarrassing tinge to it, and a lot of the pamphlets seemed somewhat hysterical. Every time we received a package from Ann, we'd tuck it away somewhere in the attic or basement, unable to actually throw it away because we loved her and knew she sent us this stuff because she loved us, too. We also knew, because she told us, that she was praying for us, which was fine. After all, we still believed in God and prayer, even though we ourselves didn't pray.

I began wondering if there had been a time, as a child, that I had prayed—other than bedtime prayers under the guidance of my mother or mealtime prayers at my grandparents' homes. I had been born and raised in Madison, Wisconsin, and usually on Sundays we went to Bethel Lutheran Church, where my father, a psychiatrist, had a ministry partnership with the pastors. There were prayers at church, of course, but I couldn't remember praying by myself, although I knew I'd written long, spiritual ramblings about the certitude of God's existence in my diaries.

After graduating from high school, Bethel gave me scholarship money to attend St. Olaf College in Northfield, Minnesota, where I eventually met the man I was to marry—not another Norwegian Lutheran, as expected, but a dark-haired, dark-eyed Scotch-Irish Presbyterian whose presence among all of us blond Norwegians gave him immediate distinction. Two weeks after graduation we were married and settled into an apartment back in Madison so he could pursue graduate studies in theater at the University of Wisconsin.

As the family breadwinner for those first few years until the doctorate was achieved, I worked as an editor at the University of Wisconsin Press, where nearly every day from my office window I could watch National Guard tanks roll up to campus. It was the protest era during the Vietnam War, and the UW was a major hotbed of dissent. Although we sympathized with peaceful protests, Buzz and I were too busy with work and studies to be a part of this; however, like the rest of the country, we simply watched the events as they unfolded on television. Most Sundays we attended services at Bethel, and when our daughter, Keri, was born, that's where she was baptized.

It was only in 1970, when Buzz became an assistant professor at the University of Virginia in Charlottesville, that we stopped going to church. The war was a big factor in our decision, since we considered ourselves "doves" while most of the people in the little Lutheran church we attended assumed a more "hawkish" position. For Christians to support such an atrocity, we thought, was major hypocrisy. Then, too, Buzz and I dressed a little differently than most of the congregation. Our hair was a little longer and perhaps our clothes were more flamboyant, and because of this, I think that some people assumed we were "hippies." Actually, this couldn't have been farther from the truth. Like them, our lives revolved around our family and our jobs, although academia, the arts, and liberal politics had definitely been turning us toward assorted lies like "zero population growth."

Still, we felt like outsiders when we joined this particular congregation on Sundays and so, eventually, we just stopped going. Instead, the three of us would head up into the Blue Ridge Mountains for hiking, picnicking, and communing with God as we found Him in nature. For the next fifteen years, the outdoors became our church.

I go looking for answers

After hearing the singing at the lodge, however, I knew I had to figure out why I was being drawn back toward Christianity. If Ann had lived nearby instead of in California, I might have gone to talk with her. As it was, the only nearby Christian friend I could think of was Pat Crisman. Several years before, she and her husband, Jim, had fled a fast-track existence in suburban Chicago to begin a new, simpler life in the New Hampshire woods with their three children, the oldest of whom was the same age as Keri, who'd just graduated from high school. Pat and Jim, along with our landlords, the Healys, were "ardent Catholics"—which was fine with us. As lapsed Protestants, we didn't care what anyone believed, as long as they didn't try to foist it on us. Neither the Crismans nor the Healys had ever tried to do this during the five years we'd been coming to New Hampshire. Now, however, I was curious about their beliefs.

The fact that they were Catholic, instead of Protestant, made no difference to me. I'd never experienced anti-Catholicism as a child—except for my grandmother's refusal to attend a wedding if a family member was marrying a Catholic (and I remember thinking: I love Grandma, but I know she's wrong on this one). In fact, an elderly babysitter of mine, whom I'd nicknamed "Nana" and considered my third grandmother, had been a devout Catholic who'd take me to Mass with her, letting me prop my feet up against her back while she knelt down to pray. Both Catholics and Protestants, I thought, were part of a somewhat divided but definite whole, the only difference being that Catholics had a higher, more ornate liturgy and had retained certain practices that we Protestants had done away with, like Confession, as the Sacrament of Penance (or Reconciliation) is popularly called.

Although Pat had never spoken to me about her faith—at least, not in any proselytizing sense—I now wanted to find out what had led her to become a practicing Christian. One day, when Buzz had driven into town to do an errand, I seized the opportunity and walked through the woods and down the tree-lined road to her house. As always, she welcomed me in as though I was exactly the person she'd been hoping to see. Over cups of tea, we discussed initially the ups and downs of our lives, particularly my anxiety over the fact that Keri was traveling in France with a boyfriend. This, and the fact that we hadn't received a postcard from her for several weeks, was doing little for my peace of mind. Finally, after we'd spoken for a while about the pangs of being a mother, I pushed these worries aside and plunged into the heart of my curiosity. "Pat, why are you a Christian?" I asked.

At first I could see that my question shocked her, but she recovered quickly and without showing that her heart was leaping—although it must have been—she began describing the fact that all history revolved around the figure of Jesus. Even time itself, she said, was divided into B.C., before Christ, and A.D. (*Anno Domini*, "in the year of the Lord"), after His birth. Then she told me, citing something C. S. Lewis said in his book *Mere Christianity*, that each person had to decide for himself or herself who Jesus was and is, and that it's not possible to maintain that He was only a great moral teacher. Because of the claims Jesus makes about Himself, she said, there are only three choices: Either He was a lunatic, a liar, or who He says He is—the Son of God.

Sensing my receptivity, Pat said that when she began reading and meditating on Holy Scripture she realized that Jesus was, in fact, the Second Person of the Trinity. Pulling out a well-worn Bible, she opened it and read:

> In the beginning was the Word, and the Word was with God, and the Word was God. . . . And the Word became flesh and dwelt among us, full of grace and truth.[14]

---

[14] John 1:1, 14.

If a person reads the Bible, she said, Jesus explains who He is. Turning to another passage, she read:

> I am the bread of life; he who comes to me shall not hunger, and he who believes in me shall never thirst. . . . I am the light of the world; he who follows me will not walk in darkness, but will have the light of life. . . . I am the resurrection and the life; he who believes in me, though he die, yet shall he live, and whoever lives and believes in me shall never die.[15]

When she looked up at me, her eyes were shining. "There are so many passages I'd like to show you," she said. "But maybe I could write out a list, and you could look them up when you have the time. Do you have a Bible?" The only Bible I had, I said, was back in New Jersey. Pat crossed from the kitchen into the living room and returned carrying an enormous blue *Jerusalem Bible*. "You can borrow this one, if you'd like," she said, holding it out to me.

At that moment—as she stood there in front of me, extending that Bible—time suddenly seemed to stand still, as if someone had pushed the "pause" button on a video. In my brain, I sensed a kind of violent ripping, like cloth being split from top to bottom while an agonized inner voice cried out: "No, not the Bible!" Simultaneously there was also, inside me, the formation of a still, sure "Yes."

I reached out and took the gargantuan book, flinching a little as its weight sank into my arms. "I'm sorry it's so large," Pat said, apologetically. "It's the only extra one we have on hand right now."

"That's okay," I said, wondering if it would be rude to ask her for a bag to put it in. Resisting the temptation, I said my thank-

---

[15] John 6:35; 8:12; 11:25-26.

you's and good-bye's and headed off down the road, enduring the Bible's heaviness and the fact that nothing could hide its shameless religiosity. An inner, whining voice complained as I walked along: "What are you doing? Why did you agree to this?"

Fortunately, Buzz was out canoeing when I arrived back at our cottage. Relieved, I slid the bulky volume under our couch, thinking: If he sees me with this thing he'll know I've finally lost my mind. The first time I was alone, however, I slid it out from its hiding place and headed for our screened porch where I opened it and read, looking up the passages Pat had given me, but also wandering around through the Psalms and Isaiah. "Just as a literary exercise," I told myself. Although *The Jerusalem Bible* was a different translation than what I remembered, coming back to these words again as an adult was like surviving a famine and then, wandering through the woods one day, finding a long, white banquet table spread out under the trees with the finest of foods. Day after day, I would read and feast and read and feast.

I come face to face with the truth

One weekend when Buzz had gone off in the canoe on an Indian spirituality-inspired "vision quest," I settled down for a long, uninterrupted reading session. This time, I opened *The Jerusalem Bible* directly to Isaiah 43:

> Do not be afraid, for I have redeemed you; / I have called you by your name, you are mine. / Should you pass through the sea, I will be with you; / or through rivers, they will not swallow you up. / Should you walk through the fire, you will not be scorched / and the flames will not burn you. For I am Yahweh, your God, / the Holy One of Israel, your savior.

Suddenly the words "For I am Yahweh, your God, your Savior" seemed transformed into bold print right before my eyes. For a moment I sat there, surprised, and then went on reading, moving through the verses to Isaiah 55, where the words started to turn into boldface again:

> Oh, come to the water all you who are thirsty.... /
> Why spend money on what is not bread, / your wages on
> what fails to satisfy? Listen, listen to me, and you will have
> good things to eat.... / Pay attention, come to me; /
> listen, and your soul will live.

I paused again, wondering at what was happening. It was as if these words were directed specifically at me. Continuing to read, I landed at last in Isaiah 60 and 62 (60:1, 19; 62:10; 60:16; 62:10), where the words became insistent, demanding action:

> Arise, shine out, for your light has come, / the glory
> of Yahweh is rising on you.... / Yahweh will be your
> everlasting light, / your God will be your splendour.... /
> Pass through, pass through the gates ... / and you shall
> know that I, Yahweh, am your saviour / ... your
> redeemer.... / Pass through, pass through the gates....

And suddenly it cut through me, through my brain and my heart into the center of my being: This is all true—everything written in this book. It's all pure truth.

I got down on my knees in thanksgiving.

What about Buzz?

That weekend I went back to Pat's and told her what had happened. She rejoiced and prayed with me, and in my heart I knew everything in my life had changed. I now had a center, a rock. But what about Buzz? I wanted him to have that rock and center, too, for him to possess the joy I felt. How could I convince him that Jesus was the Way, the Truth, and the Life?

"Pray for him," Pat said. "Just pray for him, and I will, too." Actually, she said, she and Jim and Nick and Jane and friends of theirs had been praying for us for years. I was astounded. Then I remembered that Ann had been praying for us, too, probably for ten years before they had. I'd have to sit down and write her a long letter. And then, repenting for our hard-heartedness, I resolved to dig out all her books and pamphlets when I got home.

In the meantime, Buzz was returning from his time alone in the wilderness, and I had to tell him what had happened. Sitting on the screened porch, I saw him gliding the canoe toward the dock, smiling and raising his paddle to me in greeting. I went down to meet him.

"How are you doing?" he asked, and then, seeing my face: "Is everything okay?"

"Everything's great," I said. "Tell me about your trip."

"Wait a minute—you look funny. What's wrong?"

"Nothing," I said, laughing, and gave him a hug. Then, finally: "I think I've just become a Christian."

He only stared at me, wondering.

I am a Christian; now what?

Pat had suggested that I call a friend of hers in New Jersey when I got home. The problem was, she was a Catholic and I was a Protestant. I assured Pat that I'd keep up the daily prayer time I'd started and would also search immediately for a church, beginning with the Lutherans and progressing through other mainline denominations until I found my "home."

In the end, after attending a different church every Sunday for about six weeks, I settled on one that was Presbyterian, mostly because its interior reminded me of Bethel and because its members were friendly and welcoming. After a few months, the pastor started talking to me about becoming a member. It took a while to overcome all my intellectual objections about joining up with "organized religion," but time spent in prayer finally convinced me that this, indeed, was the way I should go. It wasn't long afterward that I was asked to be a deacon and joined our pastor's weekly Bible study.

Meanwhile, I was listening to Christian radio hungrily, soaking up as much teaching as I could while tolerating the annoyingly saccharine music often interspersed between programs. I also enrolled in religion courses at Drew University's Methodist-oriented seminary, but after a series of classes in which the name "Jesus" was never mentioned and reading lists included books like *Beyond Liberation, The Predicament of the Prosperous,* and *Diving Deep and Surfacing: Women Writers on Spiritual Quest,* I realized that I'd unwittingly walked into a bastion of agenda-driven, liberal theology—hardly rich territory for learning about absolute truth.

Fortunately, I'd learned that one of the members of my women writers' group, Shirley, had become a "born-again" Christian. Although I cringed at the fundamentalist tone in this description, I had to admit that, most probably, this is what had happened to me, too. At Shirley's invitation, I joined a large women's Bible study held at the conservative, nondenominational church she attended, and for the first time I experienced the emotional sway of powerful contemporary Christian music, which we'd all sing together during the opening of each session. Then one day, back at the church I'd joined, I received a warning from the director of religious education about this particular Bible study and "those born-again Christians," who really went too far in their religious zeal. Too far? I'd just begun realizing that my little church wasn't going far enough. I also wasn't happy that Buzz didn't like the church the few times he attended with me. He thought the interior dark and the pastor's sermons uninspiring, and once, at a coffee hour after the service, actually introduced himself to several of the other deacons as "Kris's pagan husband."

God answers my prayers for my husband's conversion

Even though Buzz usually stayed home on Sundays reading the *New York Times* while I went to church, I began trying to live out the biblical truths I was meditating on, hoping to become a more loving person, a better wife. Paul's exhortation in Ephesians 5:22 to "be subject to your husbands, as to the Lord" was particularly challenging, not to mention annoying, since I'd always preferred doing things my way. Realizing, however, that submission (or "subjecting oneself") meant honor and respect, not doormat passivity, I decided to try a truth-experiment. The next time Buzz and I disagreed on something, I'd state my case as persuasively as possible, but if in the end he still held out for doing things his way, I'd acquiesce to his judgment as head of the family. After trying this for several months, I was amazed at the results. Buzz not only became more loving and receptive, but started taking on a new sense of responsibility and even looked taller, more sure of himself. Furthermore, he told me he'd noticed a change in me, that my faith was making me a better person. Maybe, he said, he'd better take a closer look at Christianity for himself.

About this time, a friend mentioned that her mother was a member of the Presbyterian Church at New Providence, where an inspirational pastor named Tom Tewell was receiving wide acclaim. Since this sounded intriguing, I asked Buzz if he'd like to visit New Providence with me, and he agreed. That Sunday, Tewell was just beginning a series on Romans, and he was, indeed, a gifted preacher, so gifted that Buzz said after the service: "Let's go back next week. This is the way church should be!" We returned every Sunday after that until finally I had to officially resign as a deacon and member at my old church. But God was answering my prayers about Buzz's faith. He still had a lot of questions and reservations, but was coming closer every day.

That summer back in New Hampshire, Pat's husband, Jim, came down to help Buzz put a new roof on our cottage. I was inside doing some cleaning when I heard Jim, up on the roof, singing: "Change my heart, oh God, make it ever true, change my heart, oh God, may I be like You. . . ." And then I heard Buzz's voice, joining in: "You are the potter, I am the clay, mold me and make me, this is what I pray. . . ." About a week later, Buzz knelt down on our dock, all by himself, and prayed that Jesus would come into his heart and change his life.

Conversions continue

Once Buzz and I were united in our faith and began praying together, interceding for friends and family, our primary concern and regret was that we'd never taken Keri to Sunday school or given her any religious training. Despite our parental failings, however, she was a warm, loving child whose nature was open and receptive to things spiritual. In fact, a strange thing had occurred when she was fifteen, and we were on a year's sabbatical in France. Once, while traveling, we paid a visit to Rocamadour, a twelfth-century church that since the Middle Ages had become a popular pilgrimage destination because of its famous "Black Virgin," reportedly responsible for numerous miracles over the centuries. The moment we entered the "Holy of

Holies," the Chapelle Miraculeuse, Keri left us and went to kneel before the statue of the Virgin, staying there in a kind of reverie until finally, after almost an hour, we had to tap her on the shoulder and suggest moving on.

After our conversions, Buzz and I would talk to her as much as we could about what and why we believed, but at first the whole thing bewildered and puzzled her. During most of this period, except for summers, she was away at college. When she was home, she'd often attend church with us, but was reticent about talking in depth concerning spiritual things—mostly because, she told us years later, she knew Jesus was calling to her and that she'd have to give up too much of her lifestyle to follow Him.

We kept praying, however, and then, during her junior year as an art student in Paris, an amazing thing happened. Through a visiting pastor at New Providence who'd spent some time in France, we found out about an evangelical group in Paris, a kind of French Campus Crusade for Christ, and passed this information along to Keri. During a particularly difficult period in her studies, she decided she needed some new friends and, spontaneously one evening, took a cab to one of their services. ("Even that was mysterious," she said later. "When I came out of my building, there was a cab, as if it were waiting for me; usually I'd have to walk blocks to find one.")

Some weeks later she called us joyfully and said that her life had changed, that she, too, had opened the door of her heart and become a Christian. She began attending Bible studies and later, during a trip to England, experienced what she felt was a baptism of the Holy Spirit. Returning home for her final year of studies at Parsons School of Design in New York City, she broke up with the boyfriend she'd been seeing and started living a whole new life. But dating was difficult for her now; she wasn't interested in young men without a Christian perspective, and yet the Christian men she met at church didn't have an interest in the arts, her passion and vocation.

So we started praying for a Christian husband for her. And then, suddenly, along came a young, exceptionally talented Jewish actor named Tyagi Schwartz. Buzz had hired Tyagi to work at the theater he'd founded some years previously, the Playwrights Theatre of New Jersey, and both of us had liked him immediately. Keri liked him, too, when she finally met him at a cast party, and the two of them stayed up late that night talking about art and religion. As it turned out, she informed us, Tyagi was also interested in spiritual things. The only problem was that he wasn't a Christian, and isn't that what we had prayed for?

Our view proved shortsighted. Tyagi was born Aaron Schwartz to a mother of Italian Catholic descent who had converted to Judaism before marrying her Jewish husband. At the age of five, his parents renamed him Tyagi, which means "surrender to God," when they turned away from Judaism and began following an East Indian guru. When Tyagi and Keri began dating, they'd talk together about her beliefs, and often he'd accompany her to Sunday services at Calvary Baptist Church in New York. They read the Bible together as well, and one day it struck him: If all this was true, and he was beginning to think it was, then Jesus was the Messiah his people had been waiting for!

I long for unity with my Catholic friends

Two months after her graduation from Parsons, Keri and Tyagi were married in the Presbyterian Church at New Providence, which the two of them attended when they came to visit us. During the first few years of their marriage, Tyagi auditioned for and landed several parts in television shows and series and for a while they lived in California, where they attended Bel Aire Presbyterian Church and became acquainted with Jews for Jesus. Then, after a series cancellation and feeling homesick for family and familiar surroundings, the two moved back to New Jersey, which meant that they often joined us during holidays at our cottage in New Hampshire. Eventually, both became good friends with the children of our friends and neighbors, the Crismans and the Healys. Everyone in this large and extended family had become devout Catholics, most of the children having graduated from Franciscan University of Steubenville, where Nick Healy, by this time, had become head of development. Although the Healys lived in Ohio for most of the year, they, like us, traveled often to New Hampshire.

Keri, Tyagi, Buzz, and I had a lot in common with our New Hampshire neighbors: All of us had become orthodox Christians, albeit Protestant on one side and Catholic on the other. Although this divide existed, there were more things that united us with the Crismans and the Healys than with liberal Protestants, and more things that united them with us than with liberal Catholics. Our core beliefs were the same.

Because of this, whenever a visiting priest was in the area—and the Healys, rich with the gift of hospitality, entertained many priests, theologians, and philosophers during the summer—we would all receive an invitation to attend Mass, held either at the lodge or at the Healys' home. The problem was, we couldn't receive Holy Communion. When I asked Pat why this was, since we were all Christians, she said it was because we didn't believe in the Real Presence of Christ in the Eucharist—we believed it was a symbol. "No," I said. "Ever since I first received the Body and Blood of Christ as a Lutheran, that's what I always thought I was receiving: the real Body and Blood. Otherwise, why bother?" Buzz, Keri, and Tyagi agreed.

"The sad truth is that the Reformation has divided us," Pat said. "Protestants are no longer in communion with Mother Church; therefore, we can't honestly take the Eucharist together." Although the words "Mother Church" jumped out at me, hauntingly, and while it was becoming increasingly painful not being able to receive Holy Communion with our friends, the idea of becoming Catholic never occurred to any of us. Instead, we prided ourselves on being Protestant "salt" in the midst of so many Catholics.

Then Pat and Jim's daughter, Julie, who was studying for her theology licentiate in Rome, became engaged to one of the Pope's Swiss Guards. A trip was arranged for Julie and the young man, Mario Enzler, to visit New Hampshire. Before Mario left Rome, Pope John Paul II gave him ten papal medals, stamped with the Pope's image and that of the Virgin Mary, to give to whomever he wished. We were in New Hampshire when Mario and Julie arrived and, after visiting with them, Mario gave one medal to me and another to Buzz. Touched by his gesture, we decided to begin praying in earnest for unity within the body of Christ. Julie also gave me a pearl Rosary with the papal cross. Although I had no idea what to do with a Rosary, I was similarly touched that she would offer me such a precious gift. Although we were Protestants, we looked up to the Pope as the world's greatest Christian leader.

Toward fullness of faith

When we arrived back in New Jersey, Buzz was invited to join a weekly men's discipleship group led by our new pastor, Ben Patterson, who had become a good friend. Not long afterward, I became part of a newly formed women's group. Instead of focusing solely on the Bible, these groups studied issues like the nature of the Trinity, the divinity of Christ, and the fruit of the Holy

Spirit. The topic that began to cause problems for me and Buzz was a study of the sacraments. What we discovered shocked us. We Protestants had only two sacraments, Baptism and the Lord's Supper, while our Catholic friends had seven; worse yet, Protestants didn't even consider marriage a sacrament. What? Of course it was—that was something you just knew!

Our next crisis came during discussions about the Lord's Supper. In my women's group, an argument arose about the words "This is My Body; this is My Blood." I suggested that Jesus meant exactly what He said when He used the word "is." He didn't say "like" or "stands for"; He said "is." But our leader, Barbara, an ordained minister, only looked at me sadly and shook her head. "When we celebrate the Lord's Supper," she said, "the bread and wine do not actually become the Body and Blood of Christ; they're symbols that point to Him." At this, a woman who'd been a Presbyterian all her life shouted out: "What are you talking about? Of course it's the Body and Blood of Christ!" Barbara shook her head again. "That's not what Presbyterians believe," she said. "That's what Catholics believe."

Driving home that night, I wondered if the difference in belief stemmed from the fact that I'd been raised Lutheran. That must be what Lutherans believe, too, I thought. After researching the matter, however, I discovered that Barbara was right. Only Catholics believe fully in the Real Presence of Christ in the Eucharist, while Lutherans dance around the issue, raising terms such as "consubstantiation," in which the bread and wine remain bread and wine, while also being the Body and Blood of Christ. Episcopalians adopt an "it is what you think it is" stance.

Finally, I realized I needed to study the Reformation in order to find out what had caused these differences in the first place. Looking at both Protestant and Catholic accounts, I became convinced that Luther wasn't a hero but a heretic, which my

Random House dictionary defined as "a professed believer who maintains religious opinions contrary to those accepted by his church or rejects doctrines prescribed by his church." A rebellious, politically manipulated priest, Luther defied the Pope and the authority of the Church, instead of taking a more prayerful, obedient stance, like many of his peers, and working for reform from within.

These conclusions about Luther were highlighted in our daily life when Ben Patterson called the New Providence Presbyterian Church to obedience, something few Protestant ministers ever dare to do, and received ferocious opposition from a vocal minority. During a heated church meeting one night, the word "*Protest*-ant" became a living reality. Then, in my daily prayer time, I came across a passage from Romans 13 that seemed applicable to this situation and to Luther's:

> Let every person be subject to the governing authorities, for there is no authority except from God, and those that exist have been instituted by God. Therefore he who resists the authorities resists what God has appointed, and those who resist will incur judgment.

Ever since Luther, I realized, Protestants have been protesting whatever they don't like—usually authority of any kind—and since the system is democratic and not ecclesiastical, whoever has the most votes wins. This democratic system was proving to be increasingly problematic for orthodox Presbyterians and for orthodox Christians in every mainline Protestant denomination. It was now apparent that the more liberal factions had been inserting themselves into various power positions and were able to cast more votes on hot-button issues like abortion and homosexuality. One by one, every mainline Protestant group was sliding dangerously downhill toward official sanctioning of these practices. Only the Roman Catholic Church held uncompromisingly firm.

Heading home

More and more, our family realized this "firmness" and "fullness" of faith was what we admired and wanted to be a part of. Gradually, we began making secret forays into various Catholic churches in our area, sometimes together, and sometimes alone. What we found, initially, was disappointing: The singing—or lack of it—was a huge letdown; sermons were often far from inspiring; and many parishioners didn't even seem to follow along with the liturgy. Despite all of this, however, there was an unmistakable, mysterious sense of the Holy. Here was the awesome reality of the Eucharist, of the fact that Jesus was appearing and offering Himself daily—Body, Blood, Soul, and Divinity. Either this was blasphemy and idolatry or it was the absolute truth. We opted for the latter.

Still, in moving toward the Catholic Church there were other issues that had to be studied, grappled with, and understood, such as Mary and the saints, the Pope, purgatory, and the Church's position on contraception. For us, reading books and listening to tapes by converts such as Scott Hahn, Tom Howard, and Peter Kreeft shed light on many of our questions. Another enormous help was watching the Eternal Word Television Network (EWTN). In New Hampshire, of course, we were aided by the Crismans and the Healys, along with a newcomer to our neighborhood, Margaret Farren, who became a dear friend and gave us what she called our "Catholic Kit"—an old *Baltimore Catechism*, along with a *Liturgy of the Hours*, Rosary, and worn prayer book.

We were also gifted with the friendship of Dr. Alice von Hildebrand, widow of the famed Catholic philosopher Dietrich von Hildebrand, who came to New Hampshire every summer to work on her books and articles. Alice, whom we all called by her nickname, Lily, often enriched the neighborhood by giving extemporaneous talks at the Healys, with whom she stayed, on topics like metaphysics or the principles of true art. Lily loved to take long, daily walks, and I often accompanied her down the leafy, tree-lined road that stretched between the Healys' house and our new place, a cottage Buzz and Tyagi had built on a piece of high, mountain-view property we bought from the Healys. With her arm linked into mine for steadiness, Lily and I would stroll along discussing whatever happened to be going on in our lives, in the world, or in the Church, which she loved with an enormous, holy passion that was, for me, a wondrous thing to observe and absorb. Books by her husband, who converted to Catholicism in his mid-twenties, were another special source of inspiration, particularly his brilliant works *Transformation in Christ*, *Marriage*, and *Liturgy and Personality*.

Then, too, there was Father David Tickerhoof, a warm, gentle Franciscan priest who also visited every summer and, during July of 1992, gave a series of talks at the Healys that he called "The Good Shepherd Seminar." Urging those of us who sat in on his talks to be "fruit-bearers in unconditional love," Father Dave was the person that we all decided to ask, at the end of that summer, how we could become Catholic. Father Dave explained that first we'd have to take instruction from a priest, and he knew an excellent one in New Jersey, Father Brendan Murray.

When we arrived home, Buzz and I called Father Brendan, who invited us to join his RCIA group at St. Pius X in Montville, about twenty minutes from our home. Keri and Tyagi, meanwhile, had decided to join an RCIA program at a local parish. After several unsatisfactory sessions, however, in which it was clear that a watered-down, de-Romanized training was being presented, they joined us with Father Brendan, who personally taught us for three hours every week.

We arrive at last

Six months later, at the April 10, 1993, Easter Vigil, all four of us became confirmed members of the Roman Catholic Church, with Tyagi as a catechumen receiving Baptism, as well. Amazingly, during our six years as Protestant evangelicals, no one had ever thought to have him baptized. Father Brendan, with a sense of theological theatricality, fully immersed Tyagi's head in a basin of water three times, crying out: "In the name of the Father . . . and the Son . . . and the Holy Spirit . . . !" Then, with a white robe and candle, Tyagi went up and down the aisles lighting everyone's candles, including those of our friends who had traveled to New Jersey to celebrate with us: Pat and Jim Crisman and their son, Ted, whom Tyagi had asked to be his godfather, Nick and Jane Healy, Margaret Farren, and Alice von Hildebrand. It was a glorious night, ablaze with candles and bells and joy.

While our journey had taken us "home" at last, because of the Reformation, it also separated us from friends and family members with whom we no longer shared a church pew, especially my parents, who were the last to learn of our decision. However, at my Lutheran confirmation, my father wrote these words in the Bible he and my mother gave me, words that I hope I've lived up to:

> On this day you assume full responsibility for your own religious faith. Believe in yourself, for the truth will always be in your heart. Think, contemplate, and reason in your beliefs. Never accept only because someone else has said it is so, for faith that does not remain consistent with reason soberly done cannot stand. May God bless

you in your efforts, shared with everyone on earth, to find a meaning in life and an integration with God that places your soul and mind at peace.

To his memory, to my loving mom, and to my three little high-spirited cradle Catholic grandchildren, Justin, Zoe, and Brendan, I dedicate this true story.

Ad Dominum omnia gloria.

Kristen McLaughlin has worked in publishing for more than thirty-five years as a journalist, book and magazine editor, and public relations writer. With her husband, playwright Buzz McLaughlin, she has written scripts for The Family Channel, as well as several screenplays and teleplays. A member of the Writers Guild of America, she is currently at work on a book about the conversion experiences in her family. She and her husband live in New Jersey in the winter and New Hampshire in the summer and spend much of their time playing with their three young grandchildren.

4

A Matter of Conscience

Linda Poindexter

I am in awe of the pattern and the plan God lays out for each person. As I grow older and more reflective, His plan becomes clearer to me. I now recognize all the signs and helps along the way, and the pattern is beautiful to behold. I am also filled with pain, chagrin, and embarrassment when I think about how many times in life I ignored His direction and went my willful way.

I can remember, at times in life, being sure that God only spoke to and guided certain select souls, thinking that it was presumptuous to suppose that I, a common sinner, could have genuine spiritual experiences and could come to know Christ intimately. My small, finite mind could not conceive of a God who wished to have personal contact with every single person in the world and had a plan for each one of them. I couldn't imagine a God so immense, so powerful, so loving. However, I now know it must be true because He has a plan for me, and I know that I am not unique.

Christian roots

I was blessed from birth to be part of a Christian family. I went to church every Sunday, and in the years of World War II, when my family lived in my grandparents' home, I learned many beautiful old hymns that my grandmother sang as she went about her chores. Faith and church were things I took for granted.

The church of my youth, the Disciples of Christ, was Protestant, but unusual in its practice of having communion at every worship service. I viewed it as nothing more than a symbolic memorial; nonetheless, I learned at an early age the importance of the Eucharist.

There was something unique about the particular church I attended, Third Christian Church of Indianapolis, Indiana. It was a very large church with a small chapel called the Madonna Chapel. It had a painting of the Blessed Mother on the wall above the communion table, which was a very unusual thing, indeed, to see in a Protestant church in the Midwest. Recently, I learned the chapel actually had several paintings of Mary on the front and side walls. The chapel was the project of a pastor's wife in the early nineteenth century. Apparently, she was a devout Christian and great devotee of European art. She dreamed of having a chapel adorned with copies of great paintings of our Lady. I now believe that chapel introduced me to our Blessed Mother and that she has remained with me throughout my life. These two early gifts—weekly communion services and the presence of our Lady—set me on the journey that would finally lead me home to the Catholic Church.

As a youth, I had many Catholic friends. I heard about the Mass, Confession, and first Holy Communion. I even visited Catholic churches and found them to be beautiful places of awe and mystery. I actually envied my Catholic friends. At times, I wanted to be a member of a Church that offered such beauty and mystery and, further, demanded so much of her people, helping to sanctify them.

In high school, I dated a very nice boy from the local Catholic boys' high school. I was too young and inexperienced to recognize the training in purity and respect for young women he had been given. (I only wish young people today had the benefit of the education in purity and decency that was part of Catholic education in the past.) My parents' friends were outraged I was allowed to date a Catholic. What if we should marry? There was a wall of separation between Catholics and Protestants at that time. While I admired the Catholic Church and envied my Catholic friends, it would never have occurred to me that I could become Catholic myself.

We moved to the Washington, D.C., area when I was in high school, and I continued to be active within the church and to enjoy the fellowship of a youth group. I attended a conference for youth at Bethany Beach, Delaware. It was a memorable week. At the final service, we were asked to pray and consider giving our lives to service within the church. I signed that pledge. Later, I dismissed the idea of going to a church college and becoming a Christian educator. I was young and wanted to party. I concluded I had been overly influenced by the conference and youthful emotions. Much later in life, however, when I felt called to the ordained ministry, I thought perhaps God was calling on me to honor that pledge.

Marriage and the Episcopal priesthood

Instead of a Christian college, I attended the University of Maryland. While I was there, I met my future husband, John Poindexter, a midshipman at the Naval Academy. All midshipmen had to attend Divine Service on the weekend, and the majority chose to attend the main chapel service, which was Morning Prayer, according to the rites of the Episcopal Church. The midshipmen marched to chapel, resplendent in their uniforms. Their "dates" sat in the balcony. John and I became so accustomed to the Episcopal liturgy that it seemed only natural to enter the Episcopal Church together a few months after our marriage.

John's naval career caused us to move many times, but wherever we went, we always made the Episcopal Church our home. Our five sons were baptized and raised in that faith communion, and we were strengthened and nurtured by it. I will always be grateful to that faith community. In 1976, the Episcopal Church began to ordain women, and although I was for the change in tradition, I did not immediately consider becoming a priest. In 1980, I suddenly felt called to think about it. One Sunday, while watching our Episcopal priest distribute communion, I thought that perhaps God was calling me to the ordained ministry. My boys were at a stage in their lives when they no longer needed my undivided attention, and I had begun to think and pray about my own future.

I soon discovered that to become an ordained priest was not an easy thing to do. We had moved back to the Washington, D.C., area. At that time, there were more Episcopal priests than there were positions for them, thus the bishops were becoming increasingly more selective about those whom they admitted to postulancy and sent off to seminary. At age forty-three, I was considered a bit old.

After two years of preliminary work, my bishop finally said that I could go to seminary and be ordained upon graduation. I commuted to the Episcopal Theological Seminary in Alexandria, Virginia, while continuing my responsibilities as wife and mother to the two sons remaining at home. To make matters more complicated—much more complicated—my husband was with the National Security Council. Eventually, he became the National Security Advisor in President Reagan's White House. He was very busy! I don't quite know how we all survived the three years of seminary, but by God's grace we did. I was ordained a deacon and went to work at a nearby church, and in December 1986, I was ordained to the priesthood.

What do I now make of that time when I was an ordained priest? I don't believe it was a mistake or that I did not hear God right. Rather, I am convinced it was part of God's plan that I do the work of priest and pastor for a time, before I was allowed to come all the way "home." I liked being a priest most of the time, and I think the Lord used me to do some good work. A colleague once suggested to me that perhaps the purpose of my training and experience was to put me in place to assist one family who went through a crisis of love and trust. Perhaps, with my help, they ended up stronger and back with God. I like that thought. It certainly was a great privilege to be with people during extraordinary times in their lives and to be able to bring God's blessing or healing to them. Yet, I always felt torn between the needs of my husband and family and the needs of the parish. It was very difficult to leave one for the other. Emotionally, I constantly felt pulled in two directions. Though my sons no longer live at home, I have discovered motherhood never ends. Once the grandchildren start arriving, it is hard not to be with them. While I was a parish priest, I began to understand the blessing of the celibate priesthood.

During my time as a priest, I met many former Catholics who had become Episcopalian. Many had joined the Episcopal Church because they were divorced and wished to marry again and still be able to receive the sacraments. Others had fallen away from the Catholic Church for a long time, no longer wanted to be practicing Catholics, but found in the Episcopalian denomination a place that felt like home. (I hope and pray these Catholics have found their way back to their true home.) Part of my job as a priest was to prepare such people for reception into the Episcopal Church. I always found that former Catholics were very interested in what the rules were going to be in their new church home. I took pride in explaining to them there were few rules. I was not, and never had been, anti-Catholic, but my theological mindset was typically Episcopalian. Episcopalians take great pride in their liturgy and in their ability to think and decide for themselves. They believe every person can read the Bible, pray, and know what God wills. While I was a priest, this view of things suited me just fine. Being by nature rebellious, I liked not having rules to follow. I had much to learn about humility and obedience. It took a long time for me to understand and accept there is a truth beyond all our individual conceptions of truth.

I begin to see the truth about abortion

Eighteen years ago, I was willing to leave some very important issues up to the individual. For instance, on the subject of abortion, I would have characterized my own position as personally antiabortion but politically pro-choice. The good Lord was kind enough not to let me continue thinking this way. Slowly, I began to see that abortion is always and everywhere in opposition to the will of God. I came to that knowledge through the witness of the Catholic Church and the witness of individuals, both Catholic and Protestant. President Reagan, for instance, never wavered in his support for life from the moment of conception. On the tenth anniversary of *Roe* v. *Wade*, he wrote an essay called "Abortion and the Conscience of a Nation."[16] He consistently supported the Republican Party's pro-life plank and worked to prevent public funding of national and international programs that advocate for or perform abortions. At the time, I wondered

---

[16] For the complete text of "Abortion and the Conscience of a Nation," see http://humanlifereview.com/reagan/reagan_conscience.html.

why he placed such importance on an issue that could have been a political liability. He sent the President's Pro-life bill to Congress in 1987; it would have put Congress on record against *Roe v. Wade* and denied federal funding for abortions. Of course, it did not pass, but even when such legislative initiatives fail, they provide valuable witness, which may change minds and hearts in the end.

As I began to recognize the horror of abortion, I became painfully aware of the incapacity of the Episcopalian Church to address the issue in any coherent fashion. The Episcopalian Church in the United States meets in a general convention every three years. A house of bishops and a house of deputies vote on matters of policy brought to the convention. The deputies are laypeople and clergy, elected by their dioceses. In many conventions, that body reiterated the position that abortion always has a "tragic dimension" and should never be used as a form of birth control or simply for convenience. However, the conventions also always stated that they were against any legislation restricting the right to abortion. I responded by joining the National Organization of Episcopalians for Life (N.O.E.L.). They are a wonderful group of people. Although they are not highly respected in the Episcopal Church as a whole, they maintain a witness for life that I hope has won over hearts and souls and perhaps has saved the lives of many unborn children. A convention in 1997 refused to condemn even partial birth abortion, saying that the Episcopal Church viewed it with "grave concern." I was gravely concerned about a church that could not condemn the murder of innocent children!

The tyranny of the individual conscience
The Episcopal Church is completely preoccupied with the human sexuality issues with which the whole world has been

dealing. Over time, I became disheartened by many of the clergy who were coming to believe that homosexual unions were something that could be blessed by the church and that sexually active homosexuals could be ordained. I know they were trying to be compassionate and just; but instead, they were leading people astray, encouraging that which is not from God. Those of us who disagreed—and there were many—were told that we were unchristian and unloving. No longer was it acceptable to love the sinner but hate the sin.

I was now beginning to see the problem with leaving it up to individuals to decide for themselves what is right and what is wrong. I felt great sadness and pity for the people who had been faithful and devout members of the Episcopal Church their entire lives, trying to come to grips with the constantly changing standards for truth in their church. For many others, the changes in the Episcopal Church's positions were a source of pride; Episcopalians were keeping up with the world. Colleagues defended their pro-choice position by pointing to the fact that the Anglican Church did not always approve of contraception, as if it were self-evident that contraception is a good thing.

As a priest, I was scandalized by a certain Episcopalian bishop who openly supported "gay rights" and even ordained self-professing homosexuals to the priesthood.

He wrote increasingly strange things about Christianity. Finally, he wrote a book that trashed just about everything in the creeds. For instance, he claimed there is no saving efficacy in the Cross. This was the bishop of a diocese, a person who had taken vows to uphold the teachings of the faith. What was even more disturbing, however, was the reaction of the hierarchy: No one rebuked him or officially rebutted his heretical teachings.

These matters deeply pained my conscience, but I had no thought of leaving—at least no conscious thought. Often, I gave thanks for the consistent witness of the Catholic Church in matters of doctrine, especially on those issues pertaining to the culture of life. I came to greatly respect and pray for our Holy Father. The good Lord was gradually teaching me that there are reasons for authority, for a Church that is unafraid to speak God's will and Word to His people.

Surreptitious forays into the Catholic Church

I worked in five different parishes: two as an assistant and three as the priest-in-charge during the two years it takes for a parish to search for and call a new rector (pastor). There came a time in one parish where I was an assistant that I simply could not pray within the confines of the building's walls. So many interpersonal and spiritual problems were in the air that prayer had become impossible for me.

Seeking haven and peace, I walked around a circle to our neighboring Catholic parish. I now believe this was no idle decision on my part but an example of firm guidance by a loving Father. I entered the church, genuflected to the presence of our Lord, and knelt to pray. From the moment I entered, I felt a peace and comfort that filled me with awe and wonder. Almost immediately, I began to wonder if I could become Catholic. I began to cross that circle on a regular basis for prayer. Later, I came to understand that my sense of peace and comfort flowed from the Blessed Sacrament, which strangely enough is the name of the church where I went to pray.

Addictions, even good ones, grow. The next thing I knew I was sneaking over for midday Mass. I would remove my clerical collar and wear a sweater just to maintain anonymity. Sometimes, I received the Eucharist. As I said, I liked making up my own rules. I believed in the "Real Presence" of Christ in the Eucharist, and I thought that made it all right to receive. I still had much to learn about obedience and humility. I was becoming infatuated with the Catholic Church; however, infatuations need time to grow into true love.

The Virgin Mary had intrigued me for years. Perhaps it would be more accurate to say I felt drawn to her. I kept thinking I would prepare and teach a course on the meaning of the Blessed Mother for Episcopalians. To that end, I purchased several books, but never found the time to read all of them. Though still in its infancy, my devotion to Mary led me to think about praying the Rosary. I bought a nice, modest Rosary and a little booklet to teach me what I did not know about praying the Rosary. I began to pray the Rosary in the early morning while I walked my dog in the park. Though I was not always attentive, I still believe that daily repetition made the mysteries a part of my inner life and drew me closer to our Lady and our Lord.

The importance of authority

I decided to do some further study of Catholic belief and doctrine. I bought the *Catechism of the Catholic Church* and eventually began to read it. Cradle Catholics often do not realize the great gift of having the beliefs of the Church so clearly presented. According to many Episcopalians, God is essentially mysterious; therefore, the truth, as much as we can know of it, lies in the questions and not the answers. I started to really wonder about this kind of thinking. Does God want us to wander in the dark? Is He not a God who has chosen to reveal Himself to us? I began to have a new appreciation and respect for the teaching authority of the Church, that is, the Magisterium. Previously, I had been appreciative of definitive Church teachings only when they coincided with my own thinking. Now, I felt myself drawn to that most famous of Anglican converts, John Henry Cardinal

Newman. In Newman's *Apologia pro vita sua*, I came across this powerful argument for the Magisterium:

> I am brought to speak of the Church's infallibility, as a provision, adapted by the mercy of the Creator to preserve religion in the world, and to restrain that freedom of thought which is one of the greatest of our natural gifts, and to rescue it from its own suicidal excesses.

Not long after the time when I began to pray in that church near my place of ministry, I felt the need to be free to spend time with my husband and family. The difficulties in my parish, coupled with the demands of family life, were taking a heavy toll on my physical, emotional, and spiritual well-being. I was blessed to have the option of not working. I gave my pastor six months' notice, so that I could bring about an organized departure. God's guidance and preparation in light of our needs is often breathtakingly marvelous. Within weeks after I left, our oldest son was suddenly widowed, leaving him devastated, with two small children to care for. I was free to be with them and support them through this time of crisis. (God has since greatly blessed our lives. My son is now happily married to a lovely lady with a daughter, and they have added another daughter to our family.)

For a few months after the death of our daughter-in-law, I enjoyed a period of relative peace, although it was tinged by sadness and concern for my son. John and I visited different Episcopal churches on Sundays. Though I hate to admit it, we sometimes skipped worship altogether. I started attending weekday Mass at St. Raphael's Church near our home, once or twice a week. I began to think and pray seriously and deeply about converting.

I return to the parish one last time

This reverie was broken, however, when I received a call to ministry that I decided I must answer. A nearby parish was in dire need of an interim priest after the sudden departure of their priest. It was a parish that had many problems and needed some tender loving care. I didn't really want to accept the call because I felt that I had, in many ways, left the Episcopal ministry. I seemed to have little in common with my colleagues, and I wondered if I could do justice to these people who appeared to have so many needs. I also wanted the freedom to spend time with my husband on our sailboat. Having to work on Sundays precludes sailing weekends; nevertheless, I believed the Lord wanted me to accept this position, and I did so. I determined to put my longings for the Catholic Church on hold. Perhaps, I thought, returning to the parish would put a stop to this love affair of mine.

It turned out to be a wonderful parish. I lived in the same vicinity of the church and had known some of the people for many years. It was a beautiful church with a long history and a "high church" tradition, that is, a more "Catholic" form of worship. The Stations of the Cross were mounted on the walls, and there was a tabernacle for the Blessed Sacrament. In other Episcopal churches I had served, the Sacrament was reserved in the sanctuary in an ambry, a recess in the wall usually on the side of the sanctuary. It is difficult to explain the Episcopal understanding of the Eucharist because there is no defined doctrine, at least none that I have ever found or been taught. Generally speaking, Episcopalians believed in the "Real Presence" of Christ in the consecrated bread and wine; however, Anglican teaching has historically rejected the Catholic teaching of transubstantiation. The church's *Thirty-Nine Articles,* the historical statements of belief of the Anglican Church, state:

Transubstantiation (or the change of the substance of Bread and Wine) in the Supper of the Lord, cannot be proved by Holy Writ; but is repugnant to the plain words of Scripture, overthroweth the nature of a Sacrament, and hath given occasion to many superstitions. The Body of Christ is given, taken, and eaten, in the Supper, only after a heavenly and spiritual manner.

In point of fact, there are many views and practices associated with the "Real Presence" within the Episcopal Church, and all are tolerated. They range from those held by the Anglo-Catholics who reserve the consecrated bread and wine in a tabernacle, genuflect before the Eucharist, and regularly have Benediction of the Blessed Sacrament, to those of the "Protestants," who show no reverence for the remaining elements. I always followed the Anglo-Catholic practices and beliefs. As with many other issues, Episcopalians consider it a strength to have no clearly defined doctrine. I now believe such an attitude leads to the false impression that there is no knowable truth.

Parting is bittersweet

Try as I might, I could not renounce my Catholic ways. Before I received the Eucharist, I always whispered: "Lord, I am not worthy to receive You, but only say the word, and I shall be healed." Those words are not part of the Episcopal liturgy, and each time I said them, I felt I was somehow touching the Catholic Church—touching what was beginning to seem like home.

My ministry in the parish was blessed and happy, but I was glad when it was time to leave. Once more, I was free to spend time with my husband. I was free also to begin thinking again about the Catholic Church. On Sundays, when John wanted to go to church, we went to an Episcopal church together; however, the liturgy had become flat to me and devoid of meaning. This feeling was overwhelming; thus no matter how lovely the music, how beautiful the liturgy, how excellent the homily, I did not feel I was at worship. I felt a bittersweet sort of sadness; I was sad for my loss, but alive with longing for the Catholic Church.

I began to look forward to the Sundays John did not choose to attend church, because then I would go to Mass. I went back to attending weekday Mass once or twice a week. I had not taken the step of talking to anyone in the Catholic Church, but I began to read stories written by converts. I went to see video presentations by the Catholic convert Scott Hahn at the local Catholic parish. His story was much more dramatic than mine, since he originally despised Catholicism and actively sought to convince Catholics to leave the Church. Compared to him, I was a pushover.

I talked to my spiritual director, a wonderful, holy Episcopal priest who was as troubled as I by the goings-on in the Episcopal Church. He understood why I was attracted to Rome, but he could not really share my enthusiasm. It was hard to think about leaving the communion of this good Christian. (Fortunately, we have remained good friends.) Other considerations held me back. My sons are all active within their churches: two in the Episcopal Church, two in independent Protestant churches, and one in the Presbyterian Church. I am grateful they are all men of faith and committed to raising their families in the Christian faith, and I did not want to do anything to drive a wedge between us. Moreover, my family and many friends had made sacrifices and prayed hard for my ordination and my priestly role. I was truly reluctant to disappoint them, to make them feel they had in some way been cheated and deceived. Furthermore, I worried about those whom I had served as an ordained minister. What would they think? What would it do to their faith? Would they think I had been faking it as a priest?

While I had it much easier than many Protestant pastors who must give up their livelihoods to become Catholic, I still found it all very difficult. Was I being selfish? Perhaps God really wanted me to stay right where I was and work for reform and change. I also felt a lingering reluctance to accept all of the Church's teachings. At that time, I still had questions about some teachings, such as the ordination of women, contraception, the validity of the Anglican orders, and the definition of new dogma. I knew I could not convert and become a "cafeteria Catholic," picking and choosing the beliefs that appealed to me. It is a lesson in humility to accept authority, and humility has never been one of my virtues.

Finally, I did a fateful thing. I decided to go to Mass every day during Advent of 1998. The blessings were momentous; I felt surrounded by love and warmth, but I was on the outside looking in. I yearned with all my heart to be at one with those people. Whenever Father Mike prayed for our Holy Father, I wanted to know that he was my Holy Father, too. I became suspicious of my emotional reactions. Sometimes, it is hard to believe that God could want us to do that which we so much desire to do. For me, it is easier to believe that God wants us to be tough, to do the hard, disagreeable thing.

I am ready

It is amazing how little bits of information can sometimes fall into one's lap. I picked up my recent copy of *First Things*, a journal centering on religion and public life, and read an article by Jennifer Ferrara in which she described some of her journey to Rome. She said that she had "arrived at the doorstep of *Lumen Gentium* (no. 14)":[17]

---

[17] See *Lumen Gentium* (no. 14) in the *Documents of Vatican II*.

Whosoever, therefore, knowing that the Catholic Church was made necessary by God through Jesus Christ, would refuse to enter or to remain in her could not be saved.

Her article, and especially these words, not only gave me food for serious thought, but a positive reason to convert. I was convinced the Roman Catholic Church was the fullest expression of the Church established by Jesus Christ. I believed the Church taught the truth. I believed the bread and wine became the actual Body and Blood of Jesus during the Eucharist. How could I, then, in good conscience, keep myself apart from this communion of faith? I had made the long journey from valuing freedom of thought and decision, to gratitude for the Magisterium and for centuries of Tradition that offered assurance of the timeless beliefs of the Church—ergo, true freedom. Jesus Christ is the same yesterday, today, and forever, and so are God's laws and God's promises.

Ideally, I would have liked to wait until my husband, John, was ready to convert, so that we could come in together. He, however, was not ready at all, and I was. He believed that it was the right thing for me to do but had not yet reached the same conclusion for himself. I am not a patient person and wondered if God was calling on me to be patient, but I did not think so. John and I decided that to wait for him would put undue and unfair pressure on him, as he knew how very much I wanted to be Catholic. We arrived at a compromise: With my pastor's permission, I would join the RCIA program already half done for that year and be received into the Church at the Easter Vigil of 1999.[18] If John chose, he could come to Mass with me. If he

---

[18] RCIA, or the Rite of Christian Initiation for Adults, is a catechetical program for adults seeking full, sacramental communion within the Roman Catholic Church.

wanted to attend Episcopal services, I would first go to Mass and then accompany him to his church. As it turned out, John came to Mass with me most of the time. What turned out to be yet another example of God's preparation and planning, John was received into the Roman Catholic Church and confirmed by our pastor on August 14, 2001. In response to the tragic events of 9/11, John was asked to return to government service as Director of the Information Awareness Office of the Defense Advanced Research Projects Agency. His Catholic faith was a major source of strength for this strenuous new undertaking at a time when we thought we would be looking at full retirement.

Remaining questions

I can honestly say I have never looked back. Almost every time I pray, I give thanks for being Catholic. I have come to a fuller understanding of most of the teachings I once questioned. When it comes to those that still trouble me, I am more able to honestly say I am not the final authority; I can trust and rely upon the authority of the Catholic Church. To members of my former church, this may seem like mental laziness or simplemindedness. I believe it's faith. I am often asked by those near and dear to me how I can reconcile my former beliefs with those of the Catholic Church. Of course, they needn't be reconciled, for one's beliefs can change in light of greater revelation.

I am asked most often about the ordination of women, and I admit to being troubled by the issue. I do not fully understand the reasons for not ordaining women, but I do believe that if the Holy Father says the Church cannot ordain women, then it is true. I believed when I was an Episcopalian that the Anglican communion was one of the three branches of Catholicism and that if the ordination of women was God's will, then someday the whole Catholic Church would ordain women. If these ordinations were not God's will, the practice would die away. Such reasoning became irrelevant when I came to realize the Episcopal Church was not Catholic.

Although I have always intuitively felt the Protestant and Catholic understanding of ordination was profoundly different, I did not have the words to explain the difference. I am indebted to George Weigel for his excellent exposition of the difference in *The Truth of Catholicism*. He identifies the Protestant view of ordained ministry as a functional one; the pastor is the one who does certain things. By contrast, in the Catholic sacramental imagination, the priest is an icon. He represents Christ the High Priest. Since Christ's relationship to the Church is spousal, the priest, acting as an icon of Christ, makes Christ's loving gift of Himself present in the consecration of the bread and the wine. In order for the priest to truly represent Christ, the priest must be male.

Though the Catholic priest is always male, the Church has a softer, more feminine side, which I never recognized until I actually became Catholic. I suppose all of the anti-Catholic rhetoric about the Church being a male-dominated enterprise had soaked into my subconscious. The reality is much different. I find it to be a communion where women are valued, admired, and appreciated. I suspect this is most true for women who really like being women, as I do. I have found in the Church a high regard for the holiness of the family (the domestic church, as John Paul II calls it). This respect for the importance of the home and family has much to do with an atmosphere that values the feminine.

Falling in love with Jesus

At the core of my spiritual journey has been the desire to draw closer to Jesus in the Eucharist. I believed that He was truly present in the consecrated bread and wine of the Episcopal Church, and I still think He may be present somehow to those who receive communion in that faith. However, there is a difference in the Catholic Church. The bread and the wine *are* the Body and Blood of Jesus. It was His presence that spoke to me as I entered the church for prayer. It was that for which I yearned, which gave me the "falling in love" feeling. I wasn't just falling in love with the Catholic Church; I was falling in love with Jesus. Of course, I cannot prove Jesus is present in His Body and Blood, but I know this is true, and I see the fruits of His presence in my own life and in the lives of others. I am not gifted with being focused in prayer, but I can be quiet and enjoy longer periods of prayer when I am in the presence of the Blessed Sacrament and even more so when the Sacrament is exposed for adoration.

Being received into the Catholic Church was a major spiritual high for me. It bore no resemblance to "joining a church." I floated on air. I reveled in the great privilege of receiving the Body and Blood of our Lord. But as the newness of the experience wore off, I missed the anticipation and the preparation and the intense prayer that accompanied it. I knew that I was coasting. However, at this point of spiritual dryness, I began to discover the deep benefits and riches that the Church has to offer to those who seek them. I sought out a spiritual director, as I am a person who needs to be held accountable. He helped me establish a rule of life and began to introduce me to great classics of spiritual reading, some of which I owned and had never read. There is so much help in the Catholic Church for those seeking ways to become more holy. Devotions to the Divine Mercy or the Sacred Heart, to the Blessed Mother, or to particular saints, all give blessings of understanding and closeness to Christ. Being able to enter a church at almost any time of day and to pray in the presence of the Blessed Sacrament makes mental prayer so much easier. Adoration has its own special joys and gifts. Finally, and centrally, there is the ultimate intimacy of receiving the Body and Blood of Christ into our own bodies. If you think on that for a time, as the consecrated Host is still dissolving in your mouth, it is awe-inspiring. When I receive the Eucharist, I feel not only the closeness of Christ but intimacy with His entire body—the whole company of the faithful around the earth and throughout the ages.

In my quest for intimacy with our Lord, I have developed an understanding and appreciation of mortification. Although I, for many years, "gave up something" for Lent and found the practice to be spiritually beneficial, I never truly understood the idea of mortification. This word always brought to my mind pictures of medieval people flagellating themselves. It always sounded a little "over the top." However, under the gentle prodding of my spiritual director, I have come to understand and value the offering of little sacrifices, the forgoing of pleasures or gratifications. Like most Americans, I am addicted to instant gratification of my desires, and "addicted" is the right world. It is extremely difficult, for me at least, to value Christ above all things when I am surrounded by so many pleasures and attractive things. If prodded by the Spirit to make some small offering of something I love, like giving up bread for a whole day, I notice that I begin to bargain and quibble, as if a single day without bread were too painful to contemplate. The training that comes from abstaining or offering up little sacrifices awakens my mind to my very real attachment to comforts and luxuries, and it helps me achieve a small detachment from the goods of this world.

All things come together in the Catholic Church

Ultimately, those little sacrifices deepen my understanding of suffering as redemptive and purposeful, not meaningless evil cast onto us by fate or a capricious god. When I was a priest, people often asked: "How could God allow such a terrible thing to happen?" I often encountered people who believed it was up to God to remove suffering and pain. If He did not, they believed it was due to a failure of prayer or a lack of faith. In my experience, Protestants often do not know what to do with their sufferings. Granted, we all ask for protection and relief from sorrow, illness, pain, or difficulty. I certainly do. Only in the Catholic Church, however, do I hear it is imperative that we "offer up" our sufferings, use the pain or sorrow as prayer for others, use it as "cross" and be creative within that. Even the mere thought there is a use for pain (a redemptive purpose) seems to help. But how and why is it used? In seeking an answer, I read the Holy Father's apostolic letter "On the Christian Meaning of Human Suffering." Nothing John Paul II has written is light or easy reading, but I highly recommend it. The ideas that impressed me the most were those about Christ's own suffering. In the Passion of Christ, love and human suffering become linked, and redemption is accomplished through suffering. In the great mystery of God's plan for our salvation, we are privileged to participate in the redemptive suffering of Christ. We do so through our own suffering, and we do so through the Mass, as all things Catholic come together in the Eucharist.

I often wish I had converted to Catholicism at an early age and had been the beneficiary of the teachings of the Church in my youth. Had I heard and followed the teachings, I might have saved myself from some painful and foolish times. I especially wish we would have become Catholic in time to raise our sons in the faith. I like to think I would have been more patient and more intentional in my mothering if I had received the benefit of a Catholic understanding of marriage and family and parenting. While there is no opportunity to do it all over, I am grateful to have come to this time of life and to have this wonderful new blessing of being Catholic.

Linda Poindexter was born in Indiana. She received her undergraduate degree from the University of Southern California and her Master of Divinity from the Episcopal Theological Seminary in Alexandria, Virginia. Linda has been married to John Poindexter since 1958. They have five sons and thirteen grandchildren. Linda and John have considered the Maryland suburbs of Washington, D.C., home since 1966, although they have often been away for Navy tours of duty. Linda is currently writing a full-length story of their spiritual journey and conversion, to be published by Ignatius Press.

5

The Lord Never Gave Up on Me

Victoria Madeleine

The Lord never gave up on me, though I lived in darkness for many years. Even though I tried to fill my emptiness with everything under the sun except Him, He continued to pursue me and to invite me to live in His love. Yet, I kept refusing His invitation because I felt there was no way God would take me back. I thought I had offended Him too often. I gave up on Him, but He never gave up on me.

I was born into a Catholic family. My father attended Mass every Sunday; however, my family never prayed together. I remember almost nothing of my Catholic childhood, not my lessons, and not even my first Holy Communion, which I received at the age of seven in May 1967. The few scattered memories I do have are not positive. I was in Catholic school at the time, but I hated it so much I transferred myself right out of it. Sometime later, I told God I wanted nothing to do with Him or His Church. Hence, my life of sorrow and misery began at a young age.

Encounters with the occult
I was a bingo rat. All the Catholic churches in my neighborhood had bingo. My mother spent most nights at these

churches. While she played bingo, I played with my friend Gianna.[19] Through Gianna, I had my first encounter with the occult. When Gianna wasn't around, I sometimes played in the grotto in the yard of my home parish. A statue of Our Lady of Peace was in it, and I now believe many seeds must have been sown in my heart in that place, lying dormant until grace helped them to grow. I also like to think Mother Mary placed me in her heart there. As mothers know, we cannot make our children do anything, for the Lord has given us free will. All we can do is pray for our wayward children. I believe Mary always prayed for me.

At the time, though, I was under the spell of Gianna. Her father was an alcoholic and often became very abusive. Her mother was addicted to gambling. Gianna was a "bully," but I was attracted to her seeming power over situations and people. She beat me up often, but I still hung out with her whenever she showed up on bingo nights. Sometimes, I went home with her to spend the night. There were many abandoned houses in her neighborhood, and Gianna claimed to see the spirits of people who lurked around these places. She practiced "white witch-craft" and said she had ESP. I don't know how much of this was serious and how much was dabbling, but I do know now that it opened up the door for evil to enter my soul.

My search to fill the void that only God could fill—a search that began when I was very young—is what led me to be attracted to this power that Gianna had. She lived far away, so we lost contact when I was old enough not to have to go with my mom to bingo. I continued to dabble in witchcraft through slumber-party séances, Mary Worth, levitation, and Ouija boards. It was "all in fun," as people say, but these seemingly innocuous activities opened the door wider for the evil one.

---

[19] Gianna is a pseudonym.

My descent into darkness

By the time I reached high school in the mid-1970s, I was far from God and His Church. I was totally messed up. I partied all the time and never knew where I was going to be from one day to the next. Deep inside I wanted God, but I refused to acknowledge my longing. I was intrigued by Carl Sagan and questions about science and space. I loved John Lennon and the lyrics of his song *Imagine.* I even thought about running away and joining a communist group. My English classes were, what were then called, "alternative classes." They included "Mind over Matter," "Self-communication," and "The Occult and New Age." In these classes, I was introduced to spells and tarot cards. I felt both drawn toward and repelled by this stuff, but the darkness won out.

During these times, I struggled with fitting in and being accepted and, as a result, felt most comfortable in a gang. We hung out at the cemetery. Although everyone had boyfriends, I didn't have one because I wasn't "easy." Plenty of girls were. When the senior prom came around, I didn't have a date. A friend of mine fixed me up with a friend of her boyfriend; he was twenty-two and wanted to go to the prom. I was very attracted to him and determined that I was not going to lose him. I thought the way to hold on to him was to have sex, and I lost my virginity at the age of seventeen. It is obvious to me now that peer pressure and my own feelings of hopelessness led me to do this.

I had fallen into a crowd that was always in trouble and always seeking ways to find relief from feelings of despair by altering their senses. Substance abuse was my life. Therefore, when I met this attractive twenty-two-year-old man, it was easy to give myself sexually to him. I knew deep down I was doing something very wrong, but I ran from the truth and fell more deeply into sin. My sin led to tragedy. I found myself pregnant and was scared to tell my parents, so I had an abortion. That was in 1977. It seemed so very easy. Sex was such a casual thing; nobody thought of the consequences. I would guess a third of my graduating class had had abortions. Many others had their babies; some kept them and others gave them up for adoption. After my abortion, my life became a living hell for the next six or seven years. It would be many more years before I would finally experience complete healing and reconciliation.

Three years later, I married the father of my aborted child. I pushed for the marriage because somehow I felt we had to get married. We didn't have a Christian wedding, as I wanted to be married outdoors, and we couldn't find a priest or Protestant minister who would marry us. Eleven months after our wedding, we had a baby boy. His father wanted to name him after Joshua. I didn't know who Joshua was, but after my husband explained to me the battle of Jericho, I knew this was the perfect name for our baby.

From the beginning of our marriage, my husband was abusive, but I thought he was a dream come true because he was sober and took me out of the world of drugs. It wasn't long, however, before drugs came back into our lives. My husband became addicted and got me started using drugs all over again. Our drug use continued to intensify until it led both of us into promiscuous lives.

When I was in high school, my older sister and her husband became "born again." They left the Catholic Church and began attending a fundamentalist Baptist Church. Wow, had they changed! I thought they were nuts. At first, I really didn't like this Jesus whom my sister and brother-in-law talked about. They burned all of their rock music and became "savers of souls." Every time I was with my sister, all she seemed to talk about was the beast and the mark of the devil and the number 666. It was pretty creepy. However, she gave me a copy of the New Testament, which I would read from time to time. I would also watch Hollywood portrayals of Jesus at Easter time, and I was drawn to Him. However, I couldn't understand why God would allow Jesus to be killed, so I never understood the whole picture. I fell in love with Jesus, but was mad at God. I now realize God was working mightily in me during those times, and I wanted so badly to have Him in my life. Still, I refused to go to church, and I really knew nothing about God. Even though I had fallen in love with Jesus, I wasn't living a Christian life. I figured I had done too much evil for God to ever take me back. I didn't understand the crucifixion, so for years I was angry at God for letting Jesus die on the cross.

My initial reaction to my husband's abuse was to try to change him and, thereby, bring the abuse to an end. I also thought I had to make my marriage work for the sake of my son, but my husband only became more abusive. Finally, I left the marriage for my son's sake because I had begun to fear for his life. I was no longer in anything I could call a relationship. My husband did not contest the divorce, and it was final in one year.

Despite my rejection of Him, God continues to look after me

After our separation, I fell even more deeply into a life of sin. Yet, God still did not give up on me and continued to send me messengers of His love; however, I rejected most of them. Just when I thought I couldn't go on with my life, the Lord sent John into my life. At first, we moved in together because we wanted to be with each other all the time. He accepted my son. I felt secure, and I loved him very much. My parents were opposed to our living together. My father was ill and didn't have long to live, and my mother pleaded with me to make things right before he died.

After a year of living together, in October of 1986, John and I were married by the mayor of the town in which we lived.

John, who is eighteen years older than I, had been through a prolonged and messy divorce, and he had raised two children, both of whom were teenagers. Meanwhile, we had many struggles raising my son who was four years old when John and I first met. Joshua was very troubled, which was not surprising given all he had been through in his short life. John and I decided it would be best if we didn't have any more children, yet deep down I knew this was wrong. Two months after we were married, I planned to have my tubes tied. When I went to the doctor to make the arrangements, I learned I was two weeks too late. Somehow, I knew this had to be the work of God. He had heard my silent prayer that I might have a child with this man whom I loved so much; however, the joy that attends the feeling of having a prayer answered passed quickly. I struggled with intense feelings of hopelessness.

When I was four months pregnant, my father died. My whole life flashed before my eyes as I looked down into his casket before they were about to close it. I collapsed into my husband's arms. He tried to comfort me by assuring me I would see my dad again, but I cried in sheer agony, "No, I won't because my daddy will be in heaven, and I am not going to be with him."

My second little miracle boy was born four and half months later, on September 25, 1987. I was reading my New Testament from time to time, but I still hadn't returned to church. I wanted to have Michael baptized because both my family and John's were Catholic, and this is what Catholics do. My born-again older sister was furious with me. She told me it would be a mistake, and she would not come. Michael was baptized in a Catholic church on November 1, 1987. True to her word, my older sister did not attend. For the next several months, I felt very heavy of heart. I still felt I had gone too far in my life of sin and that God would never take me back. Meanwhile, a friend at the day-care center where I brought Joshua encouraged me to go to church. On Palm Sunday 1988, I found my way back to church. Only it happened to be a United Methodist church.

I finally see the light

My conversion experience was radical because I went from extreme darkness to brilliant light. As with the two disciples on the road to Emmaus, the Scriptures were opened up to me. I attended Sunday school class that Palm Sunday, and the topic was the Holy Spirit. Suddenly, everything I had been reading from time to time over the last ten years of my life made sense to me. I understood and remembered things. The teacher spent a long time talking about the power of the Holy Spirit, and everything fell into place. She ended the class with a verse from the First Letter of Paul to the Corinthians that radically changed my life: "When all things are subjected to him, then the Son himself will also be subjected to him who put all things under him, that God may be everything to every one."[20]

I had so much zeal I could not contain myself. In retrospect, I see I did more harm than good. I was involved with many devout born-again Christians (outside of my Methodist congregation), most of whom were ex-Catholics. They are a tough breed of Christian. Those with whom I associated were very legalistic and the most anti-Catholic people I had ever met. They saw it as their personal mission to "save" every Catholic from going to hell.

Something is not right

I was starving to know more, and I began to devour the Scriptures every day and to attend every Bible study, prayer

---

[20] 1 Corinthians 15:28.

group, and worship service I could. In 1989, I enrolled in a Calvinistic Bible Study correspondence course, though I didn't realize at the time that different Protestant denominations teach many conflicting doctrines and ideas. I continued to search and study, but I felt something was missing from my life—a gap in my soul. I desired Jesus in an intimate way, yet something was hindering me, and I couldn't figure out what it was. The more I searched for Jesus, the more I came face to face with myself and my guilt. I couldn't understand why I didn't experience healing. My fellow Christians believed if you weren't born again, you went to hell. But just what did this mean? There had to be more than this one teaching summed up in a little prayer found on countless tracts all over the place: "Admit you're a sinner and accept Jesus in your heart, and you will be saved." Could it be that simple or that easy? If you pray it and still go on feeling guilty, then maybe you are not born again. How can one really know in the end? On and on I went in my search. I became involved in so many ministries that I neglected the true vocation I chose when I married and had children.

The more I grew spiritually, the more I began to see my past failings. The more I repented, the more I could not deal with the guilt. The more people kept telling me Jesus had forgiven me, the more I knew there had to be more to relieving my guilt than that. I knew God had forgiven me. That wasn't the problem. The problem was I didn't feel purified. No one seemed to understand this. I became involved with many Bible studies and searched for answers no one seemed to have. In my search for the fullness of truth, I studied the teachings of one denomination after another, but never even thought of looking to the Catholic Church. I was very anti-Catholic.

Sidetracked by my decision to become a Methodist minister

Though I had a Calvinistic beginning, I was soon introduced to John Wesley in my Methodist church. He seemed to teach the closest to what I thought must be the truth. I began formal studies to become an ordained Methodist minister, and all things really began to come together for me. The more I studied Church history, the more I began to see what Jesus had been trying to teach me all along.

Three months after I began going to a Methodist church, the pastor of the church left and a new one came. Pastor Jeff was to have a profound influence upon my life. I was very arrogant and thought I had to make sure he was really "saved." I requested a meeting with him and actually asked him if he were truly a Christian, that is, born again. He turned the conversation back on me and asked about my conversion, saying I may want to consider returning to the Catholic Church. I, in turn, explained how much I hated Catholicism, reciting all that I had learned from my anti-Catholic friends. I really had no clue what the Catholic Church taught.

One day, I stopped in a Christian bookstore to pick up something for my mother. When I was checking out, the cashier encouraged me to take one of the free tapes the store was giving away. I asked what it was about, and she said it was about the Blessed Mother in Medjugorje. I dropped it like a hot potato, but I found myself drawn to it. Finally, I left with the tape, and after I listened to it, I was touched and moved and changed. None of my Protestant friends would have understood. I shared my feelings with my closest friend, and she really didn't want to hear about it, so I kept them in my heart.

Meanwhile, the more I read about and studied Church history, the more I began to see something had gone wrong somewhere and that I was missing something. When I decided I wanted to become an ordained Methodist minister, I did not have a college degree. I enrolled in Camden County Community College with the hopes of transferring to a four-year college. In the fall of 1991, I took my first class in formal religious studies: "Nature and Meaning of the Old Testament." I also took a six-week course on basic lay speaking through the United Methodist Church (UMC). In 1992, I took another course through the UMC to become a certified lay speaker. The United Methodist Church allows certified lay speakers to preach. Meanwhile, I had transferred to a four-year college. I majored in theological studies and minored in biblical studies, with the hope of one day attending seminary. In the spring of 1993, during a class on the "History and Appreciation of Art," the Mother of God touched my heart. Two classes later, in the fall of 1993, in "Biblical Themes in Art," I felt I was no longer seeing things the same way as my fellow Protestant brothers and sisters in Christ; however, I continued in my quest to become an ordained United Methodist Church pastor. I felt I was being led by the Holy Spirit to the truth. During this time, I noticed a disconcerting change taking place in my pastor. Jeff was not as supportive as he once was. He suggested there were other ways to serve the Lord besides becoming a Methodist pastor. I argued with him and couldn't understand the change in him.

I was in my "Theological Thinking" class in the spring of 1994 when I started to see some of the great flaws in the churches of the Reformation. Intuitively, I felt there was something wrong with many of the Protestant doctrines. I was beginning to think like a Catholic without knowing it. During this time, I pondered many things in my heart.

I had been at my theological training for six years, and Jeff was causing me to question the wisdom of remaining within the

Methodist Church. I pushed all such thoughts out of my mind, and I took an assignment as the local pastor of a little church.[21] I was still taking classes to earn my undergraduate degree. I was also trying to carry on with my responsibilities as a wife and mother. I was convinced this was all God's will, but, in truth, my life was chaotic.

I thought it was my mission in life to bring the Methodist denomination back to how John Wesley had conceived of it. Meanwhile, Jeff kept asking me to reconsider the path I was taking, in light of what I was learning and the reservations I had about Protestantism. I would listen to none of his arguments, and I think it was out of sheer arrogance that I took my assignment. One week before I was to begin, I felt I could no longer discern God's will. I began to slip away from God and felt overwhelmed by the needs of the people around me. Yet, I continued to be blinded to God's will by my own will.

Then, on October 13, 1994, at a Bible study I still attended with Jeff, he told two of us after class that he had decided to convert to Catholicism. I couldn't believe it! I was dumbfounded. He then gave me Scott Hahn's *Home Sweet Rome* and tape series on "The Four Marks of the Church." I couldn't put the book down, and while listening to the tape series, I had alternating feelings of relief and despair. I kept telling my husband excitedly all that I was hearing and how, during all these years of studying, I had been right all along—that it had to be the Holy Spirit who had been teaching me. This is when my internal struggle really began. What was I to do now?

It's time to go home

At first I didn't decide to do anything. However, I began to read all that I could get my hands on about the Catholic Church and

---

[21] In the United Methodist Church, local pastors are not ordained and are not permitted to conduct communion services.

her teachings. Meanwhile, in college, I was taking Greek II and a course on how to teach the Gospel of Mark. My Greek professor was a former Catholic priest who left the Church and was now a married Episcopalian priest. My other professor was a Baptist missionary on leave. Both of these men, without trying, convinced me I was definitely in the wrong place. The defining moment came when we were discussing Jesus' talk about the end times in my Gospel of Mark class. The students were asking many questions, but my Baptist professor's answers were all very ambiguous. I asked him, "What did the early Church Fathers teach about the end times?" He answered, "I don't know, I never read the Church Fathers." I was in shock. My face must have reflected this, because he went on to say that when we all got to seminary, we would be taught many different interpretations of the Scriptures and that it would be up to us to choose which ones to believe and teach. Right then and there, I knew I had to get out of my pastorate and return to the church of my childhood—God's Church, the one, holy, catholic, and apostolic Church.

Bumps along the road

Returning home would require walking a difficult road because of my marital situation. John and I both had been married before, so our own marriage was not recognized by the Church, and we could not receive the sacraments. Deep in my heart, though, I knew I was being pulled to the truth; Jesus was calling me home. My desire to be one with Him would come most fully through the sacraments, yet He was asking me to return without being able to receive Him in the sacraments. This struggle tore at my heart. Why had Jesus brought me to where I was, just to give it all up and walk away? I didn't understand, but I had to trust Him and be obedient to His command.

My first meeting with a priest was definitely preordained by God. Father Jim welcomed me home and prayed with me, but he also told me that he could not absolve me of my sins and that I was not permitted to receive the Eucharist. In the eyes of the Church, John was still married to another woman. He had to seek an annulment.[22] My former marriage did not have to be annulled because, as a Catholic, I had been married outside the Church. I only needed to provide documentation of that fact.

In the fall of 1994, I returned to the Church all alone, without my family and without friends. The more I went to Mass, the more I was drawn to it. Everything for which I had been searching was now right in front of me. I began going to Mass every day. I wanted Jesus so badly that my heart would physically ache throughout the consecration. I went through many different moods and many dark times.

John didn't return with me at first. I tried to take the kids with me, but they were understandably confused. My oldest son, Josh, my spiritual mutt, went through my initial conversion and saw Mom "go crazy." He was old enough to remember the different doctrines he had learned. He didn't understand the Mass. When he was a little boy, my mother would occasionally take him to Mass, and he would ask why he couldn't receive Holy Communion. Now he was thirteen years old and confused about the differences between Protestantism and Catholicism. He was embarrassed when we would remain seated while others received the Eucharist. A priest told me I shouldn't force Joshua to convert, but Michael was young enough. One of his friends was going to the parish school, and Michael wanted to go, too. I

---

[22] An annulment is a declaration from a tribunal of the local Catholic diocese, after careful investigation, that a true marriage never existed in a given case because one or both of the parties to the marriage were unable or unwilling at the time of their wedding to make their marital promises freely, knowingly, and sincerely.

took the opportunity to transfer him to Catholic school in the second grade.

After a few months, my husband decided to come to Mass with Michael and me. At first, he said we would have to get used to the idea that we would never be able to receive the sacraments. Michael was going to receive his first Holy Communion that year, so I began pleading with John to at least go and find out about having his first marriage annulled. His children were against the idea, and, at first, John flatly refused. However, after much prayer, he decided to go find out about what would be involved. He left the meeting with our pastor convinced he wasn't going to apply. My pastor told me: "It didn't sound good; John's heart isn't in it."

Many months later, however, John also began to want to receive Jesus in the Eucharist. I have to admit I had little compassion because I had already been suffering for over a year. For nineteen months, I had gone to Mass and not been able to physically receive Jesus. I never thought that Jesus didn't love me or wouldn't forgive me, for I knew, through my obedience, that grace was being poured into my soul. Often, though, I would lose hope or allow the evil one to tempt me to give up. At these times, the Lord always sent me instruments of His love, peace, and mercy. One of them was the original priest who received me back with open arms. Father Jim always knew when I was suffering. He would hug me and give me encouragement.

The stain of sin must be removed

One time I cried and said it was so hard and that I didn't understand anymore what I was going through. Father Jim explained to me about the stain of sin. He asked me whether or not I would forgive him if he were to spill coke on my nice white sweater. I replied that of course I would. He then went on to explain that the stain would not go away just because I had for-given him. I would have to clean it and maybe even that would not be enough. I might have to work on it by presoaking and rubbing the stain before it would be lifted out. He explained that is the way it is with our souls. He knew that I had made a per-fect Act of Contrition, and he assured me that God had forgiven me. But there was much cleansing yet to be done. I had sinned badly. I had rejected God at an early age. I denied Him many times and ignored His promptings. Over and over again, I had chosen evil over good. I had committed many mortal sins.

I had chosen to do those things, and my heart was very heavy with remorse. Jesus held me in His loving arms and said: "My child, your sins are forgiven; go and sin no more." Now the healing process needed to take place. This is what I had known in my heart all along. This is why I persisted in my search for all those years. This is why I knew there had to be more than just accepting Jesus in my heart and knowing I would be saved.

Besides going to Mass most days, I would go into church and kneel before Christ in the tabernacle every chance I got. Many times I felt as if God had forsaken me. Yet when times seemed darkest, God would shine the brightest in my heart. I remember writing many prayers of pain to Jesus. Only He could feel my pain, and only He understood my internal sufferings. I wrote:

> I feel as if I am going through some kind of dark night of the soul, yet not completely. It's like I cannot sense the presence of God, yet He is assuring me in ways that He is with me and in control.

Many people could not understand why I put myself through this kind of fire. The Lord called me to this place, and as much as I suffered through every Mass, the joy far surpassed it. But my moods would often remain dark. The more joy the Lord granted me, the more intense the desire burned within me to have Jesus in the Eucharist. I had many ups and downs. I took a measure of comfort in the knowledge that Jesus was allowing me to share in the suffering of the holy souls in purgatory. In one of my letters I wrote: "At this point in my life, the fires of purgatory have to be raised so high, and may I enter them with joy. So much needs to be burned away. Help me, Lord Jesus, to endure."

I would often find myself praying:

> Father, may I trust in Your timing. For You see through eternity, and You know all things, and Your ways are holy, pure, and just. May I not depend on my finite mind. May I not seek to always understand, but to just trust in You that all will be well. Help me to trust You, Lord Jesus Christ. Help me to endure and be patient.

I was so consumed with the sacraments that I would dream about receiving Holy Communion and being forgiven through the Sacrament of Reconciliation. I thought I was going crazy, and those around me thought I had taken leave of my senses, especially my Protestant friends. There was no way they could understand because Protestants and Catholics don't view sin in the same way. Protestants don't believe we are ever truly cleansed, just covered over with the righteousness of Christ. Jesus stands between us and God, so the Father sees only Jesus, not us. By contrast, according to the teachings of the Catholic Church, we are being divinized. We are being made whole. We will be united totally with God, and He will be able to look directly at us and we at Him. This is the process of sanctification. It is a process of purification, for in addition to forgiveness, we must be purified in order that we might be one with Him who is pure holiness. I saw the truth, but I couldn't yet receive it. I could not go to Confession, but I needed to do penance. Who could give it to me? Jesus gave it to me, as not receiving the Eucharist was the toughest penance of all. I had chosen to offend God over and over again, and now I had to suffer.

John and I put our trust in God and bear the cross of chastity

Throughout the year I suffered from not being able to receive the Eucharist, John changed his mind several times about applying for an annulment. Then one day, God powerfully, yet so gracefully, moved mightily in John's heart. God worked through a letter from Jeff, my former Methodist pastor, who had left the pastorate in order to become Catholic. After I read it, I knew it was from the Lord and immediately showed it to John. Jeff wrote:

> What's really at stake here . . . is much more than just a technicality of canon law. It's a matter of the most holy will of God. Do you believe that John's first marriage never happened? If so, you must proceed vigorously with the application for annulment. If you don't believe that John's marriage was sacramentally invalid, then you have no choice but to try to live from now on as brother and sister. Otherwise, you are knowingly and deliberately turning away from the commandment of Jesus. But, then again, how would you know whether or not his marriage was valid? By what criteria can you judge such a thing? Obviously, you are not in a position to know. So, you are thrown back again on the Church, whom God created to

be our Mother in faith. I guess what I am trying to say is that the most important thing is that you and John are completely surrendered and supplicant to the will of God, as He speaks to you through His Church. This means you must be willing to bear the cross of chastity, if that's what it comes to. As the Holy Father frequently exhorts, "Do not be afraid!" God is love. Happiness is only found in conforming our lives to His perfect will. And He will give you the grace to accomplish whatever He requires of you. Perhaps you can join St. Augustine in praying, "Command what You will, and give what You command."

Within hours after I read the letter to John, he told me he felt the Lord was asking us to live together as brother and sister. We had to assume he was married to another woman. Shortly thereafter, he filed for an annulment. Because we were no longer living as husband and wife, we were able to seek and receive absolution through the Sacrament of Reconciliation. We were restored to full communion in the Catholic Church.

Through the process, John came to understand that truly his first marriage was not a sacrament and that he had to trust God's Church. After about seventeen months, I was beginning to give up and thought we would have to decide if we were going to live for the rest of our lives as brother and sister or live without the sacraments. Just when it seemed hopeless, the Church granted the annulment.

During the nearly two years of uncertainty about our future, when John and I took up the cross of chastity[23] in obedience to

---

[23] The *Catechism of the Catholic Church* defines the virtue of chastity as "the successful integration of sexuality within the person and thus the inner unity of man in his bodily and spiritual being" (no. 2337). Every person is called to live a chaste life, according to his or her state in life. "Married people are called to live

God's perfect and holy will, we lived on nothing but His grace. We cannot thank our Lord enough, especially for the supernatural grace of the sacraments, which we know gave us the strength to bear the cross of chastity without faltering.

Happily married and Catholic

On June 27, 1998, John and I entered into the Sacrament of Matrimony, and it was the most beautiful day of our lives. Since that day, we have grown ever stronger in our relationship with each other and the Lord. God truly is good. He gave us the grace to live out what He called us to do, and He continues to give us His grace every day. Our marriage is now our vocation. This is something no Protestant denomination truly understands. When I was busy running around trying to do the will of God, I was actually neglecting the will of God by not being obedient to my state in life. Now more than ever, I know my husband and my children are my priority. Ironically, Protestants accuse the Catholic Church of teaching "works righteousness," but the Catholic Church taught me how to be free of the need to do, and do, and do—for it was in the Catholic Church that I came to understand the beauty of my vocation as a wife and mother.

Understanding the Sacrament of Matrimony and my vocation as wife and mother was the answer to many of the questions for which I spent years looking. For all those years, God was telling me the truth was in the Catholic Church, but I missed it. By His grace, I came back to Him, and His grace sustains me. I am thankful I am Catholic, and I thank God for this gift every time I go to Mass.

---

conjugal chastity; others practice chastity in continence" (no. 2349). Until they received the Sacrament of Holy Matrimony, Vicky and John experienced chastity as a cross because they gave up the conjugal life they had shared and committed themselves to lead lives of sexual continence.

Victoria Madeleine returned to the Catholic Church in 1994. She resides in Laurel Springs, New Jersey, with her husband and two children. She is a member of St. Jude Parish in Blackwood, where she is involved in the RCIA program.

6

I Believe in God—So What?

Cathy Duffy

ut, Cathy, we both love Jesus, and that's really all that matters. You don't have to go to any particular church. I can understand your wanting to go back to the Catholic Church, since that's where you grew up. Really, you don't need to do *that*. Wouldn't it be better to stay at the same church with the rest of your family?"

More than one of my Protestant friends expressed this puzzled reaction when I returned to Catholicism in 1998. They assumed it was an emotional decision that could easily be set aside. The truth is, it was just the opposite. My decision was based on hardheaded logic rather than a desire to return to a childhood comfort zone. In fact, if I had chosen to return to Catholicism for emotional security, I would have been sorely disappointed, because my life was seriously disrupted, and I lost many friends in the process.

Worldviews shape spiritual journeys

I often blame my return to the Catholic Church on the saintly Protestant Reformed theologian Francis Schaeffer. In 1976, when my oldest son was about two years old, I read Schaeffer's book *How Should We Then Live?* That book opened the door for me to a serious form of Christianity that was satisfying to both my soul and my mind—at least for a time. Schaeffer asked the important questions: Does God exist? If He does, has He communicated anything to man? What does God demand of us? What is the purpose of life?

I call these the "so what" questions, because the answers we give to them shape all areas of our lives, from how we raise our children to our political ideology, from our beliefs about the origin of man to how we choose our entertainment. Through my reading, I discovered the concept of "worldviews." Simply put, our underlying beliefs about God and the fundamental questions of life make up our "worldview." Our worldview then shapes everything else about our lives. Discovering this idea of worldviews was the real beginning of my spiritual journey back to the Catholic Church. I began to realize that what I believe makes a difference in the way I live my life. Arriving at a coherent worldview, however, wasn't easy for me, and it isn't easy for most people.

Let me share two quotations that strongly highlight contrasting worldviews.[24] One is from C. S. Lewis, the famous twentieth-century Oxford scholar and author of *The Chronicles of Narnia, Mere Christianity, The Screwtape Letters*, and many other books. The other is from Karl Marx, co-founder of Communism.

The first quotation reads:

> Union with Christ imparts an inner elevation, comfort in affliction, tranquil reliance, and a heart which opens itself to everything noble and great, not for the sake of ambition or desire for fame, but for the sake of Christ. Union with Christ produces a joy which the Epicurean

---

[24] My appreciation to Bishop Norman McFarland for finding and sharing these quotations with me.

seeks in vain in his shallow philosophy, which the deeper thinker vainly pursues in the most hidden depths of knowledge. It is a joy known only to the simple and child-like heart, united with Christ and through Him with God, a joy which elevates life and makes it more beautiful.

The second quotation:

> You know, I think, that I believe in no religion. There is absolutely no proof for any of them, and from a philosophical standpoint Christianity is not even the best. All religions, that is, all mythologies to give them their proper name, are merely man's own invention—Christ as much as Loki. Primitive man found himself surrounded by all sorts of terrible things he didn't understand. . . . Thus religion, that is to say mythology, grew up. Often, too, great men were regarded as Gods after their death—such as Heracles or Odin: thus after the death of a Hebrew philosopher Yeshua (whose name we have corrupted into Jesus) he became regarded as a God, a cult sprang up, which was afterwards connected with the ancient Hebrew Yahweh-worship, and so Christianity came into being—one mythology among many.

You have probably assumed that the first quotation is from Lewis and the second from Marx, but, actually, the reverse is true.[25] Both men made these statements when they were very young. Clearly, something happened later in life that radically

---

[25] Karl Marx is cited by Eugene Kamenki, "The Baptism of Karl Marx," in *The Hittert Journal,* vol. 56, no. 3 (April 1958), pp. 345-346. C. S. Lewis wrote in a letter to Arthur Greeves (October 12, 1916), published in *They Stand Together*, by C. S. Lewis, p. 135.

129

changed the worldview of each man. Experiences that cause us to make one-hundred-eighty-degree changes in our lives are not all that uncommon. Births, deaths, marriages, divorces, successes, failures, joys, and griefs force us to confront deep life questions and potentially shape our worldview.

Unfortunately, too many people today take the path of Karl Marx and reject any belief in God, or at least any kind of God that might be concerned about our life choices. We have only to look at the erosion of belief in young people and the moral vacuum within which so many operate to understand the gravity of the problem. Look at the majority of parishes, and count the number of members around age twenty. Unless one's parish is highly unusual, the count will be disproportionately low. Yet, Christians, both Protestant and Catholic, continue to rationalize this problem with statements such as, "Sure, they all leave for a while, but we hope they will come back when they get married and have their own children." Unfortunately, many have departed for good; a few will come back the hard way, as I did. In retracing my own spiritual journey, I have thought a great deal about why we are losing so many Catholic young people and what we might do differently to prevent this tragedy.

I grew up in a Catholic family, second oldest of eight children. My parents scrimped and struggled to put us through Catholic schools, both elementary and high school, so I was a product of the Catholic education system. Even though most Catholic schools of the 1950s and '60s were more intent upon teaching children the whole truth of the Catholic faith, as opposed to many of today's schools, I believe they still had two major problems that left many of us with a hollow faith: compartmentalization and a lack of an apologetics outlook.

Stifled by compartmentalized education

Catholic schools did not invent compartmentalized education; they merely adopted it by copying what other schools did. We had classes for math, English, history, science, art, music, Latin, and physical education, but with the addition of religion and Church history. Learning was divided up into subject areas, as if knowledge operated only within these limited boxes. At that time, we still had Catholic texts that incorporated Catholic content with varying degrees of effectiveness, such as sentences to diagram that included mention of priests and the Mass. I also recall history books that included the history of Catholicism; nevertheless, none of my teachers tried to help us put all the pieces together to develop a coherent worldview. Religion teachers taught the catechism and doctrine, but they overlooked opportunities to connect what we were learning with current and historical events, scientific developments, and literary appreciation and interpretation. (Ironically, public schools today often do a better job discussing the latter topics, even raising ethical questions, but they are forbidden from making any connections to God as the ethical source.)

The other problem to which I referred—the lack of an apologetics outlook—was a practical problem as much as anything else. Classes at schools I attended were all much larger than they are now. A teacher with no aides was often saddled with fifty to sixty students. To get anything done with that size group required iron discipline, organization, structure, and limited diversions for any questions students might have. We memorized the *Baltimore Catechism* and history facts and regurgitated them on tests, but we rarely had opportunity—and were definitely never encouraged—to question or challenge anything that was presented. No child would dare ask: "Why should we learn that?" So, our Catholic faith was, in many ways, treated as just another subject upon which we were graded.

"You can't stand still with God"

Though my Catholic school education was far from perfect, I grew up knowing that God was real and personal, and many of my teachers did care intensely about our spiritual development, in spite of the structure and limitations within which they worked. I clearly remember a life-altering statement made by my second-grade teacher, a nun, who declared: "You can't stand still with God. You're always going forward or backward." Perhaps my ideas about "forward" and "backward" were fuzzy, but I took what she said to heart—at least for a few years.

By high school, my conviction that I needed to keep moving forward in my relationship with God was being displaced by other concerns. Like so many others in the "rebellious" 1960s, I wanted to do what I wanted to do. Unfortunately, some of the faculty of my high school seemed determined to exacerbate those rebellious feelings. There were a few priests and nuns who really needed psychiatric assistance. They set up legalistic, and sometimes embarrassing, rules that even I, an "A" student who never got in trouble, rebelled against. Requiring us to kneel down to make sure our skirts were long enough to touch the floor and sticking pencils in our hair to check for "ratting" were among the arbitrary and randomly enforced rules. The mindlessness of these petty tyrannies offended me so much that they made it easier and easier to ignore other ethical and religious instruction. The lack of coherence between what Catholicism should be and what was presented in my school undermined any worldview formation that might have been accomplished earlier. In my middle high-school years, I remember very consciously telling—not asking!—God to just stay out of my life. I kept going to Mass, but I effectively walked away from Him at that point.

The thing I find curious is that through this period of my life when *I* pushed God away, I maintained a sense that *He* was still hanging around on the periphery; He never cut me loose entirely. In hindsight, I describe it as God allowing me to be on a very long leash. I knew what I wanted to do, but God seemed to put roadblocks in my path. He would let me go so far and no farther, as it turned out, for my protection. Today, I marvel at the fact that God protected me in spite of my rebellion. He let the leash out a bit, but He never failed to pull me up short before I got myself into too much trouble.

Marriage, baby, and a new church
At age nineteen, I married Mike. He was raised in the Mormon Church until his mid-teens, but he had very little doctrinal knowledge of Mormonism and even less of Christianity. Sadly, at that point in my life, his religious background was irrelevant to me, and it didn't start to matter until four years later when I became pregnant with our first child. For me, it was like smacking face first into a brick wall. I *knew* that God was real and that I had pushed Him out of my life. I also knew it would be a terrible thing to raise a child without God; thus I could no longer keep Him outside my boundaries, even if I had so desired.

That meant going back to church. Since the Catholic Church was all I knew, I found the closest one and started attending Mass. It so happened this parish had a vibrant charismatic community, which was very appealing to me at that stage of my life. These people visibly loved God and generously shared their love with others. It was so different from the Catholicism of my youth, a difference I found new and exciting; I jumped in with both feet.

I found the charismatic movement in that parish to be strong on emotions and weak on theology. I was pulled back into a relationship with God, but I didn't embrace the whole of His

Church. I had entered into a relationship with Jesus, and that was all that mattered to me. As I was getting reacquainted with God, I realized that my husband hadn't even been introduced. I tried dragging him along to church, but it was too strange for him, this mix of Catholic ritual and charismatic expression. Finally, I quit dragging and prayed for two years for his conversion.

His conversion didn't happen the way I expected, however. One day he informed me he had been listening to Pastor Chuck Smith, founder of Calvary Chapel, on the radio. He had decided to accept Jesus, but he wanted to go to Calvary Chapel, which happened to be quite close to where we lived. My relationship with God at that point was rooted in emotions rather than theology; thus it didn't take much prompting for me to go with Mike to Calvary Chapel. I didn't look back for almost twenty years.

How should we then live?
Everything seemed great. We were together spiritually, growing in our knowledge of God and especially of the Bible, which I was hungry to learn. It was during this time that I read Schaeffer's *How Should We Then Live?* and began what I consider my real education. The questions Schaeffer posed caused me to start reading more history, philosophy, and theology, processing through these questions for myself. At that point, I didn't have many answers, but at least I knew that the questions and answers mattered.

My ambition to learn and understand was often confounded by the pressures of life. We had two more sons, and I was engulfed in the minutiae of meals, grocery shopping, sewing, cleaning, and child rearing; nevertheless, I kept plugging away, making my way very slowly through books and ideas.

Meanwhile, we shifted our church attendance to a much smaller Calvary Chapel that was just starting up. Nursery lines, watching Chuck Smith on the big screen in the overflow room, and the rarity of running into the same folks two weeks in a row made the idea of belonging to a smaller congregation very appealing. We heard about a new "branch" of Calvary Chapel that was meeting for only the third time. After just one visit, we felt as though we had found our home. I began putting my convictions into practice by teaching children in Sunday school at our new church. Eventually, I assumed the administration of the Sunday school program, which was growing rapidly along with the rest of the church.

Incorporating a "worldview" curriculum into our homeschool

Bible-based education became so important to both Mike and me that we enrolled our oldest son in a Lutheran school after visiting and rejecting many others. We were satisfied enough with the school and enrolled our second son in their kindergarten program. Everything was about to change, however. It was during that year the Lord confronted me with the idea of homeschooling. This was 1982, the dark ages of homeschooling; I had no idea what it would be like or even how to go about doing it. Still, my husband and I decided to give it a try, at least for a year.

I suspect that my ongoing theological quest made homeschooling a more appealing prospect than it might have been otherwise. Here, I would have the opportunity to teach my children that learning is not compartmentalized, that God is a part of everything, that there are reasons for believing in Him, and that our lives have purpose beyond getting well-paid jobs. Worldview became a significant component in our schooling, especially as we moved into the high-school years. I ended up creating my own worldview course long before anyone was publishing such things. This was essentially a two-year unit study heavily based upon Schaeffer's ideas. Using history as the organizing thread, we studied religion, art, literature, science, philosophy, economics, and government, all covered chronologically in an interrelated fashion.

I really loved teaching worldviews and wanted to help other homeschoolers figure out how to do this. I wrote magazine articles, added a chapter on worldview teaching to my homeschooling manual I was publishing and updating every few years, did many presentations on the topic, and taught classes to homeschooling teens.

Search for unchangeable truths

A crucial concept when teaching worldviews from a biblical Christian perspective is the idea that there are absolutes, that is, unchangeable truths that one must accept for life to be coherent. Ever since the Enlightenment, intellectuals have whittled away at the idea of absolutes, but the number of people who no longer believe in absolutes has grown exponentially in the postmodern era, where relativism reigns. Today, many people, perhaps most, believe there are no absolute truths, especially in regard to religion and morality. Faith and morals, then, are determined by convenience or emotions—"whatever works for you."

When teaching, I would talk about the necessity of absolute truth as a foundation for our worldview. The critical question then becomes: How do we find and define those absolutes? For Protestants, the answer is easy: the Bible. Personally, I didn't have any trouble with that answer for many years, because I had tremendous confidence in Scripture as the inspired Word of God. I was an educator, however, so I felt it was my duty to figure out a way to convince my children, as well as my readers, that they also should believe the Bible. We covered historical support for the authenticity of Scripture, the care used in its transmission, accuracy of manuscripts through the centuries, and fulfillment of prophecy. We bolstered knowledge *about* Scripture with experience *with* Scripture in their lives, that is, reading and applying God's Word.

The authority conundrum

I didn't progress far along the "knowledge about" Scripture trail before I bumped up against a problem with the canon of the Bible, namely, the question of how and why certain books were chosen to be included. I didn't have a problem with the Old Testament, as Jesus and His disciples referred to it frequently, granting it full credibility. (At this point, I wasn't even aware of the books missing from the Old Testament in Protestant Bibles.) The New Testament, on the other hand, presented a conundrum, for it could not and did not affirm itself. Protestants typically rely upon 2 Timothy 3:16 for the Bible's self-affirmation: "All scripture is inspired by God and is profitable for teaching, for reproof, for correction, and for training in righteousness, that the man of God may be complete, equipped for every good work." In this passage, however, Paul is referring only to the Old Testament, since the New Testament had not yet been compiled. As far as I could tell, there was no obvious biblical support for the New Testament canon.

The answer to this one question became an essential quest for me, so I read and asked questions to the point where I made people feel uncomfortable. I was absolutely convinced that Protestants had to have a good defense for the canon, since the Bible was the bedrock of their belief system. Protestant pastors insisted that the canon of Scripture was self-evident to the early Church, so there was no real reason for concern. They argued that the inspired books stood out easily as being different from other writings, and the Church merely recognized this fact. However, as I delved into early Church history, I grew more and more dismayed as I discovered that the inspired nature of some canonical books was *not* self-evident. The *Shepherd of Hermes* and the *Didache* were thought to be inspired by many but didn't make it into the canon. Revelation, Hebrews, and 2 Peter were strongly resisted but somehow made the cut. Decisions regarding each book were *not* sorted out democratically by the entire Church but were made by Church councils. Recognizing this historical fact brought me to a critical juncture. By what right did the Church decide? Was this simply an arbitrary imposition of authority?

The question of authority had become my biggest conundrum. If the Church did not have authority to determine the canon of Scripture, then it is possible she got it wrong. If the Church had no authority, then the Bible itself could not be proven to be the source for absolute truth. Even worse, it would mean the Church might have been wrong when she defined the Trinity, the nature of Jesus, and other key doctrinal points. I was in big trouble! I could not accept the possibility that God went to all the effort of building a relationship with us, then left us with no way of sorting out truth from untruth. From my Protestant perspective, if Scripture was not reliable, then everything else was up for grabs. I couldn't accept this; there had to be a better answer.

The Catholicity of Scripture and authority

It was only upon arriving at this dismal dilemma that I began to consider the Catholic position on Scripture and authority. I started to broaden my horizons by reading St. Augustine's *City of God*. After all, many Protestants consider him the precursor of Calvin, while Catholics refer to him as a Father of the Church. Someone with fans on both sides of the fence might be able to shed light on my dilemma without sounding too Catholic. Yet, Augustine turned out to be very Catholic. Even so, his wisdom and insight overcame my defenses. He made a great deal of sense to me, even though he clearly acknowledges the authority of the Catholic Church. John Henry Newman turned out to be another critical influence. In his book *Apologia pro vita sua,* he traces his conversion from the Anglican Church to Catholicism. Many of my questions had been his as well; the answers he discovered helped lead me out of the theological fog.

Now I had a situation where Augustine and Newman made more sense to me than all Protestant theologians. A friend tried to rescue me from the "awful mistake" of embracing Catholicism by loaning me three books by R. C. Sproul, one of the leading Reformed theologians in the country. Unbeknownst to my friend, Sproul unwittingly provided the confirmation for what I was already beginning to believe might be the truth.

In his book *Essential Truths of the Christian Faith,*[26] Sproul deals with the canon question, arriving at the conclusion that there are three positions regarding the canon:

Roman Catholic view:
> The Canon is an infallible collection of infallible books.

Classical Protestant view:
> The Canon is a fallible collection of infallible books.

Liberal Critical view:
> The Canon is a fallible collection of fallible books.

He justifies the Protestant view by saying:

> Protestants also remind Roman Catholics that the church did not "create" the canon. The church recognized,

---

[26] Sproul, R. C. *Essential Truths of the Christian Faith.* Tyndale House, 1992.

acknowledged, received, and submitted to the canon of Scripture.[27]

Sproul makes his pronouncement, however, after admitting that the Church debated the issue of which books to include. He doesn't try to reconcile an obvious contradiction: Protestantism's *acceptance* of the canon and *rejection* of the very Church that authoritatively compiled it. Nevertheless, I appreciated his honesty in properly labeling the logical and inescapable viewpoints regarding the canon.

At this point, I finally acknowledged that Protestants did not have a good defense for the canon of Scripture. On the contrary, I was finding that the Catholic Church actually owned the strongest, most logical defense for the Bible. In a way, this discovery was a relief. My entire worldview structure was not destroyed, as I had feared it might have been when Protestantism could not come up with satisfactory answers. Instead, my worldview underwent some major rearrangement, but in ways that made it more coherent and logical than before.

I challenge conflicts and ambiguities within Protestant theology

Meanwhile, my life was not lining up as logically as my theology. We had stayed with our small Calvary Chapel congregation for nearly eighteen years, and our friends and our children's friends all belonged to Calvary Chapel. A major part of our social life revolved around our church, but problems had been cropping up. The senior and assistant pastors were teaching theologically contradictory ideas, and although controversy over theology wasn't widespread, it mattered to our family. Also, worship had evolved into performance to the point where the congregation

---

[27] *Essential Truths of the Christian Faith*, pp. 22-23.

frequently applauded the musicians. This practice became the last straw as far as our particular Calvary Chapel; I was going to church to worship, *not* to hear a concert.

I had heard that for the next four weeks a well-known theologian would be speaking at the nearby Evangelical Free Church, where many of our homeschooling friends attended. I knew I would feel comfortable there, so I decided to go and listen to what the speaker had to say. The speaker was excellent, and I fit right in. My husband and sons, however, thought I was being precipitous in making such an abrupt change, and they took some time to consider what they each might do. Gradually, my husband and two of my three sons followed me to the Evangelical Free Church.

I started attending adult Sunday school and, after a few months, joined the class for prospective new members. At one of the classes, I raised some theological questions to try to pin down the church's theology regarding the nature of salvation and eternal security. I particularly wanted to know whether they held to Calvinist doctrine, but I was told the church did not take any position, and I could believe whatever I wanted to believe. They lost me completely at that point, since I had come to the conclusion that issues dealing with salvation were critical for any Christian church to address.

I kept attending the Evangelical Free Church, but their minimalist theology was a major factor in opening my heart and mind to consider the claims of Catholicism. As I began to think and believe more and more of what the Catholic Church taught, I started to feel like a heretic within the Evangelical Free Church. I was frequently questioning and challenging statements people made, and I even considered the idea of starting a home church. I had to go all the way to this logical extreme before I truly understood the necessity of Church authority to maintain doctrinal integrity.

I submit to the authority of the Church

When I finally realized that Catholicism really possesses the truth, I was faced with a huge dilemma. If I were to go to the Catholic Church, I would go alone. My husband would not even consider the idea, and two of my sons were content where they were, now that they had shifted to the Evangelical Free Church. My third son had never left Calvary Chapel, but he was asking questions of his own. I also knew that such a move would alienate most of my friends, disrupt our social circle, and undermine my business, which had been based on addressing the needs of Protestant homeschoolers, who made up at least eighty-five percent of the homeschool world at that time. Since I had been so visible and vocal about teaching worldviews, my defection to the Catholic Church would seem traitorous.

I thought perhaps I could wait a while and maybe my husband would begin to consider Catholicism, or something else would change that would make the transition easier. I stalled for a few months, but the cognitive and spiritual dissonance became unbearable. I couldn't sit quietly through a Sunday school class while disagreeing with foundational presuppositions. I was beginning to feel it wasn't right for me to be part of the congregation while undermining their theology and, more importantly, to worship in a church that held beliefs contrary to my own.

Once I had sorted out the authority issue, I was able to objectively consider other key Catholic doctrines, such as the Eucharist, the communion of saints, and the papacy. The history of the early Church confirmed Catholic positions on these issues. My reservations toppled like dominoes as I began to see Protestant doctrines as corruptions of the truth and denial of the witness of history. Participating in a Protestant communion service suddenly presented an ethical dilemma. How could I participate in communion as a "memorial" of Jesus' death when He clearly taught His Real Presence in the consecrated Eucharist as understood by the Catholic Church?

I finally reached a point where I felt there was nothing I could do *but* return to the Catholic Church. One of the first people I talked to about my decision was my mother. I was taken aback by her reaction: "Are you sure you want to do that? You know how much trouble it will cause for your family?"

I had expected her to be overjoyed, not discouraging! But my mother really understood how difficult this would be. She could see the pain it would cause my husband and sons. It actually took a month or so for my mother to come around to seeing it as a positive move and rejoicing in my return to the Church. Even before I returned, I began to call homeschool convention organizers with whom I had contracted to speak in upcoming months. My return to Catholicism was inescapable, so I believed I owed them the opportunity to withdraw their speaking contracts, since most were predicated on the fact that I was coming to speak to Christian homeschoolers who expected Protestant messages. None withdrew speaking invitations that year, but the word went out and I was professionally blackballed from then on.

Actually, returning to the Catholic Church was anticlimactic. I searched out a Magisterium-faithful parish, called up, and explained my situation. The priest informed me all that was necessary was for me to make my Confession. It seemed too little for the years I had spent separated from God's Church. I met with the priest who asked me some questions, then heard my Confession, and that was it. After years of searching, it took less than an hour to radically alter my entire life. I imagine my feelings were much like those of a novice skydiver taking that first leap out the plane door. What had I done?

The Catholic worldview withstands life's trials and the tests of time

My best friends withdrew. I had to resign from the board of an organization I had founded. We were cut off from much of our social circle, and my family was divided and angry over the trouble I caused them. My husband and two of my sons were very committed at the Evangelical Free Church by this time, a testament of sorts to the excellent job I did of helping my sons form Protestant worldviews. They were walking with God, serious about their faith, and didn't want to even consider yet another church shift.

However, my middle son, the one who hadn't left Calvary Chapel, was open to consider other possibilities. He ended up following me to the Catholic Church, went through a wonderful RCIA program, and was received into the Catholic Church a little over a year after my return.

Many people wondered why I put myself and my family through so much grief, but my questioning had led me to a point where I really could do nothing else. It would have been a terrible lie to try to continue functioning as a Protestant once I really understood the truth. I had many, many theological conversations in the course of my return and in the ensuing years. I actually got a great deal of practice presenting my theological conclusions and defending my decision even before I received the Sacrament of Penance. The more I was forced to defend my conclusions, the more I appreciated that Catholicism possessed the most logical presentation and defense of Christianity. I realized that a Catholic worldview was the only one that could stand against all the other belief systems and ideas man has concocted.

I actually reached the conclusion that Protestantism itself bears much blame for our modern relativistic society. Most Protestant denominations claim to be based on absolute truth.

For example, many claim that the sanctity of life is one of those truths. Yet Protestants contradict one another on key issues, such as the nature of salvation, how one "gets saved," whether or not Baptism is essential, and much more. These conflicts undermine the credibility of Protestants when they make claims about the truth. Why believe Protestants about the abortion issue when they cannot agree among themselves about critical faith issues? If Protestants disagree with one another, they are free to go start another denomination and make up their own doctrine—a perfect example of relativism in action. After my return to the Church, I discovered that non-Christians often hold the Catholic Church in higher esteem than they do Protestant churches, because the Catholic Church does not change her doctrines. You may not like what the Church teaches, but she will not change to suit you.

I appreciated the Church's doctrinal stability. Because of my worldview background, I was also grateful for Catholicism's demand that we de-compartmentalize our lives and view everything through the lens of faith, that is, that we follow Christ's teaching in all areas of our lives, believing and acting as Christ commanded.

As it turns out, de-compartmentalizing and developing a truly Catholic worldview are also key to keeping young Catholics in the Church. In our families, in catechetical classes, in homeschools, in Catholic schools—wherever and whenever opportunities arise—we need to help young people develop a comprehensive Catholic worldview, so they really understand what a difference being a Catholic makes in their lives now and forever.

I was successful in de-compartmentalizing and developing a worldview understanding with all three of my sons, so much so that two of them are very committed to the Protestant worldview in which I raised them. Now, I have a huge regret that I came so late to Catholicism and missed my best opportunity for teaching them the whole truth. I trust, though, that God will help them and my husband embrace the fullness of the truth of Catholicism in His own time.

Cathy Duffy returned to the Catholic Church in 1998. She is the author of three books, an international speaker on homeschooling, owner of Grove Publishing, and director for the catechumenate at her parish.

7

From "c" to Shining "C": Protestant Charismatic to Roman Catholic

Rhonda Grayson

I remember one particularly beautiful, sunny Sunday afternoon as I returned home from church. The worship service had been filled with singing, dancing, speaking in tongues, and uplifting preaching. As an ordained minister, I had assisted the senior pastor throughout the service, as I had done countless times before. To my congregation, whom I had known and loved for many years, it appeared as though I had found my calling. What they didn't know was that on this particular Sunday, as on previous ones, I was racing home to watch the Sunday Mass from the Basilica of the National Shrine of the Immaculate Conception in Washington, D.C., broadcast on the Eternal Word Television Network (EWTN). In order to appreciate how "out of the ordinary" this was for me, I need to take you back in time to 1958.

This was the year I was baptized into the Lutheran Church at the age of six. My family was very active in our congregation, which became my home away from home. I have many fond memories of those days, such as Sunday school, day camp, children's choir, Bible plays, and church dinners. A few years later, however, we moved across town and drifted away from the church.

Success at the price of faith

Instead of a church choir, I joined various secular singing groups, or "girl groups," as they were called. I sang my heart out, dreaming that one day I would become famous—like Diana Ross and the Supremes. Our groups entered various talent shows around the city, hoping to be chosen to receive a recording contract. After high school, I attended a community college, but my heart wasn't in my studies, so I left to pursue my dream of a singing career. I was soon invited to join a local singing group in the midst of promoting their first single record. I accepted their invitation, and my singing career was launched. Over the next few years, I recorded and traveled as a backup singer for various artists like Gene Chandler, who recorded *Duke of Earl,* and even had an opportunity to become a backup singer for Stevie Wonder.

I was experiencing success in my singing career, but I had strayed far from God and His Church. The bright lights, audiences, accolades, and late-night parties weren't enough to fill this void, so I resorted to drinking. The drinking only made worse the emptiness I felt inside. It had been many years since I attended a church, but I found myself crying out to God for help. Somehow, I knew that, without Him, all would be lost. I felt my prayers were answered the day I received a phone call from my sister, Beatrice, asking me to attend a week-long Christian revival service led by her husband, the Reverend Gerard "Micky" Terrell, an ordained Baptist minister. I hesitated, thinking of all the things I'd rather be doing, but she pressed me. She said they were showing a film she felt I should see, so I agreed to go.

Living for Jesus

The film *The Mark of the Beast* was about a world leader who came to power promising world peace but whose true intent was to trick people into receiving the mark of the beast, that is, the mark of Satan, 666. The film portrayed the rapture in which all the Christians disappear without a trace, leaving the world in panic and confusion. According to the film, Jesus comes back to take the Christians, who had not received the mark of the beast, with Him to heaven.

The thought of being left behind after the rapture shocked and horrified me, and I longed to know what I could do to prevent that from happening. When the film ended, my brother-in-law went through the Scriptures, showing how Jesus died for our sins out of love and rose from the dead so that we could live with Him forever in heaven. He told us that Jesus is the Way, the Truth, and the Life. We must denounce Satan and believe that Jesus died for our sins and rose from the dead for our salvation. We are to ask Jesus to forgive our sins and become the Lord of our lives, and we must live for Him from that day forward.

I knew I had caused my troubles by living for myself, so I immediately came forward to pray the sinner's prayer.[28] Afterward, I cried tears of joy to think that Jesus loved me so much that He was willing to die for me and give me another chance to live for Him. I was overwhelmed by the Lord's goodness and couldn't wait to start my new life.

The following Sunday, I attended my sister's church and joined the Bible study class on Wednesday. I purchased my first Bible and wanted to know everything I could about Jesus and how He wanted me to live for Him. It seemed as if a whole new world had opened up that I had never known existed before. I

---

[28] The sinner's prayer is usually led by the worship leader, repeated by one or more people. The following is the basic prayer, although there are many variations: "Dear Jesus, I admit I have not lived for You and that I am a sinner. I renounce Satan and all his plans for my life. I believe You died for my sins. I believe You rose from the dead and are seated at the right hand of the Father. I surrender my life to You and ask You to be Lord of my life. Help me to live for You."

devoured the Bible, reading and studying for hours on end. The more I read and prayed, the more I loved Jesus. There was no doubt in my mind that Jesus was the One who had been missing in my life, not a record deal, or fame, or success. I knew that the audience leaves the theater, and the bright lights fade to black. Late-night parties come to an end, and even the effects of alcohol wear away. The only true and lasting purpose of my life was to be found in a *person*, Jesus Christ, the Son of God. Serving Jesus became my life.

Joining the charismatic movement

I joined the Missionary Baptist Church, where my sister and brother-in-law belonged. I gave up my professional singing career and joined the choir—now I was singing for the Lord. I soon discovered that many members of the congregation had recently been introduced to the charismatic movement, which was gaining popularity throughout the country. The belief behind this movement is that the gifts of the Holy Spirit spoken of in 1 Corinthians 12 (speaking in tongues, prophecy, laying hands on the sick, healings, miracles, etc.) are still available to us today if we believe. Charismatic worship involves intense praise, which may include traditional Jewish-style dancing, waving of the arms and hands in the air, lying prostrate, and "falling under the power of the Spirit." I was drawn to this movement, along with many others in the church. It became clear, however, that the pastor of our church and others in the congregation did not accept the charismatic movement, which strained relationships. After trying to coexist for a few years, our charismatic group decided it would be best for everyone involved if we left the congregation. Rather than search for another church where we would worry about running into the same problems, we decided to start our own nondenominational church, calling my brother-in-law as pastor.

Church ministry becomes a way of life

The thought of being a part of a new church was exciting and also somewhat scary. Realizing we were in uncharted waters, we trusted God that the church would bear fruit for Jesus, and our church membership grew numerically and spiritually. Once again, I was able to use my singing talents by becoming one of four praise-and-worship leaders, a choir member, and the director of the children's Easter plays.

One day I was asked to be the main speaker at our Women's Day celebration. I felt it was an honor, but also a big responsibility. I was comfortable singing in front of thousands of people, but the thought of preaching God's Word to His people was overwhelming. I was afraid I would say something that was not scripturally sound. I prayed and worked hard, and thanks to God's grace and mercy, the day was a success; my message was well received. I became more involved in church ministry, and while things were going well in the congregation I attended, I felt I was being pulled in a different direction. When I told the pastor I was leaving to attend another charismatic church, he was very understanding. He held a special going-away service for me in which he prayed over me for God's will to be done in my life. Although I was sad leaving family and friends, I was also full of anticipation over what God had planned for me.

More ministries, burnout, and a new start

My new church was also nondenominational, and its pastor was a woman with a Pentecostal background. It was growing by leaps and bounds, due in large part to our pastor's radio ministry and dynamic preaching and teaching. Again, I sang for the Lord as the worship leader and choir member. The church was involved in dynamic evangelistic ministries. Many guest speakers from all over were brought in to hold revival services or give special healing prayer services. Several times each year we would rent a large hotel ballroom for a prayer breakfast, featuring guest speakers and attended by thousands, to whom I ministered through praise-and-worship songs.

My pastor was well known in Pentecostal circles and traveled frequently on speaking engagements. I accompanied her occasionally to lead the praise-and-worship service before she spoke. A whole new world again opened up to me as I met so many people around the country who loved God and wanted to serve Him as I did. As our congregation grew increasingly large, my ministries became more demanding, leaving me very little time for rest, as I also worked a full-time job. I turned to God, completely exhausted, asking if He required all this of me, or if it was my doing. I no longer looked forward to going to church, as it had become more like a job than something I wanted to do out of love for Jesus. Not only my prayer life suffered, but my physical state, as well. I was burned out. I resigned from my positions at the church and left to get some needed rest, but more importantly, to seek God's direction for my life.

I was without a church for the first time in many years. It felt strange not to attend worship services, especially on Sunday. After some weeks, I received a phone call from my sister-in-law, Janice, who invited me to accompany her to a church a friend told her about. It was the Full Gospel Charismatic Church, made up of over ninety percent ex-Catholic Hispanics. I returned to the church Sunday after Sunday, drawn to the spirit of the people. They danced before the Lord as I imagined the people of the Old Testament did. Using tambourines and the shofar (a trumpet made from a ram's horn), they twirled around in jubilation, kicking their legs from side to side as they shouted for joy. Then, when the music changed to slow, melodious songs of worship, the people would reverence the Lord by lying prostrate on the floor or kneeling as tears ran down their cheeks in awe of God's greatness. There, my faith deepened. I was ready to get involved; when asked, I joined the church's praise-and-worship team, as well as other ministries. I had a glorious time. Missionaries from the field would come to our church to share news of their evangelism efforts in countries near and far. We celebrated certain Jewish feasts, dressing in colorful costumes and singing songs in Hebrew.

My faith is shaken by the loss of loved ones

In 1994, my faith was shaken by the deaths of three loved ones in rapid succession. In 1986, I had lost Beatrice, the sister who had started me on my faith journey, but these new losses hit me hard. My older sister, Florida, died suddenly in January; in February, my brother-in-law, Micky, who was a pastor, died after a long battle with cancer; and in March, my niece, Cynthia, passed away. I was full of hurt and confusion, wondering how God could let these tragedies happen. My loved ones were all charismatic Christians who believed in the healing power of Jesus Christ, and yet they died, one after the other. Something was wrong; either we were being misled by our charismatic beliefs, or Jesus didn't heal. Deep in my heart, I knew Jesus had the power to heal, but I felt there was a piece missing from my understanding. I pondered these questions in my heart.

The Full Gospel Charismatic Church could not answer my questions, so I moved on. A part of me was weary of moving from church to church, but another part of me felt I was on a journey, moving closer to finding the truth. My experiences in these different churches were like pieces of the puzzle that would eventually lead me to the final piece, the one that would make the puzzle whole and recognizable. That in five years the

Catholic Church would be the final piece of the puzzle never entered my mind.

My sister-in-law, Janice, and others in my life were also on faith journeys. They came to the conclusion that we should start a church that would encompass the best from all the other churches to which we had belonged. Janice, an ordained minister and Bible teacher, became the pastor, and a young man from our previous church became the assistant pastor. I was the worship leader and choir director. We held our worship services and Bible studies in Janice's home. These were intense and exciting, and they lasted for many hours. We also had vital outreach programs that included feeding the hungry and giving to the poor.

I discover the Catholic faith

It was during this time that I discovered *Mother Angelica Live* on EWTN. A nun teaching the Word of God on TV? How interesting and unusual! Up until then I had never given thought to the Catholic Church, as Catholicism was far removed from my sphere of experience. I did remember hearing something years ago about the Pope being the antichrist, but I had no feelings for or against the Church. Now, however, I shudder at the thought of anyone saying or even thinking that.

Discovering Mother Angelica's program was just the beginning of what would turn out to be not coincidence, but Divine Providence. The next discovery I made was that one of my neighbors, Mr. Emerson Bonner, was Catholic. I had taken a part-time job in a dry-cleaning store that was located in the building where I lived. Mr. Bonner, an elderly man, would come into the cleaners often to chat with the owner. His wisdom and life experiences drew me to him, but above all, his peace and gentleness aroused my curiosity. Through our conversations, I found out that he was a cradle Catholic. I had no idea what that meant until he explained that he had been a Catholic all his life. I was very surprised, for I never knew there were African-American Catholics. I knew parents who sent their children to Catholic schools, but they did so because they wanted to give their children the best education they could. Their reasons had nothing to do with the teachings of the Church, and they left the Catholic Church behind after their children graduated. The fact that Mr. Bonner was a devout, practicing Catholic intrigued me. I have since learned there are many African-American Catholics, but they are very private about their beliefs and faith, unlike the evangelical Protestants I know.

As I got to know Mr. Bonner better, I also found myself being drawn ever more strongly to the Catholic programs on EWTN, especially its showing of the daily Mass. For a long time, however, I was unaware that God was moving me toward His Church. I continued to attend the worship services at my Protestant church, and I even was ordained to the ministry. My ordination brought new responsibilities, such as regular preaching, in addition to directing the choir and leading Bible studies.

Peace in the midst of suffering and sorrow

There was another subtle positive Catholic influence on me. It was the way Joseph Cardinal Bernardin accepted his suffering from terminal cancer. He was well liked by many Catholics in the Archdiocese of Chicago. I shared their sentiment, so I was very sad when his illness was announced. I had been through my own grief and sorrow, and these experiences only made me restless with unanswered questions about how suffering could be reconciled with faith in a benevolent God. How odd it seemed to me that the cardinal could be so peaceful and calm when he talked about his illness and the likelihood of his early death. When asked by various reporters and interviewers if he wanted

God to heal him, his response was if God wanted to heal him, that would be okay with him, but what he really wanted more than anything was that God's will be done. I had never heard such a response. It was totally contrary to what I had been taught to believe, and yet it made a lasting impression on me. People from all over the city started praying for the cardinal, including people from other religions and various Protestant denominations, coming together to hold prayer vigils outside his home. He welcomed prayers, yet he never strayed from his earlier comments about God's will, and his peaceful acceptance never wavered. When he died, tens of thousands of people from all religions and backgrounds lined the streets to pay their respects; many were crying. Looking back, I think this whole experience of faith and peace, undiminished by suffering and death, drew me closer to the Catholic faith.

The Christian witness of the Holy Father, Pope John Paul II, also moved me. I was struck by his sanctity, his humility, and his complete fidelity to Catholic teaching. I remember being especially moved by his response to his would-be assassin, Mehmet Ali Agca. He went to the jail, prayed for the man who almost killed him, and forgave him. When I recalled this scene, I was astonished by the Holy Father's mercy. I thought also about his visits to the United States and the hundreds of thousands of people who came to see him, especially the *young* people who traveled far and wide to hear his teachings. Clearly, he was not the antichrist as some taught. Gradually, I would come to love our Holy Father when, as he spoke and lived the truth in love, his sufferings became more and more apparent during his travels from country to country.

Tragedy strikes again

Then tragedy struck my life again. Without warning, Janice, my sister-in-law—my pastor—became ill and was admitted to the hospital. The doctors ran many tests but could not discover the cause of her illness. During her hospital stay, I called her after our Sunday service. While I was speaking with her, she had a heart attack. By the time I reached the hospital, she was in a semi-coma. Our whole church family prayed for her healing, and we believed God would heal her. We prayed for months, but her condition never changed. One evening, I received a phone call informing me that Janice had died. I can't express to you how shocked I was. Janice and I had dreamed of doing great things for Jesus and the kingdom of God together, and now she was gone. I cried out to God, desperate to know what was happening, or better yet, *why*. All of the people I had started my journey with were gone—dead. Now what? I was confused and hurt.

The Catholic faith answers my questions

After Janice's death, our assistant pastor became the pastor, and we moved into a church building. I preached more often but was secretly struggling with my faith—not so much my faith in God, but the Protestant faith I was called to preach and teach. I turned to EWTN to provide answers to my questions. I watched daily Mass *twice* a day, and I watched Mother Angelica every day. I began reading books about the lives of the saints and was shocked to discover that anyone could have as close a union to Jesus as they had. I was simply astounded by the sufferings and sacrifices they *joyfully* made for this union and for the souls of others. The more I learned about the Catholic faith, the more I was drawn to it, but I still had reservations about some doctrines, such as Mary's role in the Church, the Sacrament of Reconciliation, and purgatory. I spoke with Mr. Bonner about all these things, and he gave me a tape by Scott Hahn, a Protestant pastor who became Catholic. As I played the tape, I couldn't believe my ears. Here this man was talking about many of my own experiences. I laughed and cried as I discovered I was not alone on my journey. I tuned in to other shows on EWTN, such as *The Journey Home, Life on the Rock, The Abundant Life, The Holy Rosary, The Chaplet of Divine Mercy, Treasures of the Catholic Church, The Catechism with Bishop Foley*, and Bob and Penny Lord's programs on the lives of the saints. Mr. Bonner gave me many books to read, such as *Christ Is Passing By*, by St. Josemaria Escrivá, *The Catholic Source Book: Basics of the Catholic Faith*, by Alan Schreck, *The Pope Speaks to the Catholic Church*, just to name a few. He gave me my first Rosary, with a pamphlet on the various mysteries. I could recite the Rosary prayers right away from watching EWTN.

I long for union with God in the Catholic Church

Mr. Bonner also gave me my first statue of Jesus, that of the Sacred Heart of Jesus, which I fell in love with from the start. I had always wanted a statue of Jesus and other religious items in my home, but my Protestant religion had taught that this was idol worship. Thank God, through EWTN and Mr. Bonner, I learned that this was no different from having pictures of your loved ones on fireplaces, mantles, walls, or coffee tables in your home. Between reading the books Mr. Bonner gave me and watching EWTN, I was learning everything I could about the Catholic faith. The teachings that impacted me the most, though, were about the Holy Eucharist, our Blessed Mother Mary, and redemptive suffering—uniting our sufferings with Christ for the needs of others. The more I watched daily Mass, the more I hungered to receive Jesus in the Holy Eucharist, His Body, Blood, Soul, and Divinity.

I became increasingly aware of how irreverent my own church was during our monthly communion services. When I thought about it, I realized "irreverent" is the wrong word to describe the piety of the members of my church because, after all, we believed we were only taking communion as a *symbol*. I wanted to receive so much more than a symbol; I wanted to receive *all* of our Lord. There were times when I almost made the Sign of the Cross or knelt during our communion.

Finally, I understood about healing and suffering, how precious our sufferings are to Christ. Every part of my being wanted to become Catholic, but how could I leave my church, the church I helped to start? I was such a part of it, one of its pastors. What would I do if I found out I was making a huge mistake?

My longing is fulfilled

God answered my question about how I could leave my church in a direct way. When Janice died, our assistant pastor took on the role of pastor. He was a young man who really loved the Lord and wanted to serve God, but it was obvious from the start that he did not feel ready to pastor a church at his young age. He tried very hard to be a good pastor, but his inexperience undermined his efforts. The congregation stopped growing, and the members became increasingly disheartened, so much so that many left to attend other churches. The membership dwindled, and the decision was finally made to close the church. I grieved the loss of my church, but at the same time I realized that the Lord had given me the opportunity I was waiting for. I couldn't think of any more excuses to put off entering the Catholic Church, *except* for fear. I was so afraid that I thought I would never get up the courage. Then the Lord shed His light on me one providential night. I was watching *The Journey Home* with Marcus Grodi and his guests, Rosalind Moss and Kristine Franklin.[29] Both guests

---

[29] Rosalind Moss converted to Evangelical Protestantism from Judaism and later entered the Catholic Church. Kristine Franklin was a Protestant missionary who converted to Catholicism.

gave their conversion stories and were answering questions from the viewing audience. During the last few minutes of the show, Rosalind looked into the TV camera and spoke to those of us who were contemplating entering the Catholic Church. She said: *"You don't have to be afraid. God loves you."* All of a sudden, it was as if God Himself had spoken those words directly to me: *"Rhonda, you don't have to be afraid. I love you. You can trust Me."* I decided right then and there that I was going to become Catholic and that I would attend my first Catholic Mass on Sunday. I began attending the inquiry classes and was amazed at just how much I had learned from watching EWTN, speaking with Mr. Bonner, and reading the books he had given me. It wasn't long before I started RCIA classes to be confirmed in the Catholic faith.

My desire to receive Jesus in the Holy Eucharist was overwhelming. I had watched others receive Him for many years, and now that I was very close to actually receiving Him myself, my longing was almost unbearable. I was elated when I was told our RCIA class would be received into the Church in September, rather than during the Easter Vigil because of our backgrounds and knowledge. On September 11, 1999, I was confirmed in the Catholic Church and received my first Holy Communion—our Lord and Savior's *Body, Blood, Soul, and Divinity.* The inexpressible joy I felt on that day remains with me every time I partake of the Holy Eucharist. After years of searching and praying, God showered me with unimaginable blessings by calling me into His Church, the Church His Son founded. My journey was long, but the reward is priceless. Almost every day I learn something new about the Catholic faith and am ever more grateful for this gift.

Considering how different my Protestant faith and worship were from the Catholic Church, I wondered how my family and friends would react to my conversion. Surprisingly, my family was very happy and supportive. As I expected, most of my friends and my colleagues in ministry were shocked and perplexed. I received many questions, among them "Why the Catholic Church?" and "Don't you believe in Jesus anymore?" Very few friends have remained, while most have stopped calling. Although I can understand their hurt, my wish for them is that they could really and truly know the joy I feel to be finally *Home*, and I pray that one day we all may be One. From Protestant *charismatic* to Roman *Catholic,* I went from "c" to shining "C."

Rhonda Grayson was born and raised in the early 1950s on the south side of Chicago, where she received her elementary and secondary schooling, and attended college. She sang professionally for a number of years before giving her heart and life to Jesus. Rhonda is unmarried with no children, except for "the love of her life," her fifteen-year-old cat, Bunky Grayson. For the last twenty-two years, she has been employed at the University of Chicago Press.

8

‿

From Lake Wobegon to Rome

Ruth Andreas

$\mathcal{I}$ grew up, in the early 1960s, in a small Minnesota town much like Garrison Keillor's Lake Wobegon: culturally well-defined, close-knit, with many of the advantages of agrarian life. My life revolved around home, church, and school. I was blessed to live in a loving community, with many opportunities for learning. I remember the white stone statue of Jesus at the front of the Lutheran church my mother and I attended every Sunday, as well as the hymns and songs and images of the Good Shepherd hanging in the Sunday school classrooms. I also remember the prayers that we said and the stories that my parents read from *The Children's Story Bible* in our home. Thus began my friendship with Jesus.

Although my community was just a tiny spot on the map, I felt that we were part of God's larger family. As Lutherans, we were keenly aware of the great commission to go to all nations with the Gospel. I was completely captivated by the missionary families that visited my church when I was a girl. Their slide shows compiled from pictures taken in other parts of the world kept me on the edge of my seat. In a sixth-grade paper, I wrote that I wanted to be a missionary someday.

Trouble in Lake Wobegon

Simultaneous to my faith development, a trying situation in my childhood home led me to ask two very big questions for a little girl: Why does suffering have to be a part of the human condition, and is the transformation of human nature truly possible? These questions would dog me for years until I converted to Roman Catholicism in my early thirties. Both my life and my conversion have been closely linked to the struggles of my father.

My father was born in the 1920s. His life was marked or, more accurately, scarred, by the unhappiness of his own father, who abandoned his wife and four children during the Great Depression of the 1930s. My father was the oldest of those four children, and by all accounts he seems to have borne to a greater degree than his siblings the anger and frustration of his father. Sometime early in his adulthood, after fighting in World War II, my father was diagnosed with depression. By the time I came along many years later, the emotional storms he experienced had created a pattern which, like the change in the weather, seemed to be a permanent aspect of his life and, by extension, of our family life. So even though there was love and faith in my home, there was also instability. Love and faith amidst suffering, especially the suffering of depression, was a major theme that would significantly define my interior development for years to come.

The women in my father's life—his mother and his wife— were both regular churchgoers. My father, however, attended church very reluctantly during my growing-up years. I have often wondered if my father's diagnosis hindered his advance in the spiritual life. The fact that he was not raised Lutheran, as was my mother, may have accounted for some of his ambivalence. Still, could the clinical diagnosis have led my father to fail to strive for change, believing on some level that change was not possible or just plain too difficult? I often ruminated to myself: "If my father's condition is chronic and of his *nature*, can he really ever change?" My father was able to support our family financially, but over the years his level of emotional stability did not change.

The mark of suffering

I was deeply affected by my father's difficulties. I wished, at times, that I could run away from them, but the truth is I experienced my own pain and confusion relative to his. I do not remember a time when I felt at peace. I also experienced a fear of growing up to be like him, since I possessed something of his nature by birth. Still, these thoughts and fears became the cross that, in the long run, would draw me away from a life of mediocrity and into a much deeper relationship with Christ.

To all appearances, my father stopped looking for answers regarding his depression, but I did not. I didn't dwell on why things had to be this way but on how they could be changed and healed. Christianity explains the reality of original sin and resulting wounds that human persons inherit from generation to generation. This framework provided by the Lutheran Church would help me begin to understand the mark of suffering upon our family's life, but I would have to wait a long time to see the whole picture. Eventually, the Catholic Church would most totally and accurately define the human condition for me, as well as provide the full means of healing, through Jesus Christ, the Divine Physician. I would come to see how the gifts of the sacraments of the Holy Eucharist and Penance could have done much to restore balance in my father's troubled soul, had we been Catholic. As it was, we did the best we could with the resources, including psychiatry and Protestant spirituality, that were available to us at the time.

Looking for healing in all the wrong places

My search for legitimate healing became the theme of my life from early on. I embarked on the search not only for myself but also for my father, whom I love, and for others in general who suffer without understanding why. How did I go about this, and how did I respond to suffering in the early years of my life? I responded by looking for relief in the systems of thought that I had access to then, including Lutheran theology and popular psychology.

First, Luther. My Lutheran experience was, in a variety of ways, a blessing to me. As a Lutheran, I came to know Jesus as my friend and comforter. I was encouraged to read God's Word. The community life and piety of our church were a source of support for my mother and me; however, Luther's theology placed me in an intellectually and emotionally tenuous situation.

I was not a casual listener in Sunday school and confirmation class because I was a student in sincere need of hope, what Christians call "good news." As I grew older, we students heard more and more about Luther's doctrine of "justification by faith." We also often heard the phrase "saved by faith alone." Since these concepts were held up to be at the center of what Lutherans believe, I struggled very hard to understand them.

According to Luther, the justification we have gained from Christ's sacrifice on the cross is something like a cloak placed over our sins; it does not penetrate to the very essence, or nature, of man in a transforming way. While Catholicism understands human nature to be good as God created it, albeit severely wounded by original sin, Lutheranism teaches that fallen human nature is totally corrupt. Over time, Luther's view that it is not possible to change human nature brought about a passive, if not a desperate, response in me. In light of my family background, this interpretation contributed to a sense of hopelessness within me. At the same time, I looked around me to find that most Lutherans were quite content and happy with their religious identity. "I must have misunderstood something," I would tell myself, but deep down, this issue remained very much unresolved.

If Luther's view of the human condition was overly pessimistic, then that of the contemporary psychology I encountered as a high-school student was overly optimistic, looking to the strength of the individual and to his nature for the keys to healing. Furthermore, if most psychological counselors and their theories today do not outright deny the presence of God in the healing process, then the need for God is, at the very least, ignored. How else does one explain the concept of *self*-actualization? From my own experience, I knew that neither my father nor I could solve the puzzle of depression by personal strength alone. Still, as a teenager encountering popular psychology, I began to hope that an understanding of it and related theories might insulate me from the pain I experienced vicariously through my father.

In the end, I discovered that much of psychology holds out a false hope. Without a proper objective framework—that of the spiritual world, and specifically of faith in Christ—it can never deliver what it promises. Through my conversion experience, I would learn that healing could not come and suffering could not be eliminated simply through *self*-mastery. While it is true that psychological techniques may be helpful in overcoming some difficulties, they cannot be replacements for the life-giving Word and sacraments. At best, they are handmaids, just as the other sciences are rightfully placed at the service of theology and the Church. Furthermore, suffering is the result of original sin, something that comes out of the hearts of men and women. Psychological theories that deal exclusively with the perfection of human nature do not adequately address supernatural realities; nevertheless, for some time in my early years these theories captivated me. To complicate matters even further, when I was a student at a Lutheran liberal arts college in the early 1980s, I found myself drawn to cultural viewpoints different from my own, through my contacts with foreign exchange students and some of my college electives. This was not surprising, since the intellectual climate at the time encouraged it. Further, this approach to learning fed the missionary-inspired curiosity I possessed concerning the larger human family. I chose to concentrate my studies on the fields of history and anthropology.

Still blinded as to where to find the truth, I now asked myself: "Do people from other parts of the world know something we do not know regarding life's most basic questions about man?" I had stepped once again onto a slippery intellectual slope. When I had several opportunities to study abroad, I did so, investing significant amounts of energy agonizing over contrasts between cultures. I was now considering viewpoints outside of Lutheranism and even Christianity, because the world of diversity to which I was attracted offered seemingly numerous alternatives for consideration.

For a time, I enjoyed my new intellectual search, unaware of the depth of potential pitfalls when one ventures without solid guidance. A cross-cultural trip to Latin America introduced me to liberation theology, which is a deviation from Catholic teaching. It harmonized well with the *zeitgeist* of the time, when many teachers advocated a move away from traditional ways of viewing nagging social, intellectual, and even spiritual questions.

Not long afterward, I had occasion to travel to Europe. There, I found that young European intellectuals were very confident in their views, which prospered in an advancing culture of dissent similar to our own. Many were critical of the new Pope of the time, John Paul II. He seemed to represent everything from which these intellectuals sought liberation. How they misunderstood! But since I was not a Catholic at that time, I did not reflect on this deeply, nor did I appreciate that the dissent I encountered was primarily targeted at Christianity. I naïvely assumed that other young people were searching, like myself, in "good faith."

At this point in my life, what was I to do about Lutheranism? On the one hand, it was still very much a part of my identity and continued to be my only serious reference point for Christianity. I had never earnestly considered another religion, and Lutherans make good Christians by their example. On the other hand, in the wider world, Lutheranism didn't seem to be so much a universal expression of truth as a culturally defined expression of faith; it seemed narrow. Further, there was the matter of Lutheran theology itself. Despite my nagging questions about the truth of Lutheranism, the Christ I met as a little girl was still very much alive and beckoning to me, as I continued to attend worship services, although sporadically.

My search takes me to a seminary

As my college years neared an end, I was not altogether career-oriented, yet I knew the time had arrived to give myself firmly to something. The period of passive observation in which I had indulged must eventually come to an end. Around this time, I experienced what Lutherans describe as a "call" to continue my studies at a seminary. At first I couldn't believe this. Still, I was vaguely aware that ordination was something made available to women in my branch of Lutheranism, the Evangelical Lutheran Church in America (ELCA). At the same time, I felt that God was revealing to me a key to the puzzle of contemporary life, which is that the problems of our generation are spiritual, not political. I remembered the Gospel call to evangelization and, having buried my doubts about Luther, I made plans to study for the ministry.

In retrospect, I realize I entered the seminary with one foot in and one foot out. I took to my studies in earnest and even liked the idea of becoming a pastor. I was now married to a man who pursued an academic career in a field unrelated to theology, but my own passion for theology did not abate. I was still searching for an end to confusion and did not limit myself as to where to find it. As had been my pattern, I focused on the world of ideas. On the shelves of the seminary bookstore were books written by those whom I now know to be dissenting theologians, but at that time they were just part of the intellectual marketplace. Lutherans have no teaching magisterium to define the parameters of life-giving thought; instead, they have the Lutheran Confessions.[30] Those Confessions, however, continued to raise doubts in my mind. I asked myself: "With so many other theological resources available, are these what I must limit myself to in the end?"

I become a pastor, and the bottom falls out

As the day of my ordination dawned, and I was asked to swear by these Confessions, I experienced a subconscious resistance. By this point in the process of becoming a pastor, however, I felt that my resistance should simply be ignored. I had completed my education, and I would soon be ordained as a pastor in my first congregation. I wanted to preach God's Word and serve a Christian community, so I went ahead and became an ELCA pastor, and I served quite happily in the role, until the time came when my husband's career called him to another part of the country. By

---

[30] The Lutheran Confessions are a collection of documents collectively called *The Book of Concord.*

now we had adopted our first child. I was willing to move but was not prepared to seek another call.

After a few months in a different part of the country, my marriage began to deteriorate. I was trying to settle into the role of a new mother, and I felt content to stay at home with my child. Calls were not readily available where my husband had relocated. On top of this, I still struggled with the old familiar questions from my youth regarding my father and, more broadly, the healing and transformation of the nature of man. I quit going to church for a time. My husband, who had been more of a follower than a leader when it came to Christianity, did not understand why I wasn't interested in seeking another call. Didn't I want to advance my career? What about all of those years in school?

I look back now, as a Catholic, on this period of my life with an awareness of how lost I had become. I had been a pastor for a short period of time, and yet I didn't have a properly formed prayer life. Jesus was near to me, but still I had doubts and fears that I could not put to rest. I did not have the life-giving presence of the sacraments, especially the Eucharist and Penance. I was also part of a marriage relationship that was not firmly planted in Christ. I was restless and losing ground in my marriage, in my spiritual life, and, ultimately, in my health. At the end of this period, I turned my back on Jesus.

Meanwhile, my husband had found his professional niche. Settling into a new work setting, he found it difficult to deal with my troubles and eventually stated that he no longer wished to travel with me on my search. He wanted a divorce.

My turnaround
At this point, I sank into depression. My strength began to dry up, and I grew even colder in my faith. Finally, I lost all sight of how to find sustenance. I was exhausted from the journey I had

been on since my youth, and having been abandoned by my spouse, I believed things couldn't have been much worse. Although I had turned my back on Him, God did not abandon me. By His grace, a moment finally came when I was moved to speak the name of Jesus. I asked Jesus to deliver me from darkness; He was the only One who could. This was the turning point of my life.

I consider my turnaround to be a miracle because I had sunk to such a low point in human existence that it is difficult to describe. In this place, I could accomplish nothing by my own power. Since I had not found the answers I had long demanded by following the more commonly traveled paths of my generation, I was left to the raw unknown. I was stripped down, where God could begin again with me, where He could reveal to me His truths one by one. Did I ever dream that I would become a Catholic? No. But the roads of my search were about to converge in Catholicism.

My suffering finally has meaning

How quickly God worked to set me on my feet again! By God's providence, I soon met a man of faith named Mark, who introduced me to the Rosary and invited me to Mass and who, one day, would become my husband. After I obtained an annulment, he and I entered into a sacramental marriage, where Christ has truly been a welcome and active guest. This focus on Christ, along with my husband's love, has contributed to my overall sense of well-being.

I was hungry for the Real Presence of Christ in those early days of my conversion, and I continue to be today. The sacraments of the Holy Eucharist and of Penance play a vital role in the healing process. In addition, my confusion was finally ending! The holy priests I met, including but not limited to the

Dominicans, brought forth the splendor of the truth that I was longing to hear. How great God has been to me! I can still weep at the thought of my conversion. I entered into full communion with the Catholic Church on Easter of 1993.

How did the Catholic Church finally and completely end the confusion I carried with me from childhood? The first and most important point for my life has been to learn that, *yes,* transformation of human nature is possible; God's mercy and love will it. The transformation of man, body and soul, is very much at the center of why Christ, our Lord and Savior, made His sacrifice on the cross. Through faith in Christ, we are no longer the same as persons. We are set free from blindness and really do enter into a life that's new. "Therefore, if anyone is in Christ, he is a new creation; the old has passed away, behold, the new has come. All this is from God, who through Christ has reconciled us to himself and gave us the ministry of reconciliation."[31]

In recent years, I have come to cherish proper spiritual and intellectual formation, which the Catholic Church offers in totality. By contrast, the Lutheran tradition failed me. I was taught that I was saved by faith, which I know was supposed to be "good news." However, I went about conducting my life without a clear understanding of how our sufferings, our efforts, and our sacrifices are linked to God's larger plan of salvation history. For a person such as I, in sincere need of healing, much more than assent of the intellect to a particular theological formula (so heavily emphasized) was required.

John Paul II's teachings on the human person provide a particularly stark contrast to those of Martin Luther. The Holy Father's philosophy of the person (personalism) holds that every act a person makes contributes to the person he is becoming. This understanding has great implications for the moral life, and

---

[31] 2 Corinthians 5:17-18.

it holds great promise for the process of transformation. Every human act, aided by God's grace, is a potential step forward in newness. This good news is universal, that is, truly applicable to all members of the human family. All nations need Christ.

The Catholic understanding of sanctification has also given meaning to my suffering. Sometimes in life, God requires His children to undergo great losses. The Church has taught me that we really can turn our losses over to God. He, in turn, can and does use them for good. As Catholics, we learn to offer up our sufferings, even in the smaller things. We join our sufferings to Christ's own suffering and thereby enter into the process of redemptive suffering for the sins of the world. Our sufferings, our efforts, and our sacrifices become linked to God's larger plan of salvation, made tangible in human history.

Happiness as a Catholic wife and mother

I also must make mention of the importance of the Catholic Church in the formation of my family life. As John Paul II says, the family is the basic cell of society, and the Church grants legitimacy to the very important roles of husband and wife by making marriage a sacrament.[32] This is a crucial point for women, such as myself, who have chosen to be wives and mothers, according to God's plan and our primary nature. Through the grace of the Sacrament of Matrimony, husbands and wives are given special strength to carry out their parental and spousal duties. As a wife and mother of five children, I have found ongoing strength in the blessings of the Church.

My husband and I believe so strongly in the teachings of the Church about the importance of the family that we decided, amidst our babies and bills, to found a lay apostolate dedicated

---

[32] The *Catechism of the Catholic Church* is a resource which explains Catholic teaching on marriage and the family.

to the domestic church. John Paul II is bringing dignity back to family life by helping those of us in family formation to understand our high calling. The foundation for the domestic church is the Sacrament of Holy Matrimony. Grace flows through this sacrament and provides all that is necessary for the sustenance of the family. There is a particular need at this moment in history for many families to rediscover their dignity and to restore a sense of the sacred to the life of the home. And so, in the midst of building our own family, we are working to do our part to help disseminate this message in our area of the country.

In closing, I look back over my life and marvel at the course it has taken since my youth. My cross—my father's depression—which was so painful to me, set me on the search for truth. After many years of struggle, I found healing and the fullness of truth in the Catholic Church. My sufferings have borne fruit. "For everyone who asks receives, and he who seeks finds, and to him who knocks it will be opened."[33]

Ruth Andreas is a wife and homeschooling mother of five children. She also edits The Domestic Church, *a grassroots journal for families, which explores Church teachings as they relate to the family, the basic cell of society. Ruth lives in Oregon and has been a Catholic since 1993.*

---

[33] Matthew 7:8.

9

God-Haunted and Healed

Robin Maas

Some people are "God-haunted," and I was one of them. Their incidence in the general population is always a mystery. What causes the quest for God to become the central issue in the life of one individual but not another? Why do fundamental theological issues matter so much to relatively so few people? Those of us who have been invisibly "branded" in this way can usually spot one another without much difficulty. And more often than not, we find one another along the road to Rome or among the ranks of more or less recent converts to Catholicism.

Raised in a standard (for the time) anti-Catholic environment, as a newly married young adult, I found myself lurking guiltily around those shelves in the public library that contained conversion stories such as this. At the time, I could not account for my interest in this contraband literature. My Christian Science mother had made certain I knew that whatever the Catholic Church had to offer was forbidden fruit. Because she was a font of good advice and had proved herself right on countless occasions, I had no reason to doubt her. She made sure my brother and I attended Sunday school regularly, and I actually looked forward to the rather intellectually rigorous, left-brained approach to religion that I found in the Christian Science Church. In fact, I excelled at it. Thus I entered adulthood in a conflicted state: On the one hand, I considered myself a devout Christian Scientist; on the other, I was looking hard for something else—something obviously missing in the account of ultimate reality I had been given.

My first known encounter with the Church came at the age of six when my mother—on one of many shopping expeditions down Fifth Avenue in Manhattan—decided (out of curiosity) to step into St. Patrick's Cathedral and simply "gawk." The experience of entering such a dark and cavernous building filled with so much alien and religiously exotic visual stimuli was pretty overwhelming. I don't remember feeling anything more than a certain amazement and fascination at the time, but it was clear to me that I had entered a very different world—a world that had something compelling to offer. Not long after that impromptu visit I announced to my mother that I wanted to be a nun. The utter ferocity of her response—"Don't you ever say anything like that again!"—scared me, precisely as it was meant to, imprinting her fear and loathing of what she did not know or understand on my own youthful heart.

A personal loss sends me on a forty-two-year-long search

This incident came close on the heels of the first tragic loss in my life, the untimely death of my father just before my fifth birthday. One year later, my mother had remarried and relocated the family from California to New York. It has been suggested before, and I am inclined to believe it, that early suffering is a key ingredient in the psyches of those I call God-haunted. Depending on the response it meets, suffering either sanctifies a soul or sours it. In my case, it set me on a search for something that would fill the awful gap created by my father's painful and mysteriously sudden departure and the almost concurrent loss of my ancestral home and neighborhood.

Looking back on that formative visit to St. Patrick's, I suspect that what I was responding to was not the excitement of a visual "blitz"—something that would have affected me profoundly, since I am by nature what is called a "visual learner"—but, rather, my first encounter with the Real Presence. In my sorrow, the power of Christ hidden in the Blessed Sacrament spoke to me. Because it was in a language I did not understand, a long and arduous struggle to learn it was set into motion, a struggle that was to last for forty-two long years.

The next few years were relatively uneventful. My mother and stepfather soon decided to return to California, but to a different part of the state. I settled in to our new family arrangements and continued to take my religious obligations relatively seriously. Throughout this time, however, I had almost no exposure to classical Christianity apart from the limited exposure to Christian symbolism that was, in those days, still very apparent at Christmas time.

Growing up in a sect that was essentially iconoclastic, like many Protestants, I suffered a real visual starvation. Without recognizing the problem for what it was, I attempted to sate my "hunger" by collecting Christmas cards (the only religious art to which I had access) and making scrapbooks with them, something we were encouraged to do for hospitalized children. I also well recall the dramatic impact a public-school Christmas pageant had on me, since nothing of the sort was available in my church. I took great delight in performing with my classmates a selection of beautiful carols, including *Adeste Fideles*, which we sang entirely in Latin.

This was all very enticing. In contrast, my weekly Sunday school classes consisted solely of reading and discussing the Bible and Mrs. Eddy's textbook, *Science and Health, with Key to the Scriptures*,[34] an experience that fed my mind but left my soul to subsist on near-starvation rations. But nothing shook my conviction that I was a member of the "one true church." A visit to my friend's conventional Protestant Sunday school class left me scandalized. I remember telling my mother afterward, rather indignantly, that the hour I spent there was an utter waste of time, since we did nothing but color, cut, and paste. It struck me as devoid of any significant content, and I was bored silly.

Tragedy strikes again

Tragedy struck our family again when, during my freshman year in high school, my mother died of cancer. Far from disillusioning me with my religion, this crisis thrust me into it much more deeply. Almost immediately following my mother's funeral, I had an experience of consolation and assurance. I had picked up a copy of Christian Science literature lying around the house and started to read one of the personal testimonies of healing always included in them. A feeling of being loved and cared for enveloped me as I read. The message I received was clear: I needed God, and the only access I had or even knew of was the religion in which I had been raised. I rapidly took on what would normally be considered an adult-level study and practice of Christian Science. I went from fourteen to forty-four almost overnight.

Thus, in my adolescence, I acquired the habit of rising early in the morning and spending thirty minutes each day in prayerful study of the Scriptures and the writings of Mary Baker Eddy. I soon became steeped in her entirely ahistorical, "spiritual" (or allegorical) method of interpreting the Bible, and through this

---

[34] Mary Baker Eddy founded the Church of Christ, Scientist (Christian Science). Tenets of the faith include reliance on the spiritual healing of illness.

process of long and repeated exposure to biblical texts from the *King James Version* of the Bible, I learned much of this material by heart. Much later, while I was having to "unlearn" Mrs. Eddy's quirky and subjective system of biblical interpretation, I gained a much deeper appreciation for the workings of Divine Providence. I recognized what a blessing I had received in being exposed to so much Scripture early in life and especially from such a felicitous translation. I have learned that, in the last analysis, the Bible can bless and heal despite the abuse it takes from misguided or even heretical readings.

This experience of adolescent conversion and early religious formation created a kind of "template" in my soul that has remained fixed firmly in place throughout my long spiritual odyssey. First, it taught me that prayer was the very heart and soul of religion, that it was efficacious, and therefore prayer should be a first, and not a last, resort in time of trouble. Second, because Christian Science teaching stresses the importance of "truth" as a theological category and, indeed, constitutes itself a kind of "metaphysics," I grasped early on the idea that theological orthodoxy really matters and, therefore, a strong ecclesial authority is essential. Years later, these unshakable convictions were to cause me no end of trouble as I tried to integrate myself successfully into a mainline Protestant denomination. At the same time, they became powerful factors leading me to Catholicism.

Inadequate answers to the problem of suffering

These were the major assets from my past that I carried with me into adulthood. But there were also huge liabilities, such as the gnostic conviction that matter is "unreal" and that man is therefore a purely spiritual being, that sin (like disease and death) is really an illusion and, worst of all, I think, the belief that suffering was an unmitigated evil. For Christian Scientists, spiritual advancement means an increasing ability to overcome suffering and vanquish its effects. The kind of prayer with which a Christian Scientist triumphs over suffering is utterly impersonal. One "knows" the truth and thereby achieves total confidence in God. Through "knowing the truth," all evil—sin, disease, and death—are defeated. Since I had watched my mother expire from a devastating disease (and was to learn much later in life that she had, days before her death, lost her faith), this left me in a very difficult position.

I could not simply abandon Christian Science as so many disillusioned souls have done when it failed to bring healing, because I had nothing with which to replace it. To leave Christian Science meant to leave God or, worse yet, to be abandoned by Him; however, at some very deep level I lived with a profoundly disturbing "disconnect." It was years before I could gather the courage to face the problem and walk away from the only system of coping with hardship I knew.

I discover a spiritual world outside of Christian Science

Even from the grave, my mother continued to exercise great influence in my life. I knew she had wanted me to attend the only Christian Science college in existence, and so I did. I had four good years there, excelled in my studies, and met the man I would later marry. In every way, the experience confirmed me in my religious convictions with one notable exception. A strange but prophetic incident, in which I suspect my guardian angel was at work, occurred during my senior year when one day I walked into the library and saw right in front of me a rack of newly acquired titles. I headed straight for the rack, noticed one book in particular, and was drawn to check it out. It was a collection of essays by someone named Thomas Merton, entitled *No Man Is an Island*. I read it and found it strangely compelling. It cut, like a sword, through the armor that defended my religious convictions. The author was Catholic! How odd.

A similar "wounding" occurred during one of my summer holidays when, home from college, I chanced upon an appealing paperback copy of *The Imitation of Christ* on the magazine rack at my local supermarket. I bought it on impulse and started to read. In many respects, I was encountering a foreign language or at least a religious idiom that struck me as exotic, eerily *personal*, and made reading a struggle. Yet I persevered. Something made me press on with it, despite the fact that I did not understand much of what I read and sometimes felt even repelled by the extent to which this expression of faith seemed tied to material reality and the fact of suffering.

Soon after graduation, I was married, and my husband, Jack, and I moved to Oberlin, Ohio, where he was to pursue graduate studies. Our favored social outing that first year of married life consisted of walking to the town square in the evening to browse the college bookstore, eat ice cream, and then go home. Inevitably, I headed for the religion section in the bookstore, and it was there I discovered the historical novels of Scholem Asch, a Polish Jew who was deeply drawn to Christianity but who never converted. His books on Jesus, Paul, Moses, and Mary created an explosion of interest in me. I already loved Scripture, but I had never been exposed to the kind of elaborate historical treatment of biblical themes that I found here. I was driven almost wild by his rather tortured ambivalence about the reality of the Christian claims, some of which were entirely alien to me because of my unorthodox upbringing. These books raised so many questions in my mind about my own convictions that I began to devour everything about Scripture I could get my hands on. I soon found myself with an unquenchable desire to do graduate work in biblical studies, and I eventually applied to Union Seminary in New York and was accepted.

Catholic readings inspire longings and wonder

Fate intervened in the form of my first pregnancy and an opportunity given to my husband to participate in a USAID-sponsored program that would take us to East Africa for three years. I temporarily set aside my own academic ambitions but took with me on this grand safari another book I had found at the college bookstore, Evelyn Underhill's classic survey, *Mysticism*.

Three years in the Uganda bush left me with plenty of time for reading. Much to my horror, Jack was assigned to the faculty of a teacher training college in Mityana, run by French-Canadian priests who belonged to an order known then as the "White Fathers." I needn't have worried about being proselytized, for they left us quite alone and never brought up the subject of religion. Meanwhile, however, I was combing through the school's library shelves and discovering books written by the mystics I was learning about from Underhill's book, most notably Teresa of Ávila, along with an utterly compelling account of the Uganda martyrs who had recently been canonized. Our weekly shopping expeditions to Kampala usually included a stop at the Uganda Bookstore, operated by the Church of Uganda, which is affiliated with the Anglican Church. There I discovered the arcane Meister Eckhardt and a number of other Catholic writers. Anything I could find on the subject of prayer interested me; the more I read, the more I realized that there was much more to Christ and His Church than I had ever dreamed. So many questions came to mind. For instance, what was this "Eucharist" about which so many of the writers I admired spoke? I had no idea! Why was it that the average Christian's experience of prayer was so very personal compared to the kind of impersonal mental method I had been taught? What I lacked, I found both appealing and frightening. So I just kept reading and wondering and living with the same profound inner contradiction of longing for things Catholic, while simultaneously holding to the conviction that this was a religiously dangerous trap, and that what it taught was not the truth.

This uneasy and ultimately impossible position was finally shattered in my early thirties. By this time we were on our second stay in Uganda, living in the capital city of Kampala, where Jack had returned after doctoral study at Columbia University, initially, to do his thesis research and, eventually, to teach at Makerere University. With my husband's encouragement, I began a serious study of sociology (his subject of choice) leading to a master's degree. What I learned, in tandem with all of my previous religious reading, shattered the religious worldview that had sustained me through childhood, adolescence, and young adulthood.

Leaving Christian Science

At this point, it was easier to leave Christian Science than it was to embrace Catholicism, which is saying something, for the break was truly wrenching. Because I had believed in its teachings so wholeheartedly, when I finally jettisoned my belief system, I faced what seemed like an utter void. I no longer knew what was true. I continued to believe that there was a God, but I could not claim with certainty anything at all about Him. I was profoundly frightened by the loss of my previous certainties, for I had no ready substitutes. I coped by doing what I knew best: I simply continued to search, primarily in books, but I also began to attend services at the local Anglican church, which I found confusing and largely unsatisfying. In the absence of any substantial preaching, I found whatever solace I could in the visual symbols and depictions of the faith present on the walls of the church.

What the local pastor could not bring himself to say, these images preached wordlessly.

When we arrived back in New York after another three-year stint in Uganda, I was truly in a state of religious limbo. Each Sunday I went to church, but I always left unsatisfied. If I attended an Episcopal service, I was visually gratified and felt myself at least somewhat connected with the larger historical stream of Christianity that I longed to join. On the other hand, I felt a real dearth of the Word in these services, and the preaching was theologically insipid compared to what I was used to receiving in my personal study. If, out of desperation, I attended a Christian Science service, I got a large helping of Scripture, but it was dished out in very sterile circumstances. Nothing worked. Except once.

Sudden insight into suffering clarifies my path

At one of those intellectually disappointing Episcopal services at the Cathedral of St. John the Divine on the Upper West Side, I received a great gift in the form of a sudden insight derived from gazing upon something beautiful. I remember observing an elaborately decorated cross on the altar and thinking, in true judgmentally Protestant fashion, that this was an unwarranted excess, when suddenly it dawned on me that *this cross was an image of the redemptive meaning of suffering*. What looks like an unmitigated disaster turns out to be something beautiful, glorious even. It was a revelation; in retrospect, I think it clarified for me the path I was to take next. The cathedral was just beginning a special weekend program of classes in theology for the laity. I decided I would take one to see whether, in fact, I should pursue theology in a serious way, as I had earlier dreamed of doing.

I took a course, loved it, and found the opportunity I had long been waiting for when Jack was hired by the World Bank in

Washington, D.C. By this time, we had three school-age children, and soon after we arrived in the Washington area, I enrolled as a part-time student at Wesley Theological Seminary in their Master of Theological Studies program. I knew nothing about Methodism, but this seemed like a relatively safe and unobjectionable place to be—simply because it was respectably Protestant.

Well-intentioned but ambivalent Methodist

My experience as a student at Wesley, like my formation in Christian Science, turned out to be a mixed bag of blessings and frustration. I took most of my course work in Bible and biblical languages and loved it, and my strenuous struggles with concepts like the Trinity and the Incarnation were exhausting but ultimately fruitful and satisfying. Yet I was puzzled and disturbed by the ill-defined doctrinal commitments of Methodists, their lack of interest in the question of truth, and their general moral relativism. What really got to me, however, was the untempered campaign for "inclusive" language that was just beginning at this time in the mid-1970s. I had certainly not remained unscathed by the faddishness of feminism and was an avid reader of *MS Magazine* for a while, but this evisceration of the texts and the drivel it produced infuriated me. For a serious reader like myself, any attempt at bowdlerization was anathema. To my surprise, some of my classmates asked me if I were Catholic; they surmised from the kind of questions I raised in class and my attitude toward church authority that my background was Catholic. Indignant, I answered, "Of course not!" Two years into my four years at Wesley, I was baptized in the seminary chapel. I had no particular devotion to Methodism, but I had learned from C. S. Lewis that I could not be baptized into Christianity in general— as I had hoped—but must walk through one particular creedal door in order to enter the mainstream of Christian history and commitment. Frankly, I had nowhere else to go and was not willing to forgo this blessing any longer. So, at the age of thirty-seven, I became a well-intentioned but ambivalent Methodist. I must have known at the time that this would not be a final resting place for me, but I could not have told you where that place would be. If I would have stopped to think about it, my position again would have looked impossible, for I found nothing ultimately satisfying in Methodist worship. I secured a niche as a religious professional in that Protestant denomination only insofar as I found a certain receptivity among the laity to what the Scriptures had to offer.

Upon completing my master's degree at Wesley, I knew that I was not yet finished with my studies and wanted to pursue doctoral work. Because I had three children and a husband firmly ensconced in Washington D.C., I was in no position to pick up and go to wherever the best (i.e., most prestigious) biblical studies program might be. In fact, I had only one real option at the time—to enter the School of Religious Studies at Catholic University of America (CUA). I found this deeply disappointing, but in the end, I decided that this would be better than nothing. I enrolled, therefore, and spent eight years of part-time study completing a doctoral degree in religious education with a focus on biblical education.

I count myself fortunate, now, to have been thwarted in my academic ambitions. The department in which I studied was the liberal enclave within the School of Religious Studies. They welcomed me as a Protestant (and would now have enormous problems with me as a Catholic). I was given a very broad, and for that reason very helpful, exposure to mostly then contemporary Catholic thought, which affected me very differently than it did the cradle Catholics enrolled in the program.

Convinced of the truth of Catholicism—but stalled

Fresh from a Protestant seminary that paid no serious attention whatsoever to philosophical issues in theology, I found these Catholic sources to be positively bracing. I experienced an odd sense of homecoming to be suddenly immersed in readings that took metaphysical questions seriously. Because my original formation had been rooted in a system that took very little of Scripture literally, and I had just exited an institution where many believed not much of anything, I was not scandalized by the direction in which many popular post-Vatican II theologians were moving. I was conscious all along that had it not been for Vatican II, I could not have survived at CUA; I would have truly been intellectually and emotionally shut out. In effect, I received the insights of these "reformers" as someone who happened to be passing through the same intellectual point simultaneously but who was on a trajectory headed in the opposite direction.

During those eight years as a graduate student at CUA I once again entered a kind of theological limbo. Whenever I was present on campus, while engaged intellectually, I nevertheless felt "Protestant" and culturally out of place. Yet, whenever I returned to Wesley, where I had a role in founding and administering an ecumenical adult education program, I felt "Catholic." As long as I remained a graduate student, I could endure this ambiguity in my sense of identity, but when I completed my studies and was hired back by Wesley Theological Seminary as an assistant professor of Christian education, things suddenly became very difficult. Once on the other side of the desk, so to speak, the luxury of a noncommittal stance on issues of ultimate importance was no longer possible; one cannot profess what one does not believe. There is a stage through which many converts pass in which they work hard at converting those around them to the Catholic reality they have learned to love, precisely so they themselves will not have to leave them. At bottom they know that God wants it all, that nothing less than a total surrender will do, but rather than face this very real dying to life as they have always known it, they attempt to bargain. To Christ's invitation to follow Him we answer: "Lord, let me first go and bury my father," or "Let me first say farewell to those at my home," without registering His reply: "No one who puts his hand to the plow and looks back is fit for the kingdom of God."[35]

Thus I went through two very difficult years of stalling in which I tried to package what I wanted to teach in ways that would be palatable to the very mixed bag of Protestants enrolled at Wesley (everything from fundamentalists to Unitarians) and met with some success but mostly frustration. I also found that the seminary had changed considerably since my student days. Feminism was more firmly entrenched than ever, chapel worship was increasingly quirky and eclectic, and the faculty itself was painfully polarized on theological and ethical issues.

Then, out of the blue, came an invitation to team-teach a course for the Washington Theological Consortium with a Dominican priest. The consortium regularly offered courses such as this in pursuit of an ecumenical agenda, and they were look-ing for someone to provide the Protestant "ballast" for a course in comparative spirituality. Since I was the only person on the Wesley faculty at that time even remotely interested in this sub-ject, I was asked to fill this slot, and although I felt very inade-quate to the task, I was intrigued by the challenge and said yes.

A tidal wave of grace leads to my final spiritual crisis

My collaboration in this course proved to be the straw that broke the proverbial camel's back. It required me to reimmerse myself in those same mystical writers I had first discovered as a young

---

[35] Luke 9:59-62.

woman combing the shelves of a Catholic teacher-training college in rural Uganda. Now, however, I read them from the perspective of someone who had lived much longer, studied much more, and, like everyone else, suffered considerably simply from the ordinary challenges and vicissitudes of adult life. This fresh encounter with old loves came almost like a tidal wave of grace, and the highly intuitive priest with whom I worked was all too conscious of what was going on. He was ruthless in his pursuit, and I learned later that he had enlisted an army of contemplative nuns to pray for my conversion.

The course was a great success, and we decided to teach it a second time. The course was scheduled for the spring semester of 1987. The final crisis came in the fall of '86. By this time the inner conflict had become intolerable. For years I had attended an unusually liberal United Methodist Church, primarily because I had so many friends there but also because it was a place where no one was required to define himself theologically. In fact, the less defined one was, the better. What was most important to this particular group of United Methodists was the formation of a close community. But all the factors that made life difficult for me at the seminary were present in this context as well, adding to my sense of isolation and frustration. Over time, I had seen things slide further and further to the left here, too, and after a rather futile effort to convince people that we ought at least to repeat the Lord's Prayer during our Sunday worship, I gave up. I knew this church wasn't typical of other Methodist churches, so I told myself I would attend a more conventional congregation for a year before bolting.

I made a painfully awkward break with this congregation and betook myself to my neighborhood United Methodist church in the suburbs. I managed to attend for only nine months before reaching the point of despair. I remember hearing a recording of the old Protestant hymn "Once to Every Man and Nation Comes the Moment to Decide" as I was shopping in a bookstore adjacent to the CUA campus. Tears sprang to my eyes, as I thought about the "impossible" decision I was now facing. I felt "stuck"; I was miserable where I was but could not see my way out.

Catholic, I count all loss as gain

One October day, as I sat in my office at school, I picked up a slim paperback by Thomas Merton entitled *Holiness* and started to read. At some point, I paused, and weeping, said to God: "I really want to be Catholic." Immediately the answer came: "If that's what you want; that's what you will have." And that's how the deal was done.

I knew at that moment that I had, indeed, put my hand to the plow and that there was no turning back, simply because I had told the truth. For the first time in my life I had faced the reality that I had kept concealed (barely) out of fear, that I wanted to be Catholic and, indeed, already was Catholic in my convictions and tastes. Once you tell the truth to God, it is impossible to fool yourself any longer. Thus began a period, lasting two or three months, in which I was severely tested. I call it my "Oh No!" phase, in which I had to face down all of the unpleasant implications and losses entailed in my conversion and "leave the dead to bury their own dead."[36] Converting would mean having to tell extended family members and professional colleagues something they wouldn't want to hear—Oh No! It would mean losing most of the professional gains I had made over a decade (and I would soon be applying for tenure)—Oh No! It would mean worshipping without the support of my immediate family—Oh No!—and so on and so forth. Each day brought with it another fresh shock of recognition, another "Oh No!" moment, and each of

---

[36] Luke 9:60.

these moments was a test: Is it worth it? Do you really want to be a Catholic that much? Each time, I swallowed hard and answered: Yes. Even if it means losing this—or that—I want to be Catholic. Finally, there were no more "Oh No!'s." Finally, there was nothing but YES, and a great sense of peace and joy descended. From that moment on, there has never been a shadow of doubt that the Catholic Church is where I belong.

Fortunately, Easter came late during the spring of 1987, and I was able to complete almost the entire consortium course while still remaining technically a Protestant. I was received at the Easter Vigil in the beautiful chapel at the Dominican House of Studies, surrounded by my family and closest friends, knowing that the quest I had been on for so long had finally reached a successful conclusion. I was as happy as I could possibly be.

My life as a Catholic has been filled with joys and challenges. I soon discovered that facing all those "Oh No's!" simply cleared the way for new initiatives of grace I could not possibly have envisioned at the time. Three years after my conversion, I was invited to form a community for Catholic women who share a common passion for the faith and for the spiritual welfare of children and youth. The work of the Women's Apostolate to Youth gradually grew to the point where it became far more engrossing and engaging than anything I was doing at the seminary, so I retired early from Wesley and devoted myself almost full-time to this apostolate.

Soon after my conversion, I was invited to serve as adjunct faculty in spirituality at the John Paul II Institute for Studies in Marriage and Family. Eventually, I was asked to take over the role of academic dean, a job that offered me excellent professional opportunities and many spiritual challenges, until the needs of my family and my apostolate made it necessary for me to retire from that as well.

In answer to countless prayers I have had the joy of seeing, first, my daughter and then my husband, convert to Catholicism. My two grown sons, having come to recognize their need for God, are now both moving in the same direction. In short, everything I expected to lose from making this costly decision, I have received back in a much more satisfying form directly from the hands of God.

As a practicing Catholic, I have gladly abandoned the frame of mind and way of life that was grounded in the heretical denial of material reality and, hence, of the Incarnation, of the personal nature of the Triune God, and of the power of faith (rather than understanding) as the driving force in prayer. All these "losses" I count as gain.

As a practicing Catholic I receive the Body and Blood of Christ daily, pray to Father, Son, and Holy Spirit in the presence of the Blessed Sacrament, confess my sins, and beg for mercy. My prayers—no longer impersonal declarative statements about what I "know" to be "true"—pass through the hands and heart of the Immaculate Mother of God, and I call constantly upon the holy angels for guidance and protection.

While it is easy to say, with other converts, how much I might wish to have enjoyed all the blessings of the sacraments earlier in my life, in retrospect I have many more reasons for gratitude than regret. The long "haunting" that characterized so much of my life, has left me capable of consciously cherishing what I now have in a way that many cradle Catholics seem to lack. The need for a fuller and more personal relationship with God that drove me so relentlessly in my youth, has been replaced in my seniority with a healing sense of peace and the satisfying conviction that the quest I set out on at age six was, thanks be to God, successful.

∾

Dr. Robin Maas is the former Academic Dean and Professor of Spirituality at the John Paul II Institute for Studies in Marriage and Family in Washington, D.C., and she is the founder and director of the Women's Apostolate to Youth, an intergenerational community for Roman Catholic women who exercise spiritual leadership with children and youth in the Diocese of Arlington. In addition, Robin Maas directs retreats, lectures, and conducts classes and workshops in spirituality. She is the author of numerous articles and five books: The Church Bible Study Handbook, Crucified Love, The Wisdom of Saint Elizabeth Ann Seton, Living in Hope, *and* Spiritual Traditions for the Contemporary Church (*co-editor with Gabriel O'Donnell, O.P.*). *She is married, the mother of three grown children, and grandmother of six.*

10

Almost a Catholic

Barbara J. Zelenko

I almost became a Catholic two months after I was born. Preparations for my Lutheran baptism were already underway, when my Catholic Grandma Zelenko suddenly interfered at the last moment, suggesting very strongly that all this might be a mistake. She pointed out that all my cousins (none were yet born) would be Catholic, and wasn't it strange that I would be the only child in our extended family who was not?

Faced with this sudden pressure to change her plans, my Lutheran mother did consider it, but then decided to stick to her guns. "I thought how awful it would be if Barbara started asking me questions I couldn't answer," she explained in a letter to my Catholic father, who was then overseas in the Army.

I only learned about this exchange years later, and since then, I've often wondered what would have happened had my mother given in to Grandma for the sake of peace in the family. I would have become a cradle Catholic, been spared the long, slow road to conversion, with all its difficulties and uncertainties, would not have spent years on the sidelines, *almost* Catholic, believing, yet not able to take the final step. But then Catholicism would have been a given in my life, something I would have been tempted to take for granted. Perhaps I would have even shaken it off eventually, or just "lapsed," like scads of other Catholics in my generation after Vatican II. No, God knew what He was doing.

Nevertheless, my particular circumstances gave me a different background from which to approach conversion. I had none of the anti-Catholic prejudices with which so many Protestant converts struggle. I was not revolted by the Rosary or horrified by a crucifix. I had no sense of Catholicism as something scary and foreign. I was surrounded by Catholics, some of them in my own home.

Surrounded by Catholics

"You're excommunicated," the Catholic Army chaplain had told my father bluntly when Daddy told him he had married a Lutheran girl in a Lutheran ceremony. That was it. Daddy could never receive Holy Communion in the Catholic Church again, but he did not react with outrage or self-righteousness at the priest's lack of sympathy for young love. I realize now how fortunate I was to escape an "in-house" version of anti-Catholicism as I grew up. I never heard him utter a word against the faith he had disobeyed. Until his own father's funeral, my father never went to Mass because he felt he was not supposed to. He started going to Mass gradually when my Grandma Zelenko came to live with us. At first he'd take her and wait outside until Mass was over. Then, at my mother's urging, he started to stay for Mass, careful to sit in the back. "It's too late for me," he told my mother. "I'm just going in to pray for my father."

As Grandma Zelenko had predicted, all of my cousins were baptized in the Catholic Church, and so were the children of most of my parents' friends. My sister and I went to public school, but our teachers had names like Collins, Hennessey, and McCarthy. Every Wednesday afternoon, most of the children left the school for religious instruction at the nearby Sacred Heart Roman Catholic Church, leaving only three or four of us in each classroom. We got lots of personal attention from our teacher and didn't have to do any regular schoolwork. It was great fun, and I don't ever remember feeling left out.

Because my mother had refused to raise my sister and me Catholic, she took seriously her responsibility to raise us Lutheran. She enrolled us in Sunday school at St. John's Lutheran Church in Troy, New York. My sister, Dolly (Dorothy), and I loved Sunday school, which the teachers referred to as "God's house." It was a place of dark carpets, plain walls, and only one picture: the child Jesus in the temple, in sepia tones. Our teachers—all women—were very kind and seemed to love the children they taught. We were taught to sing songs like "Jesus Wants Me for a Sunbeam," "Jesus Loves the Little Children," and "How did Moses Cross the Red Sea?" The Moses song had an invigorating chorus that offered a release for any childish negativism: "Did he swim? No, no! Did he sail? No, no! Did he fly? No, no, no, NO!"

The director of the primary department, Mrs. Gulden, had a real gift for teaching children and would tell us Bible stories by placing paper figures on a flannel board. I can still see some of these figures today: Aaron as a sturdy little boy with a sailboat; Miriam as a slightly older girl in a kerchief; and Baby Moses in his basket of bulrushes. Every week, we also received a leaflet to take home with us, a beautifully illustrated Bible scene in full color with a story inside. My mother gathered all of these leaflets we took home into loose-leaf binders, one for each of us, which we looked at frequently.

Catholicism remained a presence in the background—mysterious, but never negative. After Grandma Zelenko came to live with us, we never ate meat on Fridays and added Wednesdays during Lent. Grandma walked to Sacred Heart Church every day, and I remember going with her, at least once. The Mass itself went completely over my head, of course, but I was fascinated by the dark, hushed atmosphere, trailing my hand in the holy water, and by the array of statues, pictures, and candles within. I was so taken with all of this that I remember playing "Catholic church" with my sister when I came home, using my brightly colored sand pail for the holy water font.

I was completely consumed with awe and envy of the little girls in my neighborhood and my two oldest cousins, when they made their first Holy Communions. These ordinary schoolgirls were transformed before me in beautiful white dresses and veils. Grandma referred to them as "little brides of Jesus" and someone—maybe it was one of the little brides herself—told me she had received Jesus within her for the first time. I was fascinated, and then very disappointed, when my mother explained that we believed it was better to receive our first communion in plain white robes at the much older age of fourteen, "when we could understand it." Even though I could not articulate it at the time, I sensed that this was something different from completely human activities, like wearing a party dress or graduating from school. Of course, I was mainly attracted to this external sign of the inward reality of God uniting Himself for the first time with a little human girl, but I'd had my first encounter with the beauty of the Catholic faith. As He did in the Old Testament, God first conveys truths to His people physically before they can grasp the spiritual meanings behind them. Years before I understood the meaning of Roman Catholic Holy Communion, those little brides conveyed it to me in their very persons.

Lutheranism—Missouri Synod style
By the time I was confirmed at fourteen (with my first communion a week later, almost as an afterthought), we had moved

to the suburbs of Albany, New York, and I was going to a different Lutheran church. Our new home was very close to a brand-new Methodist church, and my mother suggested that Dolly and I might like to go there for Sunday school. Both of us protested. We were only eight and nine, but we had no ecumenical inclinations. We wanted to stay Lutheran, so we started going to Sunday school at Our Savior's Lutheran Church, which turned out to be a Missouri Synod church.

Missouri Synod Lutheranism, as I remember it from girlhood, was then a pretty dreary affair, at least in Sunday school. We had dull books that had little beauty or even color. They offered a summary of each Bible story, and then we had to answer specific questions about it by looking up the answers in the Bible. I soon became bored with flipping pages back and forth to find specific Bible verses.

Bible verses were more important in Our Savior's than the stories themselves or the Bible as a whole. They were used to explain every statement in the catechism[37] and offered as the answer to every problem. Our church also had a narrow intolerance for other Christians, as well as other forms of Lutheranism, and shunned all ecumenical endeavors with them. And it was decidedly negative toward Roman Catholicism.

Our teachers told us that we were all hopeless sinners, and nothing we could do on our own could change that fact. This didn't bother me too much, as everyone else seemed to be in the same boat. Once the initial shock of that first statement wore off, it became comfortably familiar, and clicked into place every time the subject of sin came up. All of us had faults, and our only remedy was "being saved" through personal faith in Jesus, who died for us on a cross so that we might live forever. Faith, as I then understood it and saw it expressed by the church

---

[37] Martin Luther's *Small Catechism.*

people around me, was holding that truth in spite of all evidence to the contrary.

I believed that they did have the truth, but by the time I was in college I was finding the truth almost unbearably dull. I never consciously rebelled, but started drifting away, more fascinated with a particular college professor and the subject he taught than anything I heard at church. After Grandma Zelenko died, Daddy eventually joined our Missouri church. Finally, we were a religiously united family, but by this time, I was trying to become independent of them.

An uncertain time

As soon as I moved away from home, I started going to different churches on Sunday, more out of curiosity than anything else. During this period of youthful experimentation, I went to Presbyterian, Methodist, Baptist, and even Christian Science churches, but never a Catholic church. This was the period after Vatican II, when the Church was opening all her windows to let the fresh air in, and things were changing so fast that nobody knew where the Church was going anymore. The things I'd loved from afar as a child were being scorned and tossed aside.

The Catholics I knew were excited about all the changes, but I wasn't. You could now eat meat on Fridays, and people were saying that priests might even be allowed to marry in a few years. It seemed to me that the Church was trying to be just like everybody else. While I was in graduate school, I met an enthusiastic nun who dragged me to several Catholic charismatic meetings, where I was hugged and kissed by bunches of strangers. It was excessive and embarrassing. My Missouri Lutheran church, formerly so straitlaced and dull, was going through a similar charismatic revolution, and I didn't enjoy the signs of it there either.

Several personal crises brought me back to God. I had had a couple of romantic disappointments that left me terribly frustrated. I had failed to find a husband and was getting very concerned about it. I was hoping to fall in love and get married, but to do that, I had to meet someone. Once I'd finally left school and had a job in New York, the built-in social life of a student was a thing of the past, and it was hard to find friends on my own. I was very lonely.

The feminist movement was now in full swing, and my reading was encouraging me (when it was not reproaching me) to "make something of myself." According to the current secular philosophy, my failures at love were not that serious; love was not all it was cracked up to be. The many failed and unhappy marriages in our society proved that. Why did I want love and marriage so much anyway? Feminism told me that my very singleness was a chance to "make something of myself," although I was not sure what I was supposed to be. Rather than an opportunity, I felt this as pressure. I kept reading stories of women with conflicts between career ambitions and their families. I had no husband and children to keep me from fulfilling my dreams. Why, then, could I not achieve more?

My faith returns

I started attending Broadway Presbyterian Church near Columbia University. The congregation was filled with students, teachers, and other intellectuals, which was very important to me at the time. Broadway was very big on small-group Bible studies, both for learning more about the Christian faith and developing closer relationships with other Christians. We would take one book at a time and really study it, not just flip around the Bible looking for isolated verses that proved the point the teacher was trying to make. Here I started to understand the Bible, the personalities and unique circumstances behind each book, and how they all fit together.

I joined a women's Bible study group and took my turn at leading it. I got very engrossed in the preparations, and the Old Testament came alive for me. Particular events, like the breakup of David's kingdom, the differences between Israel and Judah, the Fall of the Temple, and the Exile to Babylon, were full of lessons for everyday life in 1980s New York City. Why had I never seen this before? We also shared our difficulties and prayed about them together after the study.

I started reading books on religion. My first spiritual mentor was Catherine Marshall, who wrote *A Man Called Peter.* I was immediately drawn to the romantic love story of the author and her husband, but there was something else in it beyond that. Catherine Marshall believed that faith in God could make a difference in our lives right now. Since I wasn't too thrilled with the way my life was going, this was especially meaningful to me. The whole focus of my faith had been on getting saved for the life to come, but what were we supposed to do in the meantime? We couldn't do much, because "all our righteousnesses are as filthy rags" (Isaiah 64:6, *King James Version*), an oft-quoted verse that I remembered from confirmation class. The constant dwelling on our sinfulness and hopelessness had resulted in my general passivity and pessimism about life, if not about the hereafter.

Catherine Marshall was solidly Protestant (Presbyterian), but there was something about her that, while not Catholic itself, made me more open to Catholicism when I encountered it. She used her Bible the way a Catholic woman would light a candle in church for an intention—encouraging her readers to be specific in their prayers, to pray along with some definite action, and to avoid fuzzy, too-spiritual language in prayer. She also thought that Christians should use their minds, and saw faith as "trusting [God] enough to step out on that trust."[38]

So one could be Christian *and* intellectual at the same time. I liked that. My sister had become excited by some of her professors at her Lutheran college at River Forest in Illinois, and I was so intrigued that I asked if one of her instructors, Pastor Walter Bouman, could give me a list of intellectual Christian books. He did so and annotated each book with his own comments. The first author on his list was C. S. Lewis.

Like Lewis himself when he encountered George MacDonald, "I had crossed a great frontier."[39] Even though he called it *Mere Christianity*, Lewis convinced me there was more to Christianity than I thought, leading me beyond the "justification by faith" thinking of Lutheranism. With his memorable illustration of the tin soldier who starts to come to life, he prepared me for the Catholic idea of being God's adopted child, of being *remade*, a new creation. He exposed me to a lot of new ideas, such as the harmony between faith and reason, logic and philosophy, and the understanding of virtue as habit. Moreover, Lewis believed in purgatory and convinced me to believe in it, too. Had there been a church of C. S. Lewis, I would have joined it.

Instead, I joined the New York C. S. Lewis Society, which turned out to be significant in an unexpected way, for I met Mary Gehringer there. Mary went out of her way to speak to me and make me feel at home. Like the one for whom she was named, she was quiet and rarely spoke at meetings but was always busy working behind the scenes. She wore her Catholicism lightly, but it was always there.

---

[38] Catherine Marshall, *Beyond Our Selves* 72 (Chosen Books, Baker Book House 2001) (1961).

[39] C. S. Lewis, in *George MacDonald: An Anthology* xxxiii (Macmillan: New York, 1947).

Mary never pushed me to become a Catholic but was always available to answer any questions I had about the assumption of Mary, indulgences, etc. If she didn't know the answer, she would try to find it, often sending me articles through the mail. I complained that Masses seemed cold, the people unfriendly and aloof; no one greeted you. She listened without getting defensive, although she suggested that people could do that when they got outside.

Everything's coming up Catholic

Although I was oblivious at the time, I look back now and see Catholic seeds sprouting all around me. There was my persistent inner feeling, not disturbing, but always there: "You owe it to yourself to learn more about this." It started consciously as an enjoyable intellectual hobby. I started subscribing to Catholic magazines: *Crisis, Fidelity, New Oxford Review,* and *National Catholic Register.* At that time, the *Register* offered many articles on Catholic "basics" by Peter Kreeft, which I found entertaining and full of solid Catholic teaching.

I was also visiting a Catholic church regularly. No, I wasn't fascinated by the Mass. I'd attended a few and wasn't impressed. They were more tedious than Protestant worship, with singing so bad that I was glad when it stopped. The homilies were often embarrassing; nevertheless, I had decided I needed daily prayer in a specific place, as Catherine Marshall had recommended. St. Andrew's Roman Catholic Church was right next door to my office in lower Manhattan, and it was usually quiet in the afternoons. At that time, I was totally unaware of *Who* was also there every afternoon in front of me, only a few feet away.

Fidelity magazine advertised a conference on Catholicism versus fundamentalism, which was to take place in nearby Tarrytown, New York. It was March 1988, and a program like this was something new to me. The differences between Catholics and Protestants? For over twenty years, I'd been hearing how much alike we were. I hastened to sign up.

The conference included impressive Catholic speakers, among them Father George Rutler, Tom Howard, and Karl Keating. The first one, Russell Hittinger, gave me much to think about. He was respectful toward Protestant fundamentalists but suggested that Catholicism, having been around for two thousand years, was vastly richer, deeper, and more complex. He called on Catholics to adopt some Protestant practices, such as adult education, Bible studies, and small groups—the very things I liked so much about my own faith.

The last item on the program was a question-and-answer session with Father Peter Stravinskas. He reminded me of the go-getter attorneys in my office, but he was a priest! He spoke about his refusal to say a nuptial Mass for a Catholic bride and a fundamentalist groom. Father Stravinskas impressed upon the groom that "having Jesus in your heart" was *not* the same as being Catholic. To a question about the Catholic standing of then Governor Mario Cuomo, a supporter of abortion, he said the governor should be excommunicated. I was taken aback by his strong language, but enjoyed it, too. He acted like one who believes the Catholic faith was worth defending.

During this time, the long-term women's Bible study that I had loved so much at Broadway Church had broken up, and I no longer felt at home there. I stumbled around for an extended period in what I then called the "church wilderness," hoping to find a church family again. My sister, Dolly, now a member of St. Matthew's Lutheran Church in White Plains, encouraged me to return to Lutheranism. I went to several Lutheran churches and even tried a nearby Catholic church, but it was too impersonal for me and too big a leap at the time. I enjoyed reading about Catholic ideas, but the real thing was unappealing.

Lutheranism—"evangelical catholic" style

Immanuel Lutheran Church was on the East Side of Manhattan, on 88th Street, near Lexington Avenue. I was taken aback by the formal ritual at my first liturgy at Immanuel when I saw a procession of people in robes coming down into the congregation for the reading of the Gospel. Two acolytes carried candles and took their places on either side of a third person who held the Gospel aloft, bound in gold. The minister then sang the Gospel from the gold book in the midst of the congregation. The Word coming down to dwell among us, although I only realized that much later. There were trumpets at appropriate intervals.

After years as a Presbyterian, I was barely aware of liturgy. What mattered to me was solid teaching, backed up by the Bible, and close fellowship with other believers. A little wary of Immanuel's liturgy, I waited until I saw an announcement of a Bible study class before I started to attend regularly. I feared that this elaborate ritual might distract people from the plain meaning of the Word, but it was not long before I grew to love it. Immanuel was an "evangelical catholic" church.

"Evangelical catholic" Lutheranism is a movement begun at the Missouri Synod seminary in St. Louis, by Professor Arthur Carl Piepkorn, and enthusiastically adopted by pastors who studied under him. Like Newman in his time, the evangelical catholics try to be as Catholic as possible while remaining in the Lutheran Church. They believe that Luther never meant to start a new church when he broke with Rome, but to return the Church to its "catholic" (small "c"), or "universal," state. According to Piepkorn, this "catholic church," being less than perfect, had undergone several divisions as it moved in time, the first being the separation of the Eastern Catholics from the West in 1054. After the *Augsburg Confession* in 1530, the Western Catholics continued in both the Lutheran Church (called "evangelical" in Europe) and the post-Tridentine Church of Rome. It was the old "branch theory" that Newman once believed, in a new guise.[40]

Evangelical catholicism was never clearly explained to the people in the pews, who just experienced the results: a lot of Catholic externals. For instance, we made the sign of the cross, received communion every Sunday and ashes on Ash Wednesday, celebrated a "liturgy" instead of a "worship service," and marked major feast days with special liturgies, incense, and bell-ringing. At Immanuel, the eucharistic liturgy certainly suggested transubstantiation in its gestures and sound effects. The thought was that the Church's first fifteen hundred pre-Reformation years belonged to Lutherans as much as to Catholics, and Lutherans were free to choose those elements they found most appealing. Some Lutheran pastors even went so far as to refer to themselves as "Father," and some Lutherans were so convinced of their "catholicism" that they went up to receive Holy Communion at Roman Catholic Masses. Meanwhile, under the "catholic" surface, hardcore Lutheran ideas like justification by faith and fear of Rome still prevailed. Evangelical catholics were forever talking about creating a Catholic-like teaching authority for Lutheran bishops, but no one ever proposed submitting to the perfectly good two-thousand-year-old teaching authority within the Catholic Church. They saw themselves as continually reforming the church catholic, but they couldn't even convince other

---

[40] This was an Anglican idea that appeared three hundred years after the Reformation. Even if the Church had fallen into schism, and its several divisions were no longer in communion with one another, each division might still be considered a "branch" of the true Church, insofar it kept the original faith of the Apostles and maintained apostolic succession.

Lutherans to adopt their ideas. They remain a small group within the Lutheran denomination, confined to small associations, journals, and conferences.

None of this mattered to me at the time. It seemed like the best of both worlds. I had a growing attraction to Catholic things but was turned off by the reality of Catholic worship. Immanuel, like me, was *almost* Catholic.

Shortly after I started worshipping at Immanuel, I led an adult Bible study. The class was very responsive. I enjoyed the closeness that came from being part of a small group again, as well as the status that it brought me in the congregation. Leading and preparing for this class were more satisfying to me than my regular job. Many of the commentaries I used referred to other commentaries, going back to the various Church Fathers, and I slowly began to be aware of a whole Church Tradition behind each book. This was a much bigger subject than I had previously realized.

I want Catholicism to be true

Sometime during this period I heard the now famous tape by Scott Hahn, *Protestant Minister Becomes Catholic*, although I snapped it off when I got to the part where he threw away his sainted Catholic grandmother's Rosary beads. I was annoyed. Why did every convert have to start by being so hostile to the Church? I, too, had inherited my Catholic grandmother's Rosary beads but never tossed them into the garbage! Fortunately, I got over that negative first impression, listened to the rest, and went on to buy nearly all of Scott Hahn's tapes, getting a tremendous biblical education in the process. He offered me a whole new way to approach the Catholic faith, and I never saw the Bible the same way again. I listened to his tapes regularly and started using his teaching in my Immanuel Bible study.

Because we were almost Catholic, we were open to Catholic ideas and interpretations.

I then heard that Father Stravinskas would be teaching a week-long summer course at Christendom College in Virginia, and I enrolled. The morning class on the papacy was taught by Dr. Timothy O'Donnell, then director of the theology department and now president of Christendom College. I still remember the involuntary little shiver that went through me as I prayed the Hail Mary for the first time. I wasn't expecting it—he started with the Our Father and went right into the Hail Mary. I had come here to learn more about the Catholic faith, and yet there was something primitive in me that was still protesting. Dr. O'Donnell went through a short history of the papacy, offering a convincing case for the primacy of the Bishop of Rome, and then went on to show Peter's primacy in Scripture.

Father Stravinskas started his class, "Catholicism and Fundamentalism," by listing all kinds of religious activities on the blackboard. He pointed out that all of these activities required a mediator. Most of us had been told about God by our parents, and by nuns (if we had gone to Catholic school). The Bible was mediated to us by the various writers. The sacraments mediated God's grace to us. Because of who we are, and who God is, any relationship we have with Him must be mediated.

Father Stravinskas spoke about the Virgin Mary and St. Peter. The Church became a lot more than a lumbering bureaucracy when Father talked about it; she became the Bride of Christ. He led us through the Gospel of John, showing us the "framing device" of the story of the Wedding at Cana and Mary at the Cross. Jesus had addressed His mother as "Woman" both times. Up until now, I'd just assumed He was saying good-bye to her! Then there was St. Peter and his final talk with Jesus at the sea, with a parallel to that and the ceremony of the papal crowning. Father Stravinskas had a love for the beauty of the faith, and did not just use the Bible as proof texts for every statement he made. I was overwhelmed but powerfully attracted to it as well. The final day of class he surpassed himself with a talk on fundamentalists. He started out witty, acting out conversations he'd had with Catholics-turned-fundamentalists, then became stern, giving reasons why so many Catholics had left the Church, then practical, offering suggestions for getting them back. Finally, he described their return to the Church. After Confession, he'd say: "Welcome home!" At that point, the penitent would cry.

I returned to my own home, still high. Before that week at Christendom, I'd been interested in Catholicism, had found it appealing, and was eager to learn more. But I was still looking at it objectively. Now, even though I was still not totally sure Catholicism was true, I *wanted* it to be.

I was mistrustful of the emotionalism the week at Christendom had engendered and wary of being swept away. I was also panicky about having to change my life. Feeling as I did, wouldn't I have to become Catholic? And how could I do that? I remember being relieved to return to the everyday rhythm of my life. I returned to Immanuel on Sunday and realized how much I loved it. How could I give it all up? I knew most of the people there; they were friends. And what about the Bible study group?

I had to talk to someone about all this, so I shared my experiences with my mother and sister. (My father had died shortly before I saw that first ad for the Catholic conference in Tarrytown.) Mom tried to maintain a positive attitude, but I could tell she thought this was another passing enthusiasm, like my sojourn in the Presbyterian Church. She wondered if my zeal for Catholicism would also fade.

My sister, who had gone through Lutheran colleges and actually taught at one for a few years, accused me of disloyalty to the Lutheran tradition in which I'd been raised, and to the people who had taught me the faith. Even at the beginning of my journey to the Catholic Church, this struck me as strange. We were not talking about rival schools or family traditions here. No one ever objected, except jokingly, when I joined a Presbyterian church, but converting to Rome was a different matter.

At the beginning, I had deep doubts about my own motivation. How did I know that God was leading me in this? Maybe this was just a substitute for my unfulfilled romantic dreams, or worse, a way to reject my mother and sister. There was no doubt they felt that way. My good friend, Mary, managed to keep me on an even keel by repeatedly reminding me that all of us have mixed motives.

Then there were the Catholics I knew best. If Catholicism was so great, why had so many people in our extended family shaken it off? Or were so halfhearted about it? Mom and Dolly eagerly brought up examples, but I could think of plenty of my own. There was my father, who felt he had to go to Mass, but once there, couldn't wait for it to be over. There were the people who barely opened their mouths to sing. Why did they seem so bored with it all? And how they raced out after Mass was over! Some couldn't even wait for that, taking off after they had received the Eucharist. Nobody at our church did that. People stayed for the coffee hour, catching up with one another and caring about one another. Wasn't love for other people the real test of Christian conviction? I'd be lost in that kind of environment, totally isolated. It took me a long time to feel at home in a new place, and I was terrified. Dolly tried to convince me that I had fallen in love with an idealized version of Catholicism that existed nowhere, except in books and in the occasional college course. It had nothing to do with the average, everyday Catholics I knew.

Trying to have it both ways

Was it really necessary to convert? Were the two faiths that different? After all, Immanuel was *almost Catholic*. I could still read about Catholicism and even adopt some of its practices. I started praying the Rosary. Its droning repetitions seemed tedious and boring when I saw them from the outside. But once I started praying its mysteries, I found myself dwelling regularly on things I used to think about twice a year, on Easter and Christmas. Jesus became more real to me when I considered Him in the context of specific scenes from His life. It was a totally new and welcome way of approaching Him, a break from my self-centered prayer.

I continued to pray before the Blessed Sacrament at St. Andrew's. By this time, I realized that Jesus had been there with me every afternoon in the monstrance, long before I felt a conscious attraction to the Catholic faith. The church bulletin featured a weekly column by one of the priests, Father McKeon, on the meaning of various Catholic doctrines and practices. One afternoon, I ran into this priest in a baseball cap and jacket on his way to a hospital visit nearby and mentioned how much I liked his columns. "Well," he said casually, "it's the true religion."

The truth. How could I have forgotten that? Wasn't *truth* the real issue? What did the shortcomings of some Catholics have to do with whether the faith was true or not? I thought of C. S. Lewis's story of the potential convert who insisted that Christianity must make him happy and didn't even care if it was true. I remembered what Lewis had said about the "natural" loves. My warm attachment to Immanuel, my love for its people, even my family loyalty, had to take second place to doing what God wanted.

I decided to study both faiths carefully, calmly, and prayerfully, and then come to a decision about which was the true one. Since I'd started my romance with Catholicism, Dolly had implied I knew very little of "real" Lutheranism. As it happened, our new pastor at Immanuel, Gregory Fryer, was just starting an adult education course on Lutheran teachings. We started with the *Augsburg Confession*, then Luther's *Small* and *Large Catechisms*, and even read the *Smalcald Articles*. Compared with papal documents, Luther's writings shocked me. Besides his coarseness, there was his sneering tone toward his opponents. He displayed very little Christian charity toward them.

Some people say that Luther merely reflected his times, but there were others who lived in those same times, such as his Catholic opponent, Erasmus, who made their arguments firmly but charitably. The idea that Martin Luther was the person God had trusted with the truth seemed implausible to me. He sounded much more like a lapsed Catholic who couldn't leave the Church alone. Like a divorced husband, Luther could not stop making snide remarks about his ex-wife. Nor did it seem likely that God would let His Church wander in error for fifteen hundred years or so before sending someone to bring it back to the truth. Even the more moderate *Augsburg Confession*[41]—the foundational document for Lutheran churches everywhere— reads more like a committee report than inspired doctrine. There was nothing in this document that would inspire people to change their lives, and it didn't inspire me.

Dolly brought up some horrendous examples of popes who had been gravely sinful in the past, and even Catholics agreed some popes had been awful. But I had now read enough to see that even the bad popes did not change Church doctrine to fit their sinful activities. Infallible did not mean the popes were

---

[41] Written by Luther's follower and contemporary, Melanchthon.

flawless. Meanwhile, the Evangelical Lutheran Church in America (ELCA) was proclaiming as gospel a lot of trendy ideas in the larger American culture, such as "choice" in abortion, and the need to accept the homosexual lifestyle in the name of Christian freedom and love. I had already been convinced of the need for a pope by my reading and the class at Christendom, but the ELCA's actions only made the need for a pope more obvious.

On the brink of conversion

Meanwhile, Mary had introduced me to Father Joseph Wilson, the young parochial vicar of her parish in Queens. The three of us eventually met for dinner at an Italian restaurant, and this was the start of a series of dinner meetings where I had a chance to ask questions about things I did not understand. I also began to visit his parish for Mass. Father Wilson's theological knowledge and love for Christ in the Eucharist increased my desire for the Catholic Eucharist and helped me to see it as central to the faith.

"The Eucharist is the whole point of being a Catholic, the whole of the Gospel in a nutshell," he said. "In the Eucharist we find Jesus Himself, the Divine Word, the Second Person of the Trinity. We were created to be one with Him forever, which is the mystery of Holy Communion. He came down from heaven to become one of us, just as He comes yet again to dwell among us, truly present, but veiled under the forms of bread and wine."

I asked Father Wilson about the re-presentation of Christ's "once and for all sacrifice" at each Mass. Was this the same as presenting a play over and over? "No. Every Mass makes Calvary present once again, so that when we stand before the altar as the Mass is offered, we are standing at the foot of the Cross with our blessed Lady and St. John," he answered. "The Mass is the whole of the Gospel, opened before us like a sacred text, which we're invited to step into, and all of this is effected through the sacred

Priesthood, the Priesthood of Jesus, in which the Catholic priest shares. It is in truth the pearl of great price, which the wise man will move heaven and earth to possess."

I had an increasing sureness that the Catholic faith was true. Even with the few remaining uncertainties, I was willing to trust in the Church, and I was finding it more and more appealing, to the point where I envied people who had converted. Yet, I still could not translate this faith into action. I could not do it. I could not convert. It was extremely frustrating.

I blamed myself. What was holding me back? Was it a lack of trust in God? Or was I just unreasonably attached to Immanuel and my familiar way of life? I tried to convince myself to take the step, but I was stuck.

Looking back, I am grateful for that long delay on the brink of conversion. I think it was meant to humble me, to show me how *little* the whole conversion was my own doing. For all my enthusiasm for the Catholic Church, I still saw myself as the center of the issue, trying to choose which course was right. That I could know which was right and be powerless to choose it had never occurred to me. I think God kept me *almost Catholic* for so long to show me my need for grace to do even what I now wanted to do.

The Virgin Mary intervenes

I got help from an unexpected source. After someone in our Lutheran doctrine class questioned Mary's assumption into heaven, I volunteered to research and teach a class about her at Immanuel. By this time, Mary did not provoke the involuntary shiver that I'd experienced on my first day at Christendom College. I wanted to know more about her. If we were really so Catholic, shouldn't we know more about one of the major stumbling blocks that kept us apart?

As a woman, I was drawn to Mary, although I feared a lot of Catholic preoccupation with her was just sentimental devotion. That fear fled once I started researching the subject and discovered the sixteenth-century reformers had believed in some of the Catholic Marian doctrines.

Luther, Calvin, and Zwingli accepted Mary as *Theotokos* ("God-bearer," i.e., "Mother of God"), her perpetual virginity (before, after, and during the birth of Jesus), and her sinlessness.[42] Mary had not been a big issue in the Reformation because the doctrines about her were then taken for granted. It was later, during the Enlightenment, that the various Protestant churches gradually drifted away from her.

Mary had also been an essential safeguard against heretical teachings in the Church about Jesus. The human mother of Christ prevented heresies like Docetism (the belief that Jesus only looked like a man) and Nestorianism (the belief that Mary was only the mother of Jesus' human nature). My own Lutheran church, as "catholic" as it now claimed to be, only honored Mary in one Advent sermon a year, usually for her faith, and then on Christmas itself. It treated Mary like a surrogate mother—someone to be used for an important purpose and then discarded, or at least placed safely in the background. I pressed my Bible class to question our Lutheran understanding and practices in relationship to Mary. How could Mary not be close to her Son? She is closer to Jesus than we are to our own mothers, because the rest of us come from two earthly parents, while Jesus had only one.

Protestants focus so much on Jesus' saving us from our sins that they lose sight of the shock and wonder of God breaking

---

[42] The early reformers thought that Mary was sinless from quickening (when fetal movement can be detected) rather than from conception.

into our human life. He is born, yes, but for a purpose, and they immediately rush to focus on that, losing so much else in the process. As I read and studied various texts in preparation for the class, I could feel the shift in my own perceptions. I was becoming more Catholic in outlook.

I did not want to do a purely academic study of Mary, and I began the class by asking them a question I told them I had no plans to answer—it was just something to think about. Why had Jesus chosen to be born of Mary, a human mother? He could have saved us from our sins another way, by coming to earth as an adult, or redeeming us with a wave of His hand.

The class drew a large group, most of them women. They had never been encouraged to think about Mary before—it was too dangerous. The only safe topic was that Lutheran perennial: her faith. I presented her as a woman, starting with experiences common to most of us: virginity and motherhood. In the Old Testament, virginity was valued as a temporary condition before marriage. Permanent virginity, on the other hand, was seen as a humiliating tragedy, just as a barren wife was. But Mary was chosen and elevated by God to be the mother of His only Son. Her vow of virginity led to a fruitfulness she could not have imagined when she first made it. Through her Divine Son, she became the mother of all God's adopted sons and daughters. The barren Old Testament women who later became mothers when God intervened foreshadowed Mary's fruitfulness. The last one was Elizabeth, and Gabriel specifically connects that miracle to Mary at the Annunciation.

The hardest thing for the class to accept was Mary's sinlessness, for they had been schooled, as I had been, in the idea that everyone was sinful. To claim anyone as exempt seemed to be granting that person equality with God. I pointed out that Eve, before the Fall, had been sinless, too, as was Adam. Sin was not part of being human, but a terrible wound that limits and disfigures our human nature.

Fully Catholic, at last

I found that Mary, Jesus' mother, had brought me to a different place after the class was over. It was nothing like the romantic excitement that I had had at the beginning of my journey. It was more like a dogged "Let's get this done and over with." The pull to Rome was stronger than ever. I knew that if I did not enter the Church, I would spend the rest of my life wishing that I had. My mother and sister had predicted that the romance would fade, and it did temporarily. Yet, I still knew I had to go through with the wedding.

I phoned Father Wilson. He was on vacation but agreed to meet with me right away. We met in a restaurant after a liturgy at Immanuel. My romantic side reasserted itself briefly, and I told him I would have liked to kneel before him, as Newman had done before Father Barberi. But we were in a restaurant, and I was too self-conscious to do it. He promised to light a firecracker later.

During that waiting period, I became numb. Not only my Catholic consolations, but the consolations I got from Immanuel, dried up completely. I took no pleasure in any of it. I told Pastor Fryer and my Bible study students I was "swimming the Tiber." Nobody seemed too surprised; even Dolly seemed resigned. All of this made the break a little easier for me.

My numbness started to wear off a few months afterward. I slowly realized that the things that I'd longed for while *almost Catholic*, now belonged to me, as well as much else that I could not even imagine when I was an "almost." Like the Eucharist itself, the Church has proven to be far more than she appeared when I was outside her. The façade of mediocre Masses, so-so preaching, and indifferent worship concealed much treasure. St. Thérèse of Lisieux, Father Halligan (my Father Confessor), and St. Agnes Church in Manhattan were only some of the great blessings in store for me on the other side of conversion, and I am still discovering more.

But all that came later. I was received at the "First Friday" evening Mass in October of 1995 at St. Thomas, the same day the Pope was saying Mass for seventy-five thousand people only a few miles away at the Aqueduct Raceway. Mary sponsored me and kept me calm beforehand. The church was packed. Even in my numbness, I was startled by the beauty of this Mass—Latin, incense, beautiful hymns. Father Wilson received another convert at the same time, the Baptist husband of a member of the congregation, and we were presented with baskets of cards from the congregation, welcoming us in.

I was Catholic, *fully Catholic*, at last.

Barbara J. Zelenko was born in the Bronx, raised in upstate New York, and returned to New York City as an adult after she received her Master of Library Science degree. She has been a law librarian at the federal prosecutor's office in Manhattan for many years, and she has also written articles for library and legal publications. Since her conversion in 1995, she has deepened and enriched her appreciation for the Catholic faith by taking courses at St. Joseph Seminary's Institute of Religious Studies in the Archdiocese of New York.

11

This Side of Paradise

Candie Frankel

I was born to Kenneth Walter Vandewater and Betty Marie Kurz in the summer of 1953. I was baptized two months later, on September 27, 1953, at the Lutheran Church of the Epiphany in West Hempstead, Long Island, New York. My family and extended family are Lutheran. My father's side is American, with German and Dutch immigrant roots going back to the nineteenth century and earlier. My father's family was warm and lively; there were lots of children, and I was always finding out that I had yet more relatives—like our substitute teacher, Mrs. Geiger, who turned out to be Grandma's cousin Florence. My mother is a first-generation American, born to a German Lutheran father and a Swedish Lutheran mother. Through my mother's family, I encountered foreign accents, a certain social formality, and fewer children. I sensed contrast, but not conflict, between these two family styles.

A wonderful place

The first Sunday school I attended was at St. John's Lutheran in Merrick, New York. I was three years old. We young children had to climb up a long flight of stairs to arrive at our Sunday school—a large loftlike space with a glass window and pews in one section, so couples with infants could overlook the church service taking place below. We children had our own "church," complete with altar and candles. We sat in small chairs arranged in rows, the youngest children at the front. We sang songs and the doxology with piano accompaniment, placed our offering envelopes in the collection basket, and prayed the Lord's Prayer.

After our church service, those small chairs were regrouped around tables, perhaps six or eight children per class, and we settled in for a story. We received a new lesson leaflet each Sunday, a single sheet folded in half, with a beautiful color picture on the front showing a miracle, a parable, or a special moment—like Adam and Eve in the garden before the Fall or Jacob dreaming about the angels going up and down the ladder. The text was inside the leaflet. I could not yet read, but that black-and-white page was almost as exciting to me as the front cover, because I knew it held the secret to the picture. A biblical verse in boldface type was printed at the end of the story. My teacher always recited the verse and showed us the words, and then we all said it together. I do believe that learning to read in order to read the Word of God was an intention planted early in my mind. So was the need to climb up those stairs, to get to that wonderful place of music, art, and words about God.

I was a tomboy as a child, and climbing trees went with the territory. One day, when I was about ten years old, I swung and dropped, Tarzan-style, from a tree I had climbed hundreds of times, only this time I landed wrong, on my back, the wind knocked out of me. I couldn't breathe. My brother came running up, and I managed to croak out two words: "Get Daddy." As I lay there, helpless, I faced for an instant the specter of death. In the same split second, I found myself resting unafraid in God's arms. It remains a difficult moment to describe, but one I will never forget.

Lutheran catechesis leads to deep longing for God

The summer that I turned twelve, my family moved to Smith-town, New York—in local parlance, "further out on the Island." One task my parents undertook for our family of five was find-ing a new parish. After visiting several churches within perhaps a five-mile radius, they settled on St. Andrew's, less than half a mile down the road.

St. Andrew's was a Missouri Synod Lutheran congregation, where we could receive communion every Sunday, instead of once a month. For my parents, this was new and different; for me, it would become the norm. For the next two years, I would attend both Sunday school and church on Sunday, and cate-chism class, taught by Pastor Robert C. Haupt, once a week after school.

My formal catechesis began with the Ten Commandments, a study that encompassed the "Thou shalt not's" of Sinai, along with the "Blessed are they's" of the Beatitudes. I cannot put it more plainly: I fell in love with the Commandments. Their purity, wisdom, and directness filled my young heart, as did the story of how they were first delivered to Israel. The Commandments were like a window. When I looked through one way, I saw sin. When I looked through the other way, I saw the holiness of God. I saw both of these things—sin and holiness—deep within me.

From the Commandments, we progressed to the Apostles' Creed and the Trinity: the Father who creates, Christ who redeems, and the Holy Spirit who sanctifies. Part of the theo-logical wrangling between Lutherans and Catholics has been about the way the faith, expressed in the second and third arti-cles of the creed, plays out in real life. The operative word is "jus-tification." One reason I became Catholic is that I recognized an authentic match between the Catholic understanding of justifi-cation and my experience of it.

In the Catholic faith, justification and sanctification are of a piece. Our journey home to God is initiated by the purifying Sacrament of Baptism and progresses over the course of our lives. Our salvation is not a onetime event but a lifelong story line in which we are called to work out our salvation with fear and trembling. Being holy and *becoming* holy, matters. Through our continued vigilance, repentance, refusal to sin, and prayer, God works away at our souls so that we become more and more like Christ. We genuinely change, sometimes slowly, sometimes dramatically. God Himself gives us the grace to submit to this cleansing, with Mary and all the saints urging us on. What we fail to accomplish here on earth will be completed in purgatory—"the final rinse," as Father Benedict Groeschel[43] has described it. This amazing teaching about the depth of God's grace is one of the things that convinced me of the Church's authenticity.

In Lutheran theology, justification and sanctification are treated separately. They are like two sides of a single coin. Both are essential, yet, try as you might, you cannot look at both sides at the same time. Justification refers solely to the unmerited grace part—"justification through faith by grace"—and this is where Lutherans love to place the accent. Sanctification is the "becoming holy" part, but it does not contribute to one's salvation; rather, sanctification is a fruit, or effect, of justification (the proof positive that justification has already occurred). Because God does all the redemptive work up front, so to speak, there is no need for purgatory, and the active role of the communion of saints is downplayed. It's never quite clear in Lutheranism why becoming holy *matters.*

---

[43] Father Benedict Groeschel, C.F.R., has written many books on Catholic theology and spirituality and appears regularly on the Eternal World Television Network (EWTN).

Lutheran justification is a bit like opening a photo album and looking at one snapshot. It focuses in on a particular dialectic, emphasizing that Christ loved us while we were yet sinners. Catholic justification is more like an epic Cecil B. DeMille movie. When my husband was a young boy, his mother took him to see Charlton Heston in *The Ten Commandments* six times. *That's* Catholic justification. Part of my problem (not a nagging problem, just one of those decades-long existential quandaries) was that my soul kept breaking out into full-screen living Technicolor, and I didn't understand what was going on. Hankering after God, I turned directly to God, not theological formulations. Later in my life, when I was more ready to absorb theological explanations, I found them waiting for me in Catholic teaching and spirituality.

The accurate, precise, and full articulation of the faith is vitally important (to guard against heresy, for example), but it is the crucible of faith that purifies us. Faith as intellectual knowledge and assent is one thing. Faith as Abraham telling his servant, "The boy and I will return to you," is quite another. The formation of a soul is a delicate operation. The words we use to describe this process are, at best, a dim reflection of what actually happens, but the mark on the soul is indelible. The more a soul moves in sync with God's will, the holier the soul becomes. The Catholic Church teaches and encourages all her members to pursue God's will, and through it, to obtain real-life personal holiness and a host of other blessings besides.

In my adolescent religious landscape, it was the actual examples of faith that captivated my imagination and illumined the abstract theological doctrines. I loved the Old Testament. There were so many compelling stories of people who struggled with God, and I was with them all the way. I wrestled with Jacob's angel; I went with Joseph into the pit and the dungeon; I climbed with Moses and Elijah to their mountain. Ruth totally amazed me for the way she followed Naomi. These saints of old inspired me, but I knew I could not live vicariously through them. I began to comprehend that in the same way God called Moses to *be* Moses, God created me to be a unique soul in His kingdom. There was an immediacy, an all-or-nothing quality to God's allure, that I could not cast aside. Through all of these things, I began to grasp onto the character of God: His patience, His forbearance, His holiness, His might, His mercy, His mystery, His love.

My Lutheran Confirmation

Our confirmation class also studied the Lord's Prayer, Baptism, the Office of the Keys and Confession, and the Eucharist. After two years, we were ready to be confirmed. Confirmation would take place one Sunday afternoon in May, and we would receive our first communion the following Sunday. I missed both occasions on account of a severe nosebleed and sinus infection that landed me in Smithtown General Hospital for a week. When I was better, I wasn't sure of my status. My classmates were receiving communion, but I wasn't sure I was eligible, as I hadn't yet been confirmed. My dilemma was sorted out, and one Sunday after the late service, with my family present (now numbering six), the pastor confirmed me. I remember kneeling in the center aisle of the church, closer to the narthex than the chancel. My chancel Confirmation would come some thirty years later, with my husband by my side.

Marriage as a foretaste of that which is to come

I always knew marriage was serious business—*vocation* is the Catholic term. The story of my marriage is the story of my life. I know that God chose me for Fred and Fred for me. Sometimes we talk, in all seriousness, about God looking down on us when we were small children, when Fred was five and I was two, and seeing all he had planned for us together from the time before we were even born.

When Fred was five, he lost both his parents, his mother to Hodgkins disease and his father, a few weeks later, from heart failure. I cannot fathom what his loss must have been. Fred lived with his maternal grandparents for a time and then went to live with his father's sister, Claire, and her husband, Jack Schwartz. I never knew Claire, but Fred tells me I would have loved her and she, in turn, would have loved me. I knew and loved Jack, who died a few months before Fred and I were married.

Fred and I grew up in different religious worlds. He was Jewish and I was Christian; he was a Bar Mitzvah, and I was confirmed. Our common ground? We discovered that both our mothers followed exactly the same recipe: over-broiled and ruined liver—"leatherized liver," as we dubbed it. When Fred first met me at a party in 1979, he thought I was Jewish. He confided to me many years later the flash of insight he had that very night, simultaneously surprising and pleasing him, that I would be his future wife.

When I was growing up, I never heard my parents disparage any ethnic group. My awareness that someone was Jewish, Italian, Irish, etc., was dim and in the background. Mostly, I related to my friends as people. When I look at my sixth-grade class picture, I see twenty-six children, fourteen of them Jewish. This statistic staggers me today. It is apparent that my education involved more than meets the eye.

St. Luke tells us that Mary pondered in her heart all that had happened to her. We are to follow her lead and do the same. God has given me my own things to ponder. I know they are from Him, because they always lead me directly back to Him. They also brought me my husband.

How does one enter into marriage? My dream was for holiness, by which I mean a marriage pleasing to God in every way. In the freewheeling culture of 1970s America, this was not exactly going with the flow. I kept my eyes open for that one man who was looking for me. If you truly want to discover God's will for you and ask Him to help you, a path will be carved out ahead of you, so you can get where you're going in one piece. "If you love me, you will keep my commandments."[44] A first step, of course, is knowing what God expects. A second step is desiring what God desires for your own self. Desiring it even just a little bit, I have discovered, pleases God immensely and elicits His response. I am not suggesting God can be approached half-heartedly or insincerely. God is not mocked. But if God can be said to thrive on something, there is nothing He thrives on more than our turning to Him for help in becoming holy. God wants us to love as He loves. "You, therefore, must be perfect, as your heavenly Father is perfect."[45] This is no illusion but the joy and purpose of life.

Marrying outside of my faith was not something I set out to do. The opposition of my parents, particularly my mother, amplified my own concerns about what the future would hold. Our engagement came about through Fred's love and patience and the counsel of the pastor, Raymond Schulze. I was twenty-nine years old when I married and Fred was thirty-three; our courtship lasted four years. We said our vows at Immanuel Lutheran Church in New York City on June 18, 1983.

In the Catholic Church, marriage is a sacrament. For Lutherans this is not so, but for the particular Lutheran that I was, it might as well have been so. Marriage for me was and is all bound up in fidelity. It is an earthly expression of God's faithfulness to

---

[44] John 14:15.
[45] Matthew 5:48.

Israel and Christ's faithfulness to the Church. These truths embedded themselves in my heart as I was growing up. They made divorce a preordained impossibility. They also ensured I would marry a man with the same convictions.

What strikes me most about marriage is how a couple creates a brand-new world. Their small universe can be happy and productive, miserable and full of spite, or a no-man's-land in between. A husband and wife can strive against each other, or worse yet, each can strive solely for himself or herself under the guise of togetherness, with incredible loneliness as the result. As a young single woman, I intuited the potential, as well as the dangers. Like the Apostles, I reasoned that it would be better not to marry at all than to wind up in a jam. In the private interior space of my heart, I was used to communing with God. My deep, deep longing was for a husband who communed with God, too, so I laid my heart's desire before God.

Now we get to the hard part. Love—real love—is an act of the will. Life is not easy. All kinds of stuff can happen; that's why we vow "in sickness and in health, for richer, for poorer." The opportunities to exercise this act of will, called love, abound: how we go about tackling ordinary responsibilities and dire emergencies; the things we say to each other in the process; the things we refrain from saying; the comforts we provide; and yes, the comforts that we allow ourselves to receive. When we are busy subordinating our own desires and looking out for someone else's welfare, we're not usually thinking about a spiritual return for ourselves. If we are alert, we'll soon catch on to the virtues God would have us master. The sacramental status of the Catholic marriage specially graces us with the incentive to look for and expect this instruction from God, and also to discuss it, pray for it, and rejoice over it with each other. This sacrament, in particular, places us smack-dab in the middle of that place

Christ promises to be, that place where two or three are gathered in His name.

Of course in the early years, we were Jewish and Gentile, but the seed had already been planted. Let me explain a reality of my marriage that has been present from the beginning. It is something I glimpse just barely but that I cling to with all my heart. It is my abiding awareness that, at the end, there will be the wedding. At the wedding, we are both the guests *and* the bride, and there will be no greater joy, ever, than our union with Christ the Bridegroom.

Immanuel

Life at Immanuel Lutheran Church, Sunday after Sunday, was rich with Scripture, eucharistic liturgy, and hymns. Congregational life at Immanuel was warm and gregarious, with a number of lasting friendships formed. Fred's job required him to work on weekends, but he went to church with me when he could, and people always asked for him when he wasn't there.

It was at Immanuel that I first heard the term "evangelical catholic." In the Lutheran world, evangelical catholics are those who are oriented toward the tradition of the Roman Catholic Church in matters of belief and liturgy. They tend to think of their separation from the Catholic Church as a form of exile. I did not comprehend then just how much of an enclave we evangelical catholics were. It was only gradually that I came to see that the ELCA, the Evangelical Lutheran Church in America, of which our congregation was a member, was pointed in quite a different direction.

Fred's desire to be baptized came in 1987. I can't say exactly what triggered it, as I was not particularly proselytizing. His catechesis as an adult was quite different from my catechesis as a child. It consisted of reading, coupled with discussions about the faith, with Pastor Raymond Schulze. Our pastor's basic stance was to dissuade a person from leaving the faith into which that person was born. I think this was to ensure that a change would be made for the right reasons.

Fred was baptized at the Easter Vigil. The vigil started at 10:00 P.M. and ended after midnight, at which point we all gathered in the undercroft for a potluck meal. I loved those vigils and how time and my body clock got all twisted around, a forerunner of the endless day.

Fred's understanding from the beginning, rightly so, was that he was baptized into the "church catholic." But because he entered the Christian family through a Lutheran door, he kept a special eye on Lutheran current events and exposed me to them in a way I may not have encountered otherwise. In 1990, our associate pastor, Richard John Neuhaus, entered the Roman Catholic Church, and the following year we witnessed his ordination to the priesthood by John Cardinal O'Connor at St. Joseph's Seminary. Pastor Raymond Schulze and his wife, Margaret, would also eventually become Roman Catholic.

Cataclysmic upheaval destroys my peace

In 1994, my husband and I moved from Jackson Heights to Tarrytown, New York. This entailed finding a new church home. We ended up at St. Matthew's Lutheran Church in White Plains. There is much we loved about St. Matthew's and its longtime pastor, the Reverend Frederick Schumacher, but there were also things that were different. The differences were small and seemingly imperceptible, easier felt than articulated. I began to feel discontented. St. Matthew's was not Immanuel, but I knew that was not the core of the problem. It was that I was having a harder and harder time explaining my presence within the larger Lutheran body—not that anyone was pointing an accusing finger or calling me to task. This cataclysmic upheaval occurred deep within me. The peacefulness of my meditation had been broken, and the pain was acute.

In 1995, the ELCA dropped its abortion bombshell. The ELCA health insurance policy for church employees and their families would now include coverage for abortions. The ELCA pushed this through, despite the underwriter's carefully worked-out language to exclude payment for abortions. In a *Lutheran Forum* article, Lutheran Pastor Leonard Klein responded with the riveting line: "Real churches don't kill babies." When I read Pastor Klein's words, I was stunned and persuaded by their simple truth. My husband and I had learned early in our marriage that we would most likely never have children of our own. In confronting our infertility, desperate as we were to conceive, it was obvious that there were certain medical avenues that we could not in good conscience pursue. The knowledge that the ELCA leadership condoned abortion was, therefore, particularly devastating. If my husband and I could take what we knew about right and wrong and apply it to a difficult problem and come up with the right answer, why couldn't the Evangelical Lutheran Church in America? This was no rhetorical question. The answer mattered.

In 1998, Fred and I taught the fifth-grade Sunday school class at St. Matthew's and, at the pastor's request, found ourselves covering the history of Martin Luther and the German Reformation. In preparing for our classes, we delved into both Lutheran and Catholic sources that went far beyond the scope of our class but were of interest to us. Sadly, as the *Catechism of the Catholic Church* teaches, there was sin on both sides. My heart cried out that there even were sides. I began to see the whole split as a terrible sickness, and I longed for the cure. While it did not fall to me to sort out the who-said-what's of history, it was my responsibility to work out my own salvation with fear and trembling. What did all of this mean for me, now? Was I where I was supposed to be? I had acquired my Lutheran box seat, for better or for worse, by birth and familial osmosis, but that was not the case for my Jewish husband. What were we to make of the Lutheran legacy that I had inherited, and he had adopted?

Questioning the validity of the Lutheran Eucharist

Now it's time to introduce Barbara. Barbara Zelenko is a friend from Immanuel who became Catholic in 1995. Her proselytizing was unceasing, unyielding, and sometimes exasperating. I can only imagine what St. Augustine must have felt every time he spotted his beloved mother, St. Monica, on the horizon. Barbara's zeal for Catholicism was matched by her sister Dorothy's devotion to Lutheranism. A finer polarization I have never seen, because of the great love that held it all together. Fred and I relished our invitations to Dorothy's apartment, where the four of us would banter our way through dinner, "reliving the Reformation wars," as Fred put it.

Barbara threw us a real curve ball one night by announcing that the Lutheran Eucharist is not valid, based on the nonvalidity of the Lutheran ordinations in the sight of the Roman Catholic Church. This particular point preoccupied us for months. How could the communion I had been receiving practically all my life be other than the Body and Blood of Jesus? Was that not what I had been taught and what I believed? Such a cruel deception did not seem possible in the repertoire of God, but Barbara was adamant.

The *Catechism,* I discovered, was more yielding. It used words like "certain, although imperfect" and described the Eucharist that I received as lacking "fullness." This mysterious, imprecise language, instead of muddying the waters, actually became a great comfort to me. It seemed to open a door that before had been closed. Barbara played bad cop; the *Catechism* played good cop, and together they won me over.

Through the *Catechism,* I began to grasp the cataclysmic nature of the schism. While the topic might be abortion or ordination or how we define grace, the underlying subject was the true identity of the Church. I believed in the one, holy, catholic, and apostolic Church with all my heart. I had perceived that Church to be all of Christendom and had been content to be plunked down in my particular part of it. Now, however, God was calling me out of that place into the heart and fullness of His home. He did this with extreme delicacy and artfulness, but it was not an easy or automatic persuasion. I had enjoyed a rich spiritual life as a Lutheran. Exile had blessed me enormously. What I began to see, though, is that God wanted me to enjoy Him even more.

Recognizing Jesus in the Breaking of the Bread

In early summer 1998, with our Sunday school teaching obligations complete, we did the essential thing. We began attending Catholic Mass every Sunday, visiting many different parishes to get the broadest possible exposure. With each passing week, I longed to receive Holy Communion. It was just like in the Gospel: I recognized Jesus in the Breaking of the Bread. Fred and I had moved at varying paces in this journey. We were like Peter and John running to the tomb. Sometimes Fred was John, running ahead of me; sometimes I was John, running ahead of Fred. But when we got there, we both went in together. Barbara helped us out. Everything was handled by Father Joseph Wilson, and the sacraments of Penance, Confirmation, and the Holy Eucharist were bestowed on us on September 19, 1998, at St. Luke's in Whitestone, Queens.

Conversion is infinitely more than saying yes to a creed and a way of life. It is, as our mother Mary proves, saying yes to God Himself. God does not court us to possess us, for He has already created us. He courts us so that we may be always and forever in love, so that we may intimately know that blissful eternity of love that is the Trinity. God may give us graces, visions, and consolations; however, these are only small signs of His greatest gift, which is Himself. The Eucharist comes to us straight from heaven, and we receive it this side of Paradise. A few miles from home, in a small parish protected by St. Mary Magdalene, this miracle occurs again and again in me. Like her, I fall weeping at Jesus' feet.

These days, when I visit a Lutheran church—even our beloved Immanuel, where we were married and Fred was baptized—something is palpably missing. That something is the tabernacle. Here is the fullness of which the *Catechism* speaks. In every synagogue, there is a tabernacle to hold our treasure, the Torah. In every Catholic church, there is a tabernacle to hold Christ, our Passover Lamb, the Eucharist, the Word of God made Flesh. As Isaiah foretells, the Word of God does not return to the Father empty-handed but accomplishes that for which He sends it. Bowing before His tabernacle, I am in awe of God and of the enormous grace outpoured when He makes us His temple, too.

Candie Frankel is an editor and writer specializing in needlework, crafts, and decorating. She is married to Fred Frankel, a law librarian with a federal court. The couple make their home in Tarrytown, New York. They are members of Church of the Magdalene in Pocantico Hills, New York, where they volunteer their time in various ways.

12

Running on Empty No Longer

Patricia Dixon

The first time I gave the Catholic Church any thought was when my husband, Chris, was studying for the Methodist ministry at Princeton Theological Seminary. He had read John Henry Newman's *Apologia pro vita sua* for a Church History class and was enthralled by Newman's search for the Church of the Apostles—the Church with authority and continuity. As Chris read Newman's description of his growing realization that the Catholic Church was *the* church that had always held fast to the teachings of ancient Christianity, Chris found himself inching closer to that same realization. "The thing is," Chris said one day at lunch, "I can't see where Newman is wrong." So began my husband's deeper study of Catholic theology.

For my part, I was afraid of where Chris's studies might take us. I had no particular animosity toward the Catholic Church, though I told my husband I was a convinced Protestant. At this point in my life, I didn't want any more twists and turns in the road. I had been working as a secretary for five years while Chris attended graduate school and then seminary, and I was ready and eager for him to begin parish ministry and for us to start a family. If Chris were serious about the Catholic Church, he would have to start on another career path; thus our plans to settle down would be put on hold again.

I become a Christian

That I would call myself a Protestant, a *Christian*, was unexpected enough. I grew up in a thoroughly nonreligious family that held intellectual ability in very high regard and thought it to be utterly incompatible with religious faith. My parents thought no one could be an intelligent person *and* a Christian, a view they made clear to their children. There was, however, a longing for faith inside of me, which manifested itself in my academic interests in Latin America and the Spanish language. I memorized the Hail Mary in Spanish by listening to the recitation of the Rosary on a Spanish-language radio station. When I was fourteen, I spent a summer in Mexico as an exchange student. One Sunday at Mass with my host family, I looked at the beautiful bas-relief of the Stations of the Cross on the walls of the church and found myself thinking: What a beautiful story! Wouldn't it be wonderful to actually believe all this? Years later, Chris told me that one of his seminary professors remarked: "The first stage of faith is like an orphan wondering what it would be like to have parents." I started wondering what it would be like to believe in God, angels, and miracles. Looking back at those early stirrings of faith, I see the heavenly Father's presence gently guiding me to make my home in Him through His Church.

In college, I discovered that faith and reason could really go together. High school had been easy for me. College was a different matter, for I found I had to compete for my grades. Meeting a serious intellectual challenge for the first time was exhilarating, and I loved it. I especially loved the camaraderie that came from sharing that exhilaration with other students whose intellect I highly respected. And, wonder of wonders to me, many of them were Christians! It's hard to explain how earth-shaking that revelation was, and also how freeing. Suddenly, I could discuss and explore religious questions openly, without feeling that my status was threatened as an intellectually competent and, therefore, worthwhile person. Once I accepted the unity of faith and reason, my conversion to Christianity became one of the major preoccupations of my college years, with the other being an attractive history major by the name of Chris Dixon.

Chris and I married right after I graduated in 1982 and moved to Baltimore, where Chris entered a graduate program at Johns Hopkins University, and I started work as a secretary at the same institution. Our first priority after settling in was finding a church. We had been married in a Presbyterian church, so our first stop was the local Presbyterian parish. The church was in a pleasant neighborhood and had a likable Scottish pastor. We were also drawn to the Methodist church just off campus. It was poorer but had an active young adult group and choir that seemed to need us. We attended an Episcopal church a few times but never felt comfortable with the formal liturgy. Everyone but us seemed to know when to stand, when to kneel, what to say, and how the communion procession worked. My husband, a veteran of amateur theater, complained: "I don't know the script!" At that time, church for us was less about liturgy and more about feeling comfortable at worship and fellowship with other Christians. The Episcopalian liturgy felt awkward and strange; it seemed to us to be a way of keeping strangers out. When trying to decide which church to join, we did not compare the beliefs or teachings of various denominations. We just wanted a pleasant place to worship. Eventually, the warm welcome of the Methodists won out.

Life as a minister's wife

Chris soon felt a calling to the ministry. As we were worshipping at a Methodist church, it was natural for him to prepare for ministry in that denomination. He entered Princeton Theological Seminary. His studies raised ecclesiastical issues (that would later resurface), which called into question what, exactly, "the church" is supposed to be and where authority really lies. He did not choose to study those questions more deeply at the time, perhaps because he sensed that our future plans would be threatened. Our lives were full, with the promise of a secure future. We were active in a Methodist church in the Princeton area. We loved the pastor and the congregation, and we kept ourselves busy with church activities, Chris's studies, my job, and our friends in the seminary community. In spite of the fullness of our lives, I felt empty inside. I thought it was due to the nomadic, grad-student life we were living and the fact that I wanted the children we could not yet afford. I hoped this empty feeling would end when Chris received his first pastoral appointment and we settled down, raised a family, and became part of a more permanent community.

Chris's first pastorate began in 1988 in Mays Landing, a small town in southern New Jersey. The years there were pivotal. I gave birth to my first two children, and I grew and changed in many ways. I became a passionate devotee of breast-feeding and an active advocate of mothers at home, and I started to reevaluate my pro-choice views. I was busy with my children and happy with small-town living, and although I still felt a sort of emptiness, I tried to dismiss it by "counting my blessings," of which there were many. Everything in our lives seemed right.

Then something went really wrong. Looking back, I see how naïve I was about the life of a pastor and his family. Although I was aware of certain drawbacks, especially those of living life in a fishbowl and experiencing the sometimes unrealistic expectations of the congregation, I was unprepared for the ferocity with which parishioners can turn on their pastor. When some of the people who had been a part of my social circle, my spiritual support, my "faith family," attacked my husband over what I perceived to be a few minor issues, the betrayal I felt was devastating. This crisis became the catalyst for a period of spiritual searching in which I faced the emptiness I had so long ignored. All my old doubts about the existence of God filled my head. After all, He didn't seem to be answering my prayers for relief of my painful situation. I wondered if the atheism I learned in my childhood had merit, after all.

Looking for a church with sure footings

What exactly is the church? The academic question that Chris faced in seminary years ago became an urgent, personal one for me. I had experienced the church as a loving community of like-minded people, a source of personal, spiritual, and emotional support. If that wasn't the church, what was? I had never considered it to be a supernatural entity. My understanding was summed up in the song the children sang in Sunday school:

> I am the church.
> You are the church.
> We are the church together.
> All who follow Jesus, all around the world—
> Yes, we're the church together.

I needed something deeper than a church that was just "us"; I started looking for that "something"—whatever it was. I sought out a Methodist pastoral counselor, who was very helpful in dealing with my painful emotions but who, unfortunately, had nothing to offer me spiritually. I read Methodist books on prayer and meditation, but they all seemed to lead me to find God "within myself." This conclusion was unacceptable to me, as I needed to know God was real, *independent* of my ideas about Him, not a product of my own mental processes. I asked for guidance from other people whom I respected, such as the Methodist pastor Chris had worked for while in seminary and with whom we were very close. He recommended I read a book on meditation, saying, "There will be things you won't agree with, but just take from this book what you can use." It turned out to be a New Age publication about "finding your spirit guide" and "opening yourself to the gifts of the Universe." I was desperate enough to try following some of its recommendations, but I always was uncomfortable, wondering if my "spirit guide" shouldn't be Jesus and not myself or some impersonal "Universe."

I also looked into other churches; I read some of Luther's writings and revisited the Presbyterian and Episcopal churches. None of these Protestant denominations seemed right. Like the Methodists, they all seemed to be making up their teachings for themselves, as though they had no secure roots or clear teaching authority. Luther's virulent anti-Catholic writings disturbed me, and I didn't think modern Lutherans shared his hatred for Catholics. If modern Lutheranism differed from Luther and his understanding of Catholicism, upon what foundation did today's Lutherans base their beliefs? The same went for Methodists. A Methodist leader wrote that if John Wesley returned today, he would be pleased to see what the church he founded had become. I knew that was ridiculous, for I had read enough of Wesley to know he would be appalled at the way the Methodist Church had abandoned its historic Christianity and embraced the secular worldview. I needed to find a church with sure footings.

I find a deeper union with Christ in the Catholic Church

During this time of searching, Chris and I came to know two local Catholic couples, active in the charismatic movement. They invited us to attend their prayer meetings and spent hours listening to our personal and theological struggles. We participated in a Life in the Spirit seminar and attended a Marriage Encounter weekend. These experiences—along with our friends' example of Catholic piety, devotion, and family life—presented the Catholic Church in a new, positive light. Our friend Ed, in particular, became an important mentor for me, and it was largely due to his influence that I threw out the New Age book and stopped using its techniques.

Our friends gave us a copy of Scott Hahn's tape, *Protestant Minister Becomes Catholic*. After listening to it, we both knew where we were headed: Rome. Hahn raised and answered every objection or question we had, such as those about the Magisterium and authority, the Eucharist, the interpretation of Scripture, the role of Mary and the saints. We could resonate with Scott Hahn's experiences as a former Protestant minister, as well, and it was encouraging to discover that many Protestant clergy had entered the Catholic Church. Chris wrote to Hahn, and we learned of the existence of the Coming Home Network, a ministry that assists Protestants, especially clergy, and their families to enter the Church.

The Methodist Church uses an "itinerant" system, which means that ministers are moved from one church to another every few years. In 1993, just as we were beginning to think seriously about entering the Catholic Church, Chris received an appointment to Allentown, another small New Jersey community. We had not sought out or looked forward to this move and new pastorate, but we soon came to realize the Holy Spirit had directed our course and had sent us our own messenger, teacher, and comforter: Father Joseph Procaccini, pastor of St. John the Baptist Catholic Church in Allentown. Chris first met Father Procaccini at a meeting of the local interfaith clergy association and soon began talking to him about the issues we were facing, especially our desire to become Catholic. I began meeting regularly with Father Pro, as we called him, to explore the Catholic faith further.

The farther along I went in my exploration, the more I was certain I had found that "something deeper" I had been looking for all my adult life. I was especially drawn to the idea that the sacraments were genuine openings, or points of contact, between heaven and earth. Through all my reading and searching, I had been struggling to find a more spiritual approach to life, but my reading of Protestant theologies hadn't offered much help. The Catholic faith, with its prayers, sacraments, and sacramentals, seemed to offer exactly what I needed.

There had been many times when I wanted to "make contact" with Christ in a way that the Catholic Church alone offered, through words, but also in silence. For instance, I often tried to make the Sign of the Cross many times, but couldn't bring myself to do it. I thought: "I am Protestant!" Although I was accustomed to using certain formulaic prayers in worship, such as the Lord's Prayer, I was reluctant to repeat traditional Catholic prayers like the Rosary or Act of Contrition. My Protestant way of thinking led me to associate repetitive prayers with some kind of magic spells or New Age mantras. I had come to believe extemporaneous prayers were more heartfelt. Then I came to the realization that even the most determinedly "extemporaneous" prayers could become formulaic. How many times had I heard a Protestant begin a public prayer with "Lord, we just want to thank You. . . ." As I joined my voice to the voices of Catholics throughout the world and throughout time, I gained a new understanding of Romans 8:26: "We do not know how to pray as we ought, but the Spirit himself intercedes for us with sighs too deep for words."

The sacraments as openings between heaven and earth

The Catholic Eucharist became for me the greatest opening between heaven and earth—one I longed to experience. In most Methodist churches, "communion services" are held once a month. Although the communion liturgy is similar in some ways to the Mass, the bread and grape juice (Methodists don't use wine) are thought to be purely symbolic, but with a spiritual effect. The bread does not undergo any change, but Jesus is believed to be "spiritually present" in the "communion." Our post-communion practices left me thinking Christ's spiritual presence was not all that powerful or lasting. Every month after the communion service, we would take the leftover bread home, have some for lunch, and throw the rest away. I knew something was wrong with this practice; this bread should have a deeper meaning. I started feeding the leftovers to the birds and squirrels, which felt a little better than dumping the bread in the trash. I believed Jesus was spiritually present, somehow, in that bread, so I wondered why He wasn't spiritually present in my sandwiches, or my backyard, or my garbage can. Was it that His presence depended entirely on what I was thinking, or what I alone intended when I ate the bread? The Eucharist in the Catholic Church, on the other hand, really was Jesus. He was there whether I was thinking about Him being there or not. The Eucharist did not depend on me to be real.

During the time I was exploring the Catholic Church, Chris and I went to Belgium, where we visited many beautiful, ancient cathedrals. In them, I was drawn to the confessionals, half hoping and half fearing I would find a priest inside waiting for me. Confession, the Sacrament of Penance, was starting to make sense to me. The "just me and God" version of confession found in Protestant teachings struck me as another drawback, like the Protestant understanding of communion and its general disdain for formulaic prayers. As a Methodist, I could wrap my sins in a sort of mental bubble and send it up to God in a wordless confession, without ever looking at it too closely; after all, God knew what was in there. It made the whole process seem unreal, just another mental phenomenon of my own making. I craved the personal contact with Christ that confessing through His priest would give me, especially with the superb example of His love that I saw in Father Pro.

I started attending Mass soon after I began talking with Father Pro. Phyllis, another Protestant minister's wife in town, was also on the road to conversion. In a town of less than two thousand people, the conversions of two ministers' wives was mind-boggling! (Even more so was the forthcoming conversions of several of this small town's Baptist and Protestant ministers.) I sat beside Phyllis at Mass, listening to her prayerful responses with the rest of the congregation, and I was struck by how right it all seemed: the prayers and responses, the community worshipping together but focused on God rather than one another, and most of all, Jesus truly present and among us in the Eucharist. Years ago, when I looked into the Episcopal Church, I found the formal liturgy to be a barrier to communion with God. Now, as I prepared to enter into full communion with our Lord in the Catholic Church, the liturgy became the greatest point of contact between heaven and earth. The first time I attended Mass, I came home and told Chris: "This is it!"

Catholic wife of Protestant minister

When I was ready to convert, Chris and I went to dinner with two leaders of his Methodist congregation to inform them of my decision to become Catholic and to ask for their support. They tried to give it, but the idea that the minister and his wife were a "package deal," and I was breaking up the package and reneging on the deal, was hard for them to get past. I wrote a letter to the congregation, which was published in the church newsletter, but the storm I expected never broke. Most people said nothing at all; only a couple suggested to Chris that my conversion might "hurt the church." There were members of the congregation, however, who went out of their way to encourage me to do what I thought was right for me. When the time came, a few even attended the brief, private Confirmation service in the Catholic Church.

For the next year and a half, we had a "mixed marriage." The situation was less distressing for us than for other couples, since I knew it was only a matter of time before Chris would convert; nonetheless, this period had its problems. Chris felt trapped in the Methodist Church but needed to remain longer, as it was his means of supporting a growing family. Not only our income, but our home, the parsonage, also came from his ministry. He could not leave without having a definite job to go to. The religious division within our family extended to the children. My seven-year-old daughter, Lisa, had been attending Mass with me. On one occasion shortly after my conversion, she witnessed several of her public-school classmates receive their first Holy Communion. I was almost in tears thinking how much I wished she were among them, and I noticed she seemed especially thoughtful. I talked to Chris about her reaction, and a few days later he asked her: "Lisa, do you think you might want to become Catholic?" "Yes," she answered instantly. She had been wanting it for some time but felt that family loyalty prevented her from saying anything. A few months later, she entered the Church, as well. Every Sunday, Lisa and I attended both

Catholic Mass and the Methodist worship service. Lisa also attended both CCD and Sunday school, which confused her Methodist and Catholic classmates.

A Catholic family at last

Chris attended an Opus Dei retreat for recent and potential converts the spring after my conversion and returned home knowing he had to convert soon. Father Pro approached his best friend, Monsignor James McGovern, pastor of Our Lady of Good Counsel Catholic Church in Moorestown, New Jersey, about offering Chris a lay ministry position in his parish. The parish needed someone qualified as a catechist and pastoral caregiver. Monsignor McGovern met with Chris and offered him the position, which Chris readily accepted. He would be able to work in Catholic ministry and support his family after he entered the Church. When Chris announced to his congregation that he would be converting, most people probably thought he was doing it for my sake, but actually his conversion began long before mine, ten years earlier, when he read *Apologia pro vita sua* at Princeton Theological Seminary. It was his initial interest in the Catholic faith that started me on my own journey. In the summer of 1997, shortly after we moved into our new home in Moorestown, Chris was confirmed by Bishop John Smith at a special Mass at Our Lady of Good Counsel Church, and he commenced his new lay ministry.

We have been living in Moorestown for the past five years, delighted to be raising our children in the Catholic faith. It was a special joy to have our youngest child baptized in the Catholic Church. As Cardinal Newman says in his *Apologia*:

> From the time I became a Catholic, of course I have
> no further history of my religious opinions to narrate. In

saying this, I do not mean to say that my mind has been idle, or that I have given up thinking on theological subjects; but that I have had no variations to record, and have had no anxiety of heart whatever. . . . It was like coming into port after a rough sea; and my happiness on that score remains to this day without interruption.

Patricia Dixon entered the Catholic Church in 1995. She is a former La Leche League Leader and has chaired a parish pro-life group. She is currently homeschooling her five children.

13

I Believe in Miracles

Alicia Chesser

When you grow up in a place like Broken Arrow, Oklahoma, seeing a Polish Capuchin monk is a bit like seeing the Sasquatch—an exotic, rare, somewhat terrifying being whose habits are both foreign and fascinating. If you're a nondenominational Protestant whose main experience of men of the cloth comes from camp meetings, Bible studies, and altar calls, the sight is even stranger.

I had literally never seen a Catholic priest in person before when, in eleventh grade, I saw Father Norbert—wearing a coarse brown robe and sandals, carrying a tattered Bible—walk past the door of my European history classroom. Older friends, who'd heard him lecture in our school before, said his name in the same hushed tone they used for names like "Dépêche Mode" or "U2." This guy in the robe? He was cool. There were a few other priests like him, I'd heard, at St. Anne's Parish down the street, men who lived in community and wore ropes around their waists and preached long, difficult sermons. I'd even heard that one of them grew bitter herbs in his garden, which he ate throughout the year as a sort of mortification. A few of the smartest guys in our high school would meet with Father Norbert from time to time to discuss the work of someone named Thomas Aquinas.

They'd talk with him for hours, then go out and mow the grass around the church. It sounded pretty cool, in its way.

In fact, it sounded more than cool. It sounded like these people understood something different about God than I had ever understood, like they lived in God in a way I never had. And I was ready to live in God again. I just had no idea how to start.

I drift away from organized religion

As is often the way with brainy, moody teenagers, I had come to believe in the gospel according to Jack Kerouac, Dizzy Gillespie, and a hodgepodge of Japanese poets, absurdist playwrights, and existentialist philosophers, whose works I'd found on adjacent shelves on the second floor of the public library. My mother worried that such devotion to these notorious hedonists and depressives and "live-fast, die-young" types would lead me to drugs, or worse, but there was little risk of that. My interest in the countercultural "Beat Generation" was fairly ascetical, since my real religion was the daily discipline of ballet. I had studied dance seriously since the age of five, and by junior high, it consumed nearly twenty hours of my time per week, sometimes more during the performance season of the Tulsa Ballet, with which I danced as a member of the *corps de ballet*. I worked hard, both in and out of school, and my desire to do well at everything shielded me from the profligate influences of my extracurricular reading. But something else was shielding me, too.

My parents and I had not been members of a church for a long time. Our excuse was that, because of my demanding schedule and that of my father, who owned his own remodeling business, we simply didn't have time. The deeper reason, I think, was that we had not found a denomination we could call home. My father, Wayne Mosier, raised Lutheran, and my mother, Suzanne, raised Presbyterian, had been "born again" shortly before they had me. Deeply involved in the charismatic revival that swept the Midwest in the late 1970s, they moved from Nebraska to Oklahoma to be part of the burgeoning "Faith Movement." While still in Nebraska, we traveled to nursing homes and community centers singing gospel songs, with Mom at the piano and three-year-old me taking the harmony part. We went to revivals, where people beyond number would "go out under the power," falling to the floor under what seemed to be the influence of the Holy Spirit. We read the Bible constantly.

And there were miracles. One afternoon, when I was about four, I came into the kitchen to find Mom sitting immobile at the table, in the grip of what she would later describe as "a black cloud, a satanic fog." I began to speak in tongues, and the cloud disappeared, as did the anorexia from which she had suffered for years. At a healing service around the same time, our minister laid his hands on my left leg, which curved in at the ankle and required me to wear a special heavy shoe, and as he prayed I watched my leg straighten out before my eyes. Being a dancer would never have been possible without that healing. Most of all, we prayed as a family, whenever there was something that needed praying about. We prayed in accordance with the words of St. Paul: We are washed in the blood of the Lamb, putting on the armor of Christ, treading on serpents and scorpions, believing that we may receive. We laid hands on one another and agreed that by His stripes we were healed. Jesus was as much a part of our family as any of us; in fact, He was its center, since everything that happened to us came from Him.

Before long, though, my parents became concerned about what they were seeing in the charismatic movement. The churches in which we worshipped kept breaking into factions over everything from doctrine to finances. Members could not agree on what to preach, how to pray, how to interpret Scripture rightly, and finally there would be a split, usually a bitter one. But that wasn't the worst of it. The "faith message" said that you could have anything you wanted —even a new car or a bigger salary—if only you believed enough. When our friend Greg got pneumonia, he was urged not to see a doctor but rather simply to declare himself healed. If he had enough faith, the church said, his health would be restored; going to a doctor would demonstrate, in fact, a lack of faith. Greg died soon thereafter, a martyr to what my parents began to see as an increasingly suspect and even blasphemous gospel.

Shaken and disillusioned, my parents abandoned the charismatic church, and during my later elementary school years, we shuttled between Lutheran and Methodist churches, finally settling for prayer at home, as schedules grew busier and church worship less fulfilling. "Settling" is the wrong word, perhaps, for my parents continued to be deeply devout, and we prayed together about everything; however, our lack of a faith community affected all of us. We had questions about the faith, but there was no one to answer them. I simply stopped asking. While I never stopped believing in God, He became for me just someone to talk to, someone whose help and guidance I took for granted—more a school counselor than the Alpha and Omega. Once, in a humanities course she was taking at the local college, my mom had to write an essay on the question "What is most real?" I remember scoffing dramatically when she told me her answer was "God."

I fall into nothingness

It was around this time, age fourteen or fifteen, that I began to be attracted to the writers and thinkers who described the world as a fundamentally meaningless, if more or less benign, place. I read up on Buddhism, finding its depiction of "nothingness" appealing. A common thread throughout these writings—existentialist, Buddhist, and "beat" alike—was that joy was possible despite the absence of a source for that joy, that good could be done even though no such thing as "the good" existed. I wanted to believe it. I wanted to love life, but I didn't want God interfering to tell me how or what to love. It would soon become clear that what I wanted was, very simply, a lie.

One summer afternoon, my two closest friends came to my house to tell me that our friend Rachel—the free spirit of our group, the smartest and funniest and most creative person we knew, though also the most troubled—had driven her car far out onto a rural road, climbed a hill, and shot herself in the mouth. None of us knew how to handle this: the shock of her death, the way it happened, the loss, even how to relate to one another now. At her memorial service, which we all knew she would have hated, the minister had no idea who she was, and there were prayers in the service which, in her sly way, she would have smirked at. But as we prayed the Our Father that day, tears came to my eyes, not just for Rachel, but for the emptiness that was in all our hearts. For many in our group of friends, whose homes were broken or filled with abuse and sadness, who had not grown up in the Church, the very idea of a loving Father was an absurdity. I knew that He existed, that He loved me. I grieved that Rachel hadn't lived to know it. Nothingness was now very concrete to my friends and me. It wasn't freedom. It was hell.

The path up appears

Truth, trust, community: Much later, John Paul II's *trinomial*, would teach me what was missing. True community can't exist without trust, which in turn, can't exist without a foundation in the truth. That trinomial's mirror image—untruth, fear, solitude—was the very definition of my experience in those years. I didn't know where to go, how to get out, how to return to a life that had . . . *life*. Suddenly, though, a path began to break.

My advanced placement English class had me reading stories and novels by that brilliant Catholic apostate, James Joyce. They were full of words I'd never heard before: chasuble, monsignor, transubstantiation. For help in understanding Joyce's points of reference, I went to my friend Emily, a devout Catholic and, as it happened, a member of Father Norbert's parish. An after-school talk about definitions turned swiftly into a probing conversation about the Church, in which Emily described what happened during Mass. She was calm and thorough, but when she arrived at the Canon, her voice grew intense. Her eyes shone when she said: "The whole Mass culminates in what happens here, in the Eucharist, when Christ becomes present." As she explained what Catholics believe about the Eucharist, something stirred in me, as well. "Christ becomes present." I didn't know quite what that meant, or how it happened, but I knew it was Him I wanted to see. Emily invited me to join her at Mass, purportedly to get a firsthand look at all those chasubles and things. The next Sunday, I found myself kneeling next to her near the altar at St. Anne's Parish.

I'd long had an amateur's interest in things Catholic. Having discovered Gregorian chants and books of icons at the library, I had wondered at the purity and variety of the liturgies and the richness of the art. Studying the aesthetics of the Church, however, had not prepared me for this experience of the Church *in the flesh*.

My mind was in chaos in the midst of this strange ceremony. As I knelt before the stone table, covered with an intricate lace cloth, and gazed at the mother-of-pearl icon of Our Lady of Czestochowa and the huge gold tabernacle—while Father

Norbert sang the antiphons and censed the sanctuary—I felt as though I were moving about in a dark room where strange figures brushed up against my shoulders, and strange voices guided me along. The murmur of the Rosary prayers before Mass was like a mother's lullaby, quiet and sure. I was lost, but not afraid, and when the bell rang after the words of consecration—when I looked up to see Father Norbert holding the white Host above his head—I wasn't even lost. It was Jesus. And I was home.

After Mass, Emily introduced me to Father Norbert. He grasped my hand and looked into my eyes, and I felt the Holy Spirit's power coming into my heart. It was the same steady, physically palpable force I had felt when that preacher laid his hands on my leg so many years before. Soon after, I told him that I would like to enter the Catholic Church. "Well, come and see," he said with a gentle smile, and he told me to be at the religious-education building on a Tuesday night a few weeks later, when RCIA classes would begin.

God is calling me by name

Like many Protestants of their generation, my parents had been raised with a mild form of anti-Catholicism; they weren't allowed to date Catholics, for instance, and as kids they heard the usual warnings about "statue worship." My dad had a strong religious formation in his youth, and he held firmly Lutheran views on things like the priesthood of all believers and salvation by grace through faith. Neither he nor Mom, however, had ever expressed any antipathy toward the Church, so I was fairly sure they wouldn't react negatively when I began to visit St. Anne's. To be honest, I didn't give much thought to how they would respond, and it was thanks to them that my decision could be made so freely. I knew they were confident I had absorbed what they had taught me about listening to the Lord, testing the spirits, and praying to be in God's will. It was clear that they trusted me to do that, even if the Catholic Church was strange to them. They never raised an eyebrow, at least around me. In fact, their comments when I would leave the house on Sunday mornings were amazingly nonchalant: "Oh, have a good time!" "Say hi to Emily!" They weren't sure what it was all about, but they saw that something was happening to me in that parish down the street. Mom said: "You have a different look when you come home from there. A good look. Peaceful. I don't know why, but you're different." They asked few questions; they simply let me go.

They were actually more surprised when I told them I wanted to stop dancing. Ballet had become a sort of religion for me, an all-encompassing way of life that required a single-minded devotion I was no longer willing to give. I'd had some injuries, so the likelihood of a professional career was no longer as strong as it had once been. I wanted to go to college, which would be impossible if I continued to pursue ballet full-time, although what worried me most was that dance had become my whole identity. It defined not just my schedule but my sense of self; I hardly knew who I was without it and the recognition it brought. My ballet teacher worried that I was throwing away a God-given gift. I knew it was a gift, one which, once given up, could never be retrieved. God was calling me by name—not as a dancer, or a student, but simply as me—and I knew this was a break I had to make. In the first few weeks of not going to ballet class, I had a sense of peace I had not felt in many years. Body and soul, it was a tremendous liberation.

Plus, it left me free in the evenings to attend Father Norbert's RCIA classes. There were about twenty of us: young and old, couples and singles, workers and students. We gathered once a week in a bland little room in the religious-education building and, with somewhat cautious looks, gave ourselves to Father

Norbert's care. It's no exaggeration to say that many of us were a little scared of him. He had done his dissertation on Aquinas at the Catholic University of Lublin, John Paul II's alma mater. He spoke many languages, could read Hebrew, and quote as easily from St. Athanasius as from the Sermon on the Mount, but it wasn't just his knowledge that made him intimidating. He had spent many years in Guatemala serving the poorest of the poor. He had lived under Communism in Poland. He was a Capuchin, which meant a life of asceticism and poverty. He was relatively young, perhaps in his early forties, but his face bore the signs of great suffering; his voice was low but forceful, especially when he preached about the culture of death. He was quite clearly a man who had intimate knowledge of the Cross. For us, he seemed as close to what Jesus must have been like as any man we'd ever known.

His RCIA classes were, to put it mildly, unorthodox, and by "unorthodox" I mean (in contrast to many RCIA programs I've heard about since) very, very *orthodox*. Father Norbert had no interest in making Catholicism palatable to us. He was simply there to teach us what the Church taught, to answer our questions, and to enable us to decide whether to say "yes" or "no." He began that first night by discussing a single Latin word he had written on the blackboard: *latria*, "worship." Over the next eight months, he took us through the Ten Commandments, the sacraments, the virtues, the doctrines of original sin, atonement, infallibility, the role of Mary, and on and on through the entirety of Catholic history, life, and thought. At all times, his big *Jerusalem Bible* sat before him on the table, more dog-eared even than the *Catechism of the Catholic Church* that sat beside it.

These classes were overwhelming and not a little over my head, but they were also exhilarating. It was a blessing, in a way, that I came in knowing so little theology, because I was free to absorb the Church's teachings without an intellectual struggle. Some teachings didn't quite make sense to me, but that didn't worry me; they would make sense in time. The more Father Norbert explained how the Church understood both God and human beings, the stronger my commitment became to the "body" in which the Body of Christ had been made present on the altar. The Church had me at "hello," to paraphrase a line from *Jerry Maguire*. As I began to know the Church more intimately—to learn what she thought, how she expressed herself, why she wore green on some days and purple on others—I grew more and more in love with her.

On Holy Thursday, I made my first Confession. Afterward, Father Norbert asked me to pay a visit to Our Lady of Czestochowa, whose icon had so amazed me on my first visit to St. Anne's, and spend some time giving thanks for the gift of my conversion. My friend Emily, who would be my Confirmation sponsor two days later, had given me Rosary beads and taught me the Rosary prayers. "She's a powerful woman," she'd said. "It's Mary who leads us to Christ. If you want to bring someone into the Church, go to the Rosary!" But this day, with a heart burned clean by the awe-filled gift of absolution, I sat before Mary, who looked down on the Lord in her arms and in the tabernacle underneath, and just said, "Wow!"

The following day Father Norbert asked me to meet with him one last time before the Easter Vigil. He asked if I had any final questions. He had taught us so well that most questions about doctrine had already been answered, but one thing did come to my mind. "I'm not sure I really understand humility," I said. "I know I don't have it. How can I get it?" His response astounded me. "Humility is simply telling the truth," he said, "about yourself, about others, and about who God is." Then he asked if I had chosen a patron saint for my Confirmation name.

I hadn't, so he said: "Think about Thérèse, the Little Flower. I think she would be a good friend for you." Therese it was. And that Saturday night, April 2, 1994, I became Alicia Therese, a daughter of the Church. My parents came with joy to the Vigil and sat in the front pew, where right out of the gate Father Norbert drenched my dad with a suspiciously well-aimed splash of holy water. But more on that later.

Life as a Catholic

That same night at Holy Family Cathedral in Tulsa, my boyfriend, Steven Chesser, was also received into the Church. He was among that group of young men who had met with Father Norbert to discuss theology during high school, and he was now in his first year of studies in philosophy at the University of Tulsa. His journey to the Church was completely independent from mine and very different. (He had many more, and more intelligent, questions about the faith than I did, for one thing.) Steve had not grown up in any church at all, though his mother, a Baptist, was and is a woman of great faith. In the summer of 1993, he and his family took a road trip through the Western states, and for the journey, I gave him copies of St. Augustine's *City of God* and *Confessions*, thinking he might find them interesting but never imagining their dramatic influence on him. By the time he came home, he was convinced that the Church of which Augustine was part was where he wanted to be, too. Now we were together in "the Catholic thing," and even something so basic as attending Mass together brought new depth to our love.

I started at the University of Tulsa that fall, joining Steve in the philosophy department, with a second major in English. We sat on the student interview committee that would help choose a new member of the philosophy faculty, and we were thrilled one day to find ourselves interviewing Professor Russell

Hittinger, an eminent natural law theorist who had taught at Fordham, Princeton, and the Catholic University of America. Professor Hittinger was hired, and in the next two years I took every course he offered, from "Aquinas's Treatise on Law" to "The Philosophy of Religion." We read Spinoza and John Dewey, James Madison and Justice Frankfurter, St. Francis and Gregory the Great. He became a treasured mentor, not only as a teacher of Catholic theology and religiously informed political thought, but also as a friend who unselfishly gave his time in conversation marked by singular shrewdness, prudence, wit, and zeal.

Professor Hittinger also introduced me to the world of conservative thought by encouraging me to apply for a fellowship with the Intercollegiate Studies Institute and attend conferences with the Liberty Fund. Through those organizations, I met many young Catholics who were beginning to seize the opportunity for what the Pope had called "a springtime of evangelization," searching for ways to bring their faith into public life through journalism, scholarship, and the arts. It was an inspiring time, and I was eager to be part of the work of this new generation.

In the summer of 1997, Professor Hittinger called me up with a typically bold and unexpected idea: "You should go to Poland!" What in the world would I do that for, I wondered? He explained that every summer in Krakow the Polish Dominicans hosted a three-week seminar in which George Weigel, Michael Novak, Father Richard John Neuhaus, Father Maciej Zieba, O.P., Hittinger himself, and others gave lectures on Catholic social thought to two dozen senior undergraduate and graduate students from America and Eastern Europe. In addition to the lectures, there would be discussion groups, tours of Krakow and Czestochowa and many other places, even outings to the mountains. The students would stay at the thirteenth-century Dominican priory while the brothers took a brief holiday; Mass would be said each day in the priory's chapter room. All expenses were paid except for plane fare. How could I say no? I applied, was accepted, and soon boarded a plane that would take me out of the country for the first time and into a world that would change my life in ways I could never have expected.

The lectures at the "Tertio Millenio and Free Society Seminar" were challenging and inspiring. The setting was breathtakingly beautiful. The outings (for instance, a visit to the country home of some traditional musicians who cooked us a huge dinner and laughed and prayed and taught us old Polish songs, or my visit to the real Lady of Czestochowa) were a delight, but it wasn't the trips or the discussions that made those three weeks so powerful. It was the daily Mass, intimate and unadorned, uniting our little group in trust, and it was the astonishing richness of this Church-infused culture. Everything, even the poetry of an atheist or the music of a hard rock band, seemed to exist within the sensibility of the Church. For the Poles I met, there was nothing "forbidden" about the modern world; their faith, while always ready to turn away from evil, never seemed prim or defensive. In other words, they were the first "John Paul II Catholics" I'd ever encountered: They were not afraid, either of modernity or of Christ, and their confidence drew all of us to them. This was a Christianity I'd never experienced before, and it was exhilarating.

It wasn't easy to come back. For three weeks, I had been in an environment of such abundant grace, in a culture that was so thoroughly, vibrantly Catholic, that returning to a world of shopping malls and artificially intimate liturgies was a real shock. Our American Church and culture seemed impoverished by comparison. The lack of a genuinely Catholic culture was almost physically painful in the first few weeks I was back.

Miracles continue

Little did I know what miracles waited at home. My parents had been struck by my descriptions of the Church in Poland, but perhaps just as much by how much I had changed since becoming Catholic. Soon the number of questions they were asking about Catholicism began to increase dramatically, both in number and in difficulty. I began studying my copy of the *Catechism* before going home on the weekends, so I'd be prepared to answer them. Every visit brought a new query from my father: "Now, when you talk about apostolic succession, that means there's one line of continuity from the Pope all the way down to the village priest, right? But in the Protestant church we hold to the priesthood of all believers, so there's really no difference between me and the man in the pulpit. What's so special about being in one line of succession? How does it change who the man in the pulpit is? How does it affect what happens in church on Sunday?" There were questions about the papacy, about sin and grace, about the authority of Scripture and Tradition. I wanted to give the best answers I could (and sometimes I sneaked to Professor Hittinger for help with the toughest ones), because I saw that something was happening in my parents, and I knew that if I stayed out of the way and just said what the Church said, the truth and beauty of the Church would draw them in. Later, my father would say: "Protestant ministers could never answer my questions about the faith. They'd just say: 'Read the Bible.' The Catholic Church had answers, answers that could make sense of apparently everything." He started reading *First Things*, an ecumenical magazine edited by Father Neuhaus, and he found there an abundance of food for thought. Somehow, he ended up with a copy of a book by Scott Hahn, at which point I knew he was in the final lap.

My mom didn't ask as many theological questions, but something was happening in her as well. One day, a couple of months after I returned from Poland, we were sitting in the living room talking about this and that; I think I was telling her something about the saints, whom she had begun to find fascinating. Suddenly, she turned to me and said: "Would you teach me how to pray the Rosary?" "Really?" I exclaimed. (My friend Emily's voice sang in my ears: "If you want to bring someone into the Church . . .") Heart pounding, I wrote down the prayers and took her through the mysteries just as Emily had done with me. A few weeks later, she called with words that took my breath away: "I think your father and I are going to go and see about those RCIA classes up at the Cathedral." On April 10, 1999, I was blessed to sponsor my parents as the bishop laid his hands on their heads, and they were confirmed.

After the Vigil, Dad was chuckling about something. "Remember when Father Norbert hit me with that holy water at Alicia's Confirmation?" he asked. "It was like he took a look at me standing there, all lost, and said, 'This one needs some serious help.' Well, it took a while, but he got me!"

The greatest adventure

To say that being with my parents in the Church has been an adventure would be an understatement. Faith has been so important to our family for so long. Now that we've found faith in its fullness, we are closer than ever, and it is a never-ending pleasure to explore the Church with them. They read voraciously about the faith; I go home to find volumes of the Church Fathers in the bathroom. Despite being supplemented by at least four other Catholic magazines, *First Things* continues to be the journal of choice at the Mosier house, in part because from 1998 to 2003 (thanks to a strong recommendation from Russell Hittinger) it employed the Mosier daughter on its editorial staff, getting her on her own two feet as a writer and editor in New York (and off the family dole!). Working with Father Neuhaus—my teacher in Krakow and both boss and landlord in New York—and the wildly varied group of philosophers, theologians, priests, poets, and raconteurs who surround the magazine was a joyous experience of the Church that is "catholic" in every sense of the word.

My parents got to share the experience in several visits to New York, and most dramatically, in a trip to Rome at the turn of the millennium, where they joined me at a grand reunion of the Krakow seminar alumni—and where, just eight months after entering the Church, in the Clementine room off St. Peter's Basilica, they got to meet the Holy Father. (My dad's words when greeting the Pope have become legendary in our *First Things* community. He knelt at the Pope's feet, took his hand, and said, "God bless you, heavenly father!" We've tried not to let that story get out to our Protestant family members, lest it confirm their worst suspicions about what Catholics really believe.)

There is an old French proverb which says that a coincidence is an event in which God wishes to remain anonymous. Many things in this story seem like coincidences: that I happened to get interested in James Joyce and asked my Catholic friend about chasubles; that I and my boyfriend Steve, now my husband, happened to meet the same Polish Capuchin in little Broken Arrow; that the priest who prepared us for marriage ten years later happened to be a Polish Dominican from the priory in which the Krakow seminar was held; that Professor Russell Hittinger happened to come to Tulsa, which led me to Poland and to *First Things*, all of which played a part in bringing my parents into the Church.

Looking back, it does not seem that God was anonymous at all in these events. He was always there, His extravagant, exuberant grace available at every moment. My childhood experience of a personal relationship with Him opened my heart to the fullness of that relationship in the Catholic Church. In the writings and the witness of Pope John Paul II, the Church has reasserted her ancient awareness that a *Person* stands at her center. This is not just any person, but the One who, as the Second Vatican Council put it, both reveals God to man and reveals man to himself. After all, what is at the center of the Mass but Jesus' Body and Blood? What is at the heart of our prayer, but the Man who by His death and resurrection draws us into the conversation of the Trinity? What is the beginning of the apostolic succession but Peter's realization of who this Jesus actually is?

It's not too much to say that my charismatic upbringing trained my eyes to see all this. In the rituals of the Catholic Church, in the saints, in the papacy, and in the sacraments, I was able to recognize a drawing-near to the person of Christ—in large part because another tradition taught me to recognize Him in the first place. I continue to invoke the Holy Spirit; I rely on the Word. In the confessional, there is a powerful sense of Jesus' healing mercy and my own radical dependence on it. All of this, all learned from the faith of my parents, converges with and deepens my experience of the Church. I have traveled very far, and there is far to go. Through it all, I know Christ will keep leading me home.

Alicia Chesser was until recently the managing editor of First Things *and a freelance writer and dance critic in New York City. Her work has appeared in* First Things, re: generation quarterly, UPI, The Dance Insider, *and* Pointe Magazine, *among others. She and her husband, Steve, live in Tulsa, Oklahoma.*

14

Getting It Right the Second Time

Patricia Sodano Ireland

My story begins long before I became a Lutheran, in my childhood recollections of life as a Catholic in the Church as yet unaffected by modernist cultural whims. I remember making my first Holy Communion at age six, and how I loved to carry my never-changing little missal with the English translations of the Latin Mass. I remember covering my head with a hat and, more to my liking, a long mantilla. I remember feeling awe in the presence of something so much greater than my little self every time I walked into the church, and genuflecting until my knee touched the floor. I remember how my heart skipped a beat when I stepped into the Holiest of Holy places beyond the rail, as I helped my mother change the altar linens beneath the tabernacle of the Lord. I recall memorizing the *Baltimore Catechism*, and staring wide-eyed at the holy pictures Sister Loretta Ann showed my class of Jesus' Sacred Heart and the Immaculate Heart of Mary, that we may know we are loved unconditionally. I recall frequent visits to the confessional, First Friday devotions, praying the Rosary, weekly novenas, Stations of the Cross, and veneration of the crucifix on Good Friday afternoon. I remember meatless Fridays and three-hour-long, hunger-producing, pre-Communion fasts. I can picture the altar boy holding a bright, shiny brass paten under my tongue when I received the Eucharist from the hands of the priest that not a single crumb of Christ's broken Body would fall to the floor.

These remembrances are not simply an excuse to wax nostalgic about a pristine Church in days gone by. The Church in every age is marred by sin of its members, but it was a time distinguished by its unabashed assertion of the transcendence of God. That all changed a few years after the close of Vatican II, when the insertion of the glorified *self* emerged in my little parish and parochial school in suburban New Jersey and elsewhere. Compliance, submission, and a peaceful spirit are *not* among my strongest virtues. The birth of egocentrism and irreverence as badges of honor in the 1960s gave me the excuse I desired to follow my baser instincts.

The *me* generation

It was an era characterized by self-serving dissent in culture, politics, social mores, and religion. The Second Vatican Council came and went during this frenzied decade. Capitulating to cultural trends, lay and clerical Catholics alike joined the ranks of dissenters. Professing conformity to a so-called "spirit" of Vatican II, dissenters wreaked havoc with Catholic theology, morality, and liturgy. The effects have been far-reaching and damaging to generations of Catholics since. Accommodation to the culture was in; Catholic distinction was out. While still in parochial school, I experienced a completely different Church than the one into which I had been baptized and from which I received my first Holy Communion. The nuns' habits were modified twice, and the familiar sight of the sisters pacing back and forth outside the church praying their daily *Office* disappeared. The Latin Missal was discarded in favor of solely English-language disposable missalettes. The choir loft organ went into hibernation, and guitarists strumming sentimental folk ballads stood stage left behind where the altar rails used to be. The tabernacle was shifted to the side, or even out of sight, to make room for the presider's seat, front and center. Ironically, the statues of Mary, Joseph, and the baby Jesus were removed from the sanctuary of my home parish, Holy Family. Women's bonnets disappeared, replaced by the new, preferred Sunday attire of blue jeans and sneakers. Meatless Fridays were dropped, and Saturday evening Mass was approved to accommodate convenience.

The change that made the biggest impression on me, however, was in the religion curriculum of my parochial school. Doctrinal teaching was de-emphasized to make room for individual truth-seeking. One course was called "Becoming a Person," and it encouraged a free range of irreverent expression, to which my argumentative self readily complied. I remember one particular occasion when I ranted and raved about a practice not to my liking in a church I had recently visited. My eighth-grade teacher, Sister Maureen, let me go on and on, never once attempting a sound counter-explanation.

Romantic love as the vehicle for subjective "truths" was the catechetics of choice for my junior-high years. My eighth-grade graduation Mass served up the romantic and sexy "I Don't Know How to Love Him" from *Jesus Christ, Superstar,* which we belted out with all the heartfelt emotion swooning, star-struck teenagers could muster. We sang in the person of the promiscuous Mary Magdalene, who is "moved" by this man, Jesus, whom she wants to "bring down." She can't figure out why she is attracted to Him because she's had her fill of men; He's "just a man" and "just one more." Totally confused about her hunger for this man, she cries out: "What's it all about?"

What's it all about? It was about putting Jesus and me on a level playing field and pitching Catholic practice into the

Christian pan-denominational heap. To my discredit, I lapped up this pap.

I leave the Church

College theological studies at Boston College picked up where "Becoming a Person" left off. As an undergraduate theology major, I took five graduate courses, several in B.C.'s summer pastoral ministry program, to which I returned soon after graduation to receive a Master of Arts degree. Radical feminism and liberation theology were the name of the game. Oppression was the *credo* of women and minorities. The Boston Theological Institute (BTI), a consortium of graduate and theological schools, offered a veritable smorgasbord of modernist theologies. I took courses with, attended lectures, and read voraciously the works of dissenting Catholics and Protestants, such as Elizabeth Schussler Fiorenza, Rosemary Radford Reuther, Mary Daly, Gustavo Gutierrez, Hans Küng, and Father Richard McBrien, just to name a few. I gave up the Sunday pre-Communion fast and going to Confession. I skipped Mass whenever I felt like it, yet I played piano at folk Masses and received the Eucharist. I accepted the "culture of death," which was a staple of college life. I didn't flinch witnessing the abuse of drugs and alcohol around me. My friends' experiences of sexual encounters led me wholeheartedly to advocate birth control and premarital sex within the context of "love." I listened to stories of acquaintances' multiple abortions without offering a sobering word, for fear of hurting their feelings.

Toward the end of my graduate pursuits in pastoral ministry at Boston College, I decided to leave the Catholic Church. For me, it became a *justice* issue, as it seemed all theology was reduced to justice in those days. I came to the *false* conclusion that the Catholic Church was one of the worst oppressors of women and the poor, and I was a victim, albeit a marginal one, among the "anawim"[46] described so eloquently in my liberation theology texts. My prayer life was dull. Catholic devotional life had long since given way to theological arguments. We used to joke in graduate school at Boston College, and later in seminary, that we were so busy talking *about* God, that we had no time left to talk *to* God.

Living inside my head became a sinful occupation. I made a conscious decision to leave the Catholic Church and chose Lutheranism, because its rich confessional and theological heritage stimulated my intellect, while its Catholic-like eucharistic liturgy appealed to my senses. I began instruction with the interim pastor of a small Lutheran church in Newton Centre, Massachusetts. At the end of my course, the pastor, with tears in his eyes, asked me when he should write a letter to his bishop recommending me to the Lutheran ministry. Since I was completing my M.A. at Boston College, further education was not in my thoughts; however, I accepted my pastor's suggestion as a call from God. I met with the bishop, and a few months later found myself a Lutheran seminarian at Andover Newton Theological School.

Three memories stand out about this new life. The first was my difficulty in finding a rhythm of devotion. Weekday Masses, Hail Mary's, and devotion to the saints had been part and parcel of my prayer life, dull as it had become; however, I felt that to be a good Lutheran I had to give up those things. I made a mental note that it was *not* okay to invoke a saint. On the plus side, I began praying with the Bible, something my Catholic childhood did not stress. The second memory was my excitement at seeing an ordained female professor preside at the Eucharist. It was like a taste of the forbidden fruit. I couldn't wait

---

[46] "Anawim" is a designation in my liberation-theology texts describing marginal, oppressed, and exploited people.

to do it, too. The third memory was of feeling like an outsider. Catholicism is a way of life; add my robust Italian heritage to Catholic culture, and I felt as though I were giving up my identity. I never truly felt I belonged in the Lutheran Church, especially the first two New England congregations I served, which were ethnically German and Swedish. I quickly seized upon those uncomfortable (and guilty) feelings of leaving something important behind, and deemed them to be further evidence of my victimhood as a woman and former Catholic. I embraced the feminist/womanist notion that being made to feel uncomfortable or an outsider in a male-dominated world is a good indication of one's victimization.

I soon discovered there was a benefit to being a victim: One's outsider or victim status was the entrance ticket into a whole new world of power and privilege in the Lutheran ministry. While a seminarian, I attended the fifteenth anniversary conference celebrating the ordination of women in the Lutheran Church. It was no celebration, but a lamentation orgy. Day after day was spent emoting angst over the suffering of female clergy at the hands of men. Here I was in a church where women were ordained, and I couldn't find a satisfied woman among them. While many tales of inequitable compensation and prejudice rang true, the bigger the sob story, the greater the woman's popularity. It was like a secret club I longed to join. The "best victim" award went posthumously to one of the first women ordained in the Lutheran Church who, as I remember, was disabled. There wasn't a dry eye in the house, as the story of the prejudice she encountered in her pastorate unfolded, culminating in her death in a fiery blaze in her nonaccessible apartment. I came to the crushing conclusion that the Lutheran Church was almost, but not quite, as unjust and oppressive as the Catholic Church, that is, Catholicism from the perspective of radical feminism.

By the time I was ordained in 1986, my *public* prayer life had become a political exercise. I spent more time in the liturgy listening for sexist language and changing it than I did praying. Yet, paradoxically, my *personal* prayer life deepened. Looking back, I see that the Holy Spirit was working a good in me, preparing me for my conversion. As a young pastor, I knew that to be effective I needed to develop a deep inner life. I devoted much more of each day to prayer. I still engaged in feminist activities, but they soon lost their luster. For instance, I always professed to be pro-life, yet I volunteered at Women's Way in Philadelphia, an organization that supports abortion and contributes funds to abortion clinics. I excused my involvement by saying that I worked only in the areas that had nothing to do with abortion. My volunteer days at Women's Way were numbered after my involvement at one of their conferences in which little pins resembling embryos were distributed. Conference workers and attendees were expected to wear them as signs of their commitment to "choice." I couldn't do it; seeing all those gleaming gold-toned pins on well over a thousand women made me sick. I felt ashamed to be there.

It was at that time, too, that the Lutheran Church seemed to be relinquishing much of its confessional, scriptural, and moral identity. I found myself at odds with a church ever more silent on significant moral issues, such as abortion, premarital sex, and homosexuality. I began reading independent Lutheran publications, among them *Lutheran Forum* and *Forum Letter* (the latter edited at that time by then Lutheran Pastor Richard John Neuhaus). I formed alliances with female and male clergy who struggled to assert traditional Lutheran teaching into modern discussions, most notably my friend and colleague Jennifer Ferrara, who with her husband, Steve, helped me to discover the falsehood of the feminist agenda. Especially, I learned through my pastoral ministry that sin, forgiveness, and salvation were at the heart of my parishioners' struggles. I felt *their* need for a deepened sacramental life. I openly lamented the fact that we Lutheran ministers could not offer sacramental absolution to penitents who confessed their sins. I hungered for the Eucharist, and for a time instituted a midweek communion service at my parish. I found that modernist agendas only served to alienate the laity from the Church. The "I'm OK, you're OK" motto of the majority of my colleagues at the time frankly did not cut it with believers who, with St. Paul, admitted their frequent failure to do what they ought and their penchant for doing what they ought not.

Fathers do know best

In 1993, I entered a graduate program in Historical Theology at Drew University, Madison, New Jersey. I delved into the writings of the Church Fathers, and I was amazed at their richness and truth. Regretfully, I recalled the first time I read Augustine's *Confessions* in college when I was wrongly taught that Augustine was a repressed, guilt-ridden man, obsessed with sex. The second time I read the *Confessions* was as a Lutheran seminarian. As any good Lutheran, I believed Luther's understanding of justification to be more authentically Augustinian than Augustine himself. The third time I read the *Confessions* was through the eyes of a faith wizened by life and pastoral experience, and was certain that I beheld truth. I voraciously consumed as much Augustine as I could get my hands on. Then I delved into more Fathers and discovered the Catholicity of their teachings on faith and morals. A longing to be part of the Apostolic Church began to grow inside me. I accepted the authority of the Pope and the teaching Magisterium, the seven sacraments, redemptive suffering, the way of perfection, the intercession of the saints, and purgatory. The absence of purgatory in the Lutheran Church was a source of great anxiety for me as a pastor, because there was no place in the Lutheran funeral service to storm heaven's gates on behalf of a poor sinful soul. My acceptance of purgatory, especially, meant I believed in a teaching untenable to Lutherans.

The more Catholic I became, the less confessionally and morally sound became the ELCA. What came to be a semi-scrapped but well-publicized document on sexuality audaciously pronounced that the nearly two-thousand-year-old teaching on loving the sinner and hating the sin was passé.[47] The ELCA's *Lutheran* magazine featured positive stories on alternative heterosexual and homosexual lifestyles and dubbed abortion as a tragic *choice*. Worst of all was the ELCA's insurance plan, which provided coverage for abortion. Ecclesiastically, the ELCA was forging ahead with intercommunion agreements between the Reformed traditions and the Episcopal Church, respectively.[48] One integral reason for my heretofore adherence to the Lutheran tradition was its high view of Christ's real, physical presence in the Eucharist. I believed that to grant intercommunion with denominations holding a low spiritual or memorial view of the Eucharist was tantamount to exposing Lutheran sacramental practices as a sham. I wondered how the Lutheran Church could reconcile the differences, not only in its understanding of the Eucharist, but also in ordination practices. The Lutheran Church officially, although not always in practice, required chastity from its clergy, while Reformed tradition's United Church of Christ ordained practicing homosexuals. There was also the intention of full communion with the Episcopal Church, which claims a historical episcopacy (invalid in the eyes of Rome). While many of my more "high-churchly inclined colleagues" in ministry lauded

---

[47] A mildly toned-down social statement on sexuality was released soon after.

[48] Both agreements have been passed and are in place.

such an alliance as a step closer to Rome, I was appalled because of the Episcopal Church's self-admittedly loose view of normative doctrine and morals.

Thomas Reeves, in the *Suicide of Liberal Protestantism*, speaks at length about the frenzied quest to form interdenominational alliances within mainline Protestantism. In the vast majority of instances, these unions are sought to fortify weaknesses, rather than capitalize strengths. The ELCA seemed to be in a terrible commotion on all levels of its existence. I was certain that if the ELCA stood fast in its confessional identity through its adherence to the *Augsburg Confession* and the creeds, it would *not* be making strange bedfellows with denominations radically different in their understandings of Scripture, Tradition, church teaching, sacraments, and morals. I determined what the ELCA needed most was a teaching and authoritative Magisterium; however, at the time I did not venture so far as to think that it needed to be in *Rome*.

My deepening concerns, misgivings, and restlessness over the ELCA's ecumenical intentions, as well as my growing attraction for the Church of the Fathers, occurred ironically over a period of years in which my spiritual, personal, and professional life thrived. I returned to the Bible, not as I had earlier visited, as something to be analyzed, changed, and challenged, but to be embraced and lived. Additionally, I returned to Mary. The Church Fathers' devotion to the Blessed Virgin and the Church's teaching on Mary as *Theotokos* ("God-bearer") enkindled in me a new love for Jesus' mother, unfettered by feminist mistrust of her submissiveness. I started praying the Hail Mary, and I developed a keen interest in Mary's appearances and messages of personal and corporate conversion at Lourdes and Fátima. It was through Mary that I began to accept the beauty of faithful submission to God's will.

Embracing the culture of life

I became unabashedly pro-life in my preaching and personal associations. The more deeply I entered into the mystery of life, the more richly blessed was my ministry. Once I accepted the Catholic Church's radically incarnational teaching of Christ enfleshed in all humanity, my compassion for others deepened and thus my ability to minister to them, especially to those suffering from abortion. While there were a few radical proabortionists in my Lutheran congregations, many others sought me out to confess previous abortions and to seek help in unplanned pregnancies. I regretted, however, my inability to offer sacramental absolution to those in need, and I was saddened that I could not substantiate my own pro-life position with that of my denomination, a fact which my pro-choice protagonists consistently pointed out. I knew the Catholic Church alone had denounced abortion since her inception. Years later, at about the same time I decided to return to Rome, former ELCA Pastor Leonard Klein wrote in *Lutheran Forum,* in reference to the denomination's tacit approval of abortion, that a church which condones abortion cannot be part of the one, holy, catholic, and apostolic Church.

Professionally, pastoral ministry fit me like a glove. I loved preaching and presiding at communion services, and the *Lutheran Book of Worship* provided beautiful settings for the eucharistic liturgy and services of the Word. I enjoyed the challenge of ministering to troubled people, and after I left my team pastorate in a large Lutheran congregation, I accepted several interim pastoral positions in congregations divided by internal conflicts. I relished the challenge of fostering healing and growth, preparing parishioners for their next pastor. I was respected by my colleagues and acted as unofficial mentor to several new pastors. I taught systematic theology in the New Jersey Synod Diaconate program, preparing laypersons for professional ministry. I also liked being in a position of authority, and unlike many of my colleagues, I enjoyed the administrative duties of running a parish.

In the midst of this positive professional growth, however, a nagging doubt crept in. I wondered how long I could stay in a church that seemed to be abandoning its theological and sacramental foundation. I joined a society of confessional Lutherans, bound together by our strong desire to reform our denomination, theologically and morally. Most of us longed for rapprochement with Rome, not as individuals, but as a Lutheran communion. For a time, this goal provided me with momentum to continue my ministry. Then came the conversion of several prominent Lutherans, including *First Things* editor-in-chief Father Richard John Neuhaus and patristics scholar Robert Wilken. The occasion of their conversions increased my doubts about the viability of my little society's confessional endeavors.

I picked up Father Louis Bouyer's classic Catholic apologetics, *Spirit and Forms of Protestantism*. Bouyer, a Lutheran convert to the faith more than half a century ago, provides evidence which proves that Luther's great ninety-five theses, the linchpin of confessional Lutheranism, were clearly stated centuries before in the councils of the Church. This fact was not new to me, but hearing it again prompted me to revisit my own justification for being a Lutheran. Bouyer also instructs us not to be fooled by the beauty of some Protestant liturgies. Although they may surpass many Catholic Masses in liturgical music and style, they are, at bottom, a beautiful imitation. Nearing his own conversion, former Lutheran Pastor Leonard Klein said to me: "Once you've come to the conclusion that Luther's disobedience was wrong, you're a goner." When Luther left the Church, he left behind any attempt at reform and started something new, utterly *other* than the Roman Catholic Church. For me, this was the realization that Lutheran doctrine, orders, polity, and social teaching were built on a *negation* of Catholic teaching. The early reformers did not foresee that once they negated the Holy See, they removed all positive authority, cohesion, and controls from their new church.[49] The Lutheran doctrines of *sola fide* and s*ola scriptura* ("faith alone" and "scripture alone") necessarily placed private interpretation and judgment in a conflicted and tendentious relationship with Catholic Tradition. Unbridled by the reigns of an authoritative teaching office (i.e., the bishops), the church of Luther soon found itself fractionated. Luther himself complained about the grave errors of interpretation on the part of the laity, and he also was at odds with his own colleagues, eventually parting ways with some. It was only a matter of time before Protestants splintered into churches too great to number, each incorporation resulting from a negation of a rival denomination's understanding of faith and Scripture. The Catholic Church alone offered the wisdom of two thousand years, positively expressed in the consistent teachings of the Apostles' successors.

Ironically, in the midst of my terrible spiritual torments, my personal life soared. I met my future husband, Alec, at my congregation. He was a new parishioner when we fell in love and quickly married in 1990. Our first child was born nine months later, and our family rapidly grew larger. My husband enjoyed being a pastor's spouse; he was actively involved in the congregation I served, and we became a great team. He and the children loved to hear Mom preach, and the little ones would clamor to stand next to me after church to greet people and imitate me leading worship.

---

[49] See Louis Bouyer's *Spirit and Forms of Protestantism* for a thorough discussion of the negative aspects of Protestant formation.

Prodigal daughter returns home

This relative familial calm would not last long. My professional life and personal life changed dramatically in the spring of 1996, when I decided to return to the Catholic Church. My desire to be part of the Apostolic Church and my refusal to accept the ELCA's moral decline, especially its abortion policies, left me no alternative but to leave the ELCA. Further, my rejection of Luther's disobedience meant that I believed all Lutheran ordinations were invalid; thus its Eucharist was invalid as well. I remembered a time not many years before when I claimed as my own Luther's sentiment: "Here I stand, I can do no other." I would reiterate those words when sharing my Lutheran "conversion" story with others. That sentence became the death knell of Lutheranism for me, as with difficulty I surveyed my years spent in sin apart from the Catholic faith. I felt utter sorrow and repentance over my dissenting Catholic years and my eventual break. Yet, I turned to God in hope of receiving His mercy.

My new zeal for Catholicism was tempered, however, by the continued presence of dissenting Catholics, sloppy liturgical practices, and lackluster preaching in the Catholic Church. To my happy surprise, though, I found individuals and organizations dedicated to orthodox Catholicism, a proper reform of the liturgy, and a return to Catholic devotions, like the Rosary, novenas, and Holy Hours. The Catholic Church was ever the Church, warts and all, a claim no other Christian church could make. I asked myself which church I would die for, and I immediately responded, the Catholic Church alone. I could not then deny the words of *Lumen Gentium* (no. 14), which state unequivocally that once one knows the fullness of faith is in the Catholic Church, one must be Catholic to attain salvation. Augustine writes:

284

> O God, from whom to be turned is to fall, to whom
> to be turned is to rise, and with whom to stand is to
> abide forever.[50]

Indeed, I was going home, painful as that road to reunion
would be. I had three major hurdles to cross before I could be
admitted back into full communion with the Church. The first
was telling my husband and dealing with the wide range of emotions that would accompany the news. The second was completing my commitment to the Lutheran congregation I served.
The third was to have my husband obtain an annulment from a
previous marriage.

Alec never thought I would leave the Lutheran Church.
While I had spoken to him repeatedly about my desire to be part
of the Apostolic Church and my disillusionment with the ELCA
over its confessional and moral decline, he listened to my words
in the context of my reforming endeavors *within* Lutheranism.
A lifelong Lutheran married to clergy, Alec never concluded I
would relinquish my ordination and vocation and disrupt our
family life. He felt betrayed when I confessed my intention to
return to the Roman Catholic Church. He said I wasn't the
woman he married, and he accused me of splitting the family
apart. He thought I was crazy to throw away all for which I had
worked so hard. He couldn't imagine the situation in the ELCA
was bad enough to leave, and he added that I managed to minister faithfully to the congregations I served with little interfer-
ence from the church bureaucracy. I explained that I was
returning to Rome because it is the right and only place to be,
and I hoped I would have returned anyway, despite the deterio-
rating condition of the ELCA. Those were very difficult words
for him to swallow, for he was taught as a child that the Catholic

---

[50] Augustine, *Soliloquies.*

Church was, in essence, the enemy. The Lutheran minister who prepared him for Confirmation warned him to "*never date a Catholic, for fear you might marry one*," and ticked off a shopping list of reasons why. Alec admitted he probably never would have considered marrying a Catholic.

My husband sorrowed over the religious split in our immediate family caused by my conversion, as he foresaw the children becoming Catholic, too. His prediction quickly came true, as he witnessed the three oldest receive their first Holy Communion. He acknowledges the fortification of each child's faith through our homeschool curriculum, which contains a strong religious-education component and is steeped in Catholic culture. Alec has gradually overcome his initial anger, pain, resentment, and sorrow over losing what once was, and he has been very supportive. While he is still Lutheran, though now a conservative, pro-life Missouri Synod Lutheran, he has accepted my decision and the children's Catholicism. He attends Catholic Mass with us on occasion, listens to Catholic audiotapes, and watches Catholic television programs with me. But when Sunday morning arrives, we both feel sad when we depart for Church in two different directions. There are no easy fixes, just a trust in our love for and commitment to each other, God's providence, and the confidence that we are following His will and our consciences.

After my conversion in the spring of 1996, there was a long period of waiting before I could return to Rome. I was the interim pastor of a Lutheran church in the process of calling a full-time minister. I had committed to serve the congregation through the fall, and taking their needs into consideration, I felt it was important to honor that commitment. Additionally, I was contributing to our family's income in a small but important way, so the wait provided needed time to seek another means of support, preferably in lay ministry within the Catholic Church.

Arguably, the two most important features of this waiting period were (1) the time it afforded me to work through the difficulties my conversion had caused in my relationship with Alec, and (2) the suffering I experienced leading worship in the Lutheran Church. It is to my personal suffering that I now turn.

The two most joyful and fulfilling aspects of my ordained ministry were preaching and presiding over the Eucharist. When I discovered that the fullness of truth resides in the Catholic Church, celebrating Word, and especially sacrament, became a bitter pill to me. I felt as though my heart would break in two as I uttered the words of consecration and distributed communion to my Lutheran congregants, who believed what I could not. My last pastoral act was preaching the sermon at the installation service of my childhood friend, Mary, and her husband, Steve, in their new congregation. Mary and I had gone to Catholic parochial school together. She went off to Notre Dame and I, Boston College, and then she joined me at B.C. to obtain an M.A. in pastoral ministry. I became a Lutheran a few years before she met and married a Lutheran pastor. It wasn't long after that she was ordained a Lutheran minister, too. What an irony; here she was commencing a team ministry with her husband, and I was leaving my ministry behind. I preached about the meaning of ordination and ministry. It was a very Catholic sermon, full of references to the Pope and St. Thérèse of Lisieux. When I was done, I was satisfied that I understood and lived out my ordination in the Lutheran Church, but I was grateful to God beyond words that He had led me back home.

God showered me with His graces more abundantly than I could have ever imagined: I commenced a new ministry as part-time campus minister at Princeton University. For four years, I was privileged to pray with students, teach Catholic theology, prepare converts, foster vocations, and bring

Catholic speakers to the campus. The students hungered for knowledge of the Catholic faith, and I never tired of sharing it with them.

I enter full communion with the Church

Telling Alec, completing my Lutheran ministry, and engaging in Catholic lay ministry are not the end of my story. It would be nearly three years after my conversion until I would be granted *full* communion in the Catholic Church. My husband, Alec, had been briefly married several years before we met, and thankfully, that marriage produced no children. He willingly offered to seek an annulment that I might be received back into the sacramental life of the Church. The annulment process was arduous, painful, long, and uncertain, but out of love for me, he underwent it. We had great pastoral support from Catholic friends and priests, which bolstered us along the way when time dragged on and things looked bleak. For me, it was a time of great spiritual growth, as trust in God's mercy was put to the test. The Mass was both beautiful and painful. While I was ever thankful for the gift of witnessing Christ's Body, Blood, Soul, and Divinity in the Eucharist, I could not partake of Him, and there was no certainty that I ever could. Moreover, I had a seemingly endless laundry list of sins to confess since my last Confession as a young adult, the most serious being my rejection of Catholicism. I sorrowed over the knowledge that I had put my immortal soul in peril and was unable to participate in the Church's offer of sacramental for-giveness. In my powerlessness, there was only one place to go, and that was to our Lord. I prayed that God would be merciful toward me, a sinner, and I prayed for the strength to accept whatever decision the diocesan tribunal made concerning the annulment petition. Nearly three years later, we received news that Alec's annulment was granted. Alec and I received the Sacrament of

Matrimony. I received absolution for my sins, and for the first time in years, I received the Eucharist—on the day my oldest son, Patrick, received his first Holy Communion.

Since my return to the Catholic Church, I have received calls and letters from former colleagues in the Lutheran Church who long to be Catholic. For a variety of reasons, most do not become Catholic; however, there are two reasons that stand out.

The first is the fear of an uncertain professional future for ordained Protestant men and women. Married Protestant clergymen who would like to become Catholic priests know the process is long; ordination is not guaranteed, and the types of ministry available to married priests are limited. Clergywomen are well aware that reordination is not a possibility, often a prospect too painful to consider, even for those who agree with the Church's teaching of the male priesthood.

The second reason is the Catholic Church's beautiful, steadfast position on the indissolubility of marriage. I have shared my experiences with divorced and remarried clergy and laity, encouraging them to take a leap of faith, unite *imperfectly* with the Church, and trust in God's providence. The wrenching process of applying for an annulment, knowing that it may not be granted, is often too much to bear, thus it is easier to stay away.

Becoming Catholic and *being* Catholic are not easy, for the Church requires much. Indeed, to those who have been given much, much is required. We have been given a gift beyond measure in the Body, Blood, Soul, and Divinity of our Lord and Savior every moment of every day in the Eucharist. With God, nothing is impossible.

God has also given us great *company*. St. Augustine thanks the Lord for those who led him to the Church: his mother (St. Monica), his mentor (St. Ambrose), his teachers, and his friends. Faithful disciples have walked with me along my journey, too—

from my first utterances of doubt about the veracity of Lutheranism, to my longings to be part of the Apostolic Church, to my conversion, and beyond. My longtime friend Jennifer Ferrara and I spent countless hours burning up the phone lines, discussing the decline of the Lutheran Church, and searching for truth in the Catholic Church. Throughout our shared crises, we made many trips to conferences and to seek advice from respected colleagues. A fellow convert and student at Drew University, Jeffrey Finch, gave me the push I needed to make the final decision to reclaim my Catholicism. He phoned and said: "I hear you're thinking of crossing the Tiber." Then he introduced me to a group of converting Protestant clergy who met regularly for support. The late Father Joseph Procaccini took our little convert group, Alec, and me under his wing and provided continual pastoral support. Throughout the years, faithful and concerned Catholic family and friends prayed to God for my conversion. The company I share is ever growing, and God has allowed me to be company to others. A convert to the Church and former Episcopal priest, Linda Poindexter, once wrote: "I thank God every day that I am a Catholic." Amen!

Patricia and her husband, Alec, are homeschooling parents of four young children, Patrick, Aidan, Maria Christiana, and Caroline. Patricia returned to the Catholic Church in 1996 and served four years with the Aquinas Institute, the Catholic campus ministry of Princeton University. Patricia is an adjunct instructor in the Religious Studies Department at Seton Hall University. She works intermittently as a research assistant for the multivolume Ancient Christian Commentary on Scripture *series, edited by Thomas Oden, and when time permits, she writes.*

Afterword

My search for a Protestant Church "just like the Catholic Church" ended when I stepped into Newton Centre Lutheran Church. Or so I thought. The truth is that long before I left the Catholic Church for "greener pastures" in Protestantism, I had ceased to be Catholic. I had embraced the thought of dissident Catholic theologians I read and studied in college and graduate school. When I broke the news to my parents, I really believed that Luther and Melanchthon had rediscovered pure "catholicism." As a Lutheran pastor, I spent countless hours welcoming disgruntled or divorced Catholics into my congregation, explaining the similarities between Lutherans and Catholics. In fact, I'd say: "You know, I think of myself as a *Lutheran* Catholic."

Years later, I returned to the Catholic Church because I came to the conclusion that Lutheranism, or any form of Protestantism for that matter, is *unlike* Catholicism in its essence. This is not to say that Protestants aren't Christians. The women in this book who were Protestant clearly received many graces from their faith communities, which subsequently laid the foundation for their search for the truest, fullest manifestation of the Church on earth. Catholicism is the Church of Christ and the Apostles, the creeds, the canon of the Bible, the Church Fathers, the seven sacraments, Mary and the saints, and the rhythm of unceasing and varied devotions. The more deeply I enter into the mysteries of Mother Church, the more certain I am that there is an unbreachable chasm between Catholicism and Protestantism. This difference can be expressed as the fulfillment, or *summit*, of union with Christ.

There are those rare souls we read about who experience a piercing, mystical, ecstatic union with Christ. St. Teresa of Ávila, St. Francis of Assisi, St. Faustina, and Padre Pio (St. Pio of Pietrelcina) are among the company of mystics. The vast majority of souls, however, will not know such union this side of Paradise, but we can benefit from their legacy on earth and their eternal prayers on our behalf.

Indeed, the mystic's rare gift is no cause for envy, because every Catholic soul can experience true physical and spiritual union with Christ in the Eucharist. The night before our Lord gave His life *for us* on the cross, He gave Himself *to us*—Body, Blood, Soul, and Divinity. Through his apostolic succession, the Catholic priest stands *in persona Christi* at the altar. Bread is no longer bread; wine is no longer wine. These earthly elements *become* the Host—He who is upon the altar. In a moment, He lights upon our sin-sick tongue, and we consume Him. Christ *in* me. In his translation of "Adoro Te Devote," Gerard Manley Hopkins poetically conveys the first two stanzas of St. Thomas Aquinas's adoration of the Lord in the Eucharist:

> Godhead here in hiding, Whom do I adore
> Masked by these bare shadows, shape and nothing more,
> See, Lord, at Thy service low lies here a heart
> Lost, all lost in wonder at the God Thou art.

> Seeing, touching, tasting are in thee deceived;
> How says trusty hearing? that shall be believed;
> What God's Son has told me, take for truth I do;
> Truth Himself speaks truly or there's nothing true.

Recently, I attended the funeral of a beloved former colleague in the Lutheran ministry, the Reverend Frank W. Klos. Frank, the

Reverend Richard Overcash, and I served together as ministers of a Lutheran congregation in southern New Jersey. We worked well together and were respected by our congregation. My Catholic conversion hit my former colleagues and parishioners hard, and although the latter have long known that I am now Catholic, many still think of me as their "pastor." While I had returned to that parish since my conversion, it had never been on the occasion of a worship service. This time was different.

Rich led the funeral service, and the church was packed with people who, for years, trusted me to preach the Word of God and offer the Sacrament of the Eucharist, week in and week out. From my hand, they received communion—a communion I could no longer partake.

Row after row went up to the communion rail, and when it was my row's turn, I stood to let others pass by, but I did not go up to receive. At that moment, I was acutely aware of my former parishioners' feelings of betrayal. Their pain was palpable as they struggled to understand how I could choose not to receive communion. I sorrowed over the true betrayal of Protestantism itself, which offers a false "communion" conceived in disobedience—rejection—of its Mother, the Church. Apart from her, there is no union with the body of Christ.

The women who share their stories in the pages of this book have found union with Christ in the Catholic Church. As they discovered, the beauty of the Church is that she offers the way to sanctification. The Catholic Church is the Bride of Christ, chosen by the Bridegroom Himself. She shares in the life of her Spouse.

What kind of life is this?

It is a life of fidelity: Our Lord's unconditional love, steadfast throughout eternity, is preserved this side of heaven by the Holy See, without interruption since Peter, our first Vicar of Christ.

It is a life of sacrifice: Christ, the spotless Lamb, is slaughtered to satisfy the debt of the guilty.

O Salutaris Hostia / Quae caeli pandis ostium.
O Saving Victim opening wide / The gate of heaven to all
below!

It is a life of *redemptive* suffering: We, His Bride, unite our sufferings to His own wounds for the salvation of souls.

It is a life of efficacious prayer: God listens to us and answers our pleas. We unite our hearts to the Sacred Heart of Jesus by consecrating our lives to His mother's Immaculate Heart, especially through the Rosary.

It is a life of endless joy: Heaven breaks into our world through the grace of the sacraments, especially the Eucharist—the Body, Blood, Soul, and Divinity of Jesus Christ in me. We confess with St. Paul: "I have been crucified with Christ; it is no longer I who live, but it is Christ who lives in me."[51]

Our Lord *pursues* each one of us to our last earthly moment, His mercy enduring beyond the infidelity of sin. The Hound of Heaven loves the *unlovely beloved* unto everlasting radiance:

Alack, thou knowest not
How little worthy of any love thou art!
Whom wilt thou find to love ignoble thee,
    Save Me, save only Me?
. . . .
    Rise, clasp My hand, and come!

PATRICIA SODANO IRELAND
FEAST OF THE ANNUNCIATION

---

[51] Galatians 2:20.

"Hound of Heaven"

Francis Thompson

I fled Him, down the nights and down the days;
  I fled Him, down the arches of the years;
I fled Him, down the labyrinthine ways
    Of my own mind; and in the mist of tears
I hid from Him, and under running laughter.
      Up vistaed hopes I sped;
      And shot, precipitated,
Adown Titanic glooms of chasmed fears,
  From those strong Feet that followed, followed after.
     But with unhurrying chase,
     And unperturbèd pace,
Deliberate speed, majestic instancy,
     They beat—and a Voice beat
     More instant than the Feet—
"All things betray thee, who betrayest Me."

     I pleaded, outlaw-wise,
By many a hearted casement, curtained red,
  Trellised with intertwining charities;
(For, though I knew His love Who followèd,
     Yet I was sore adread
Lest, having Him, I must have naught beside).
But, if one little casement parted wide,
  The gust of His approach would clash it to.
  Fear wist not to evade as Love wist to pursue.
Across the margent of the world I fled,
  And troubled the gold gateways of the stars,
  Smiting for shelter on their clangèd bars;

      Fretted to dulcet jars
And silvern chatter the pale ports o' the moon.
I said to Dawn: Be sudden—to Eve: Be soon;
   With thy young skiey blossoms heap me over
      From this tremendous Lover—
Float thy vague veil about me, lest He see!
   I tempted all His servitors, but to find
My own betrayal in their constancy,
In faith to Him their fickleness to me,
   Their traitorous trueness, and their loyal deceit.
To all swift things for swiftness did I sue;
   Clung to the whistling mane of every wind.
     But whether they swept, smoothly fleet,
    The long savannahs of the blue;
       Or whether, Thunder-driven,
    They clanged His chariot 'thwart a heaven,
Plashy with flying lightnings round the spurn o' their
    feet:—
   Fear wist not to evade as Love wist to pursue.
     Still with unhurrying chase,
     And unperturbèd pace,
    Deliberate speed, majestic instancy,
     Came on the following Feet,
     And a Voice above their beat—
   "Naught shelters thee, who wilt not shelter Me."
. . . .
     Now of that long pursuit
     Comes on at had the bruit;
   That Voice is round me like a bursting sea:
    "And is thy earth so marred,
    Shattered in shard on shard?
   Lo, all things fly thee, for thou fliest Me!

Strange, piteous, futile thing!
Wherefore should any set thee love apart?
Seeing none but I make much of naught" (He said),
"And human love needs human meriting:
   How hast thou merited—
Of all man's clotted clay, the dingiest clot?
   Alack, thou knowest not
How little worthy of any love thou art!
Whom wilt thou find to love ignoble thee,
   Save Me, save only Me?
All which I took from thee I did but take,
   Not for thy harms,
But just that thou might'st seek it in My arms.
   All which thy child's mistake
Fancies as lost, I have stored for thee at home:
   Rise, clasp My hand, and come!"

. . . .

About the Authors

*J*ennifer Ferrara was a Lutheran minister for eleven years before converting to Roman Catholicism in 1998. She is a full-time mother and part-time writer and speaker. She has written numerous articles on religion and culture for publications such as *Lutheran Forum*, *The Cresset*, and *First Things*. She resides in Chester County, Pennsylvania, with her husband, twin sons, and daughter.

*P*atricia Sodano Ireland was a Lutheran minister for ten years before returning to the Catholic Church in 1996. She is a full-time homeschooling mother of four and an adjunct instructor at Seton Hall University. For six years, she served as the Coordinator of Ministries for the Catholic campus ministry at Princeton University. She enjoys writing and speaking. She has published several articles on theology and preaching, and she contributed research for the multivolume Ancient Christian Commentary on Scripture series. She resides in Union County, New Jersey, with her husband, two sons, and two daughters.

Our Sunday Visitor …
Your Source for Discovering the Riches of the Catholic Faith

Our Sunday Visitor has an extensive line of materials for young children, teens, and adults. Our books, Bibles, pamphlets, CD-ROMs, audios, and videos are available in bookstores worldwide.

To receive a FREE full-line catalog or for more information, call **Our Sunday Visitor** at **1-800-348-2440, ext. 3**. Or write **Our Sunday Visitor** / 200 Noll Plaza / Huntington, IN 46750.

Please send me ___ A catalog
Please send me materials on:
___ Apologetics and catechetics
___ Prayer books
___ The family
___ Reference works
___ Heritage and the saints
___ The parish

Name _____
Address _____ Apt._____
City _____ State _____ Zip_____
Telephone (   ) _____

A91BBBBP

Please send a friend ___ A catalog
Please send a friend materials on:
___ Apologetics and catechetics
___ Prayer books
___ The family
___ Reference works
___ Heritage and the saints
___ The parish

Name _____
Address _____ Apt._____
City _____ State _____ Zip_____
Telephone (   ) _____

A91BBBBP

OurSundayVisitor
200 Noll Plaza, Huntington, IN 46750
Toll free: **1-800-348-2440**
Website: www.osv.com